ELECTROMAGNETIC WAVES

By G. TORALDO DI FRANCIA
Istituto Nazionale di Ottica, Florence, Italy

Translated from the Italian by the Author

INTERSCIENCE PUBLISHERS, INC., NEW YORK
INTERSCIENCE PUBLISHERS LTD., LONDON

Translated from
Onde Elettromagnetiche
Published by
Nicola Zanichelli Editore, Bologna, 1953

LIBRARY OF CONGRESS CATALOG CARD NUMBER 55-12142

INTERSCIENCE PUBLISHERS, INC.
250 Fifth Avenue, New York 1, N. Y.

For Great Britain and Northern Ireland:
INTERSCIENCE PUBLISHERS LTD.
88/90 Chancery Lane, London, W.C. 2, England

PRINTED IN THE NETHERLANDS

ELECTROMAGNETIC WAVES

PREFACE

This book originated from a course of lectures given by the author at the Physics Department of the University of Florence. Both the general structure and the purpose of the course have been preserved in the book.

The purpose is to give a clear and readily understandable introduction to those students who will later engage in theoretical research and also to those who will be concerned with the more and more brilliant applications of electromagnetic waves. To accomplish this the author, while attempting to present the classical theory, has always borne in mind the new and elegant standpoints suggested by modern applications.

It is worth while to mention as an example the point where the departure of the present treatment from that of classical textbooks may appear the most audacious. The dielectric constant is here assumed to have a really constant value that is independent of the frequency.

As is well known, the first reaction of the student, who, after studying Maxwell's equations and their simplest consequences, learns that in spite of the theory the refractive index is nearly always different from the square root of the relative dielectric constant, is one of dissatisfaction or even disillusion. He may even be inclined to think that Maxwell's equations and the electromagnetic theory of light are only approximations and lack some essential detail. The situation becomes more complicated rather than simpler when the student discovers that the dielectric constant is not constant but depends on the frequency; and the following assertion that the dielectric constant is complex appears to him almost absurd.

One cannot deny that in the classical formulation there is really a certain absurdity. To show this let us consider the following very convincing analogy. Suppose we are given a linear electric network of unknown structure with two accessible terminals. We want to derive the characteristic parameters of the network by merely investigating the response of the terminals. To begin with, we may apply a steady voltage and from the direct current obtained we can derive the value of the conductance. If the conductance is zero or very small we can measure a capacitance. However, as long as the voltage is maintained constant, no other parameter of the network can be derived. If now we apply an alternating voltage, that is, if we make the frequency change from zero to a finite value, we shall be able to discover some new network constants. For instance, we may be able to detect an inductance and a radiation resistance. In general the impedance will change more and more as the frequency is increased. If we persist in ascribing to the network solely a capacitance, we shall be forced to assume that the capacitance has a complex value and is a function of frequency. This formulation, however acceptable from a mathematical point of view, is physically absurd. It is much better to say that the network presents an impedance that is a function of frequency and that the actual form of this function depends upon the distribution of the different physical constants (capacitances, inductances, resistances) of the network.

By analogy with these considerations we shall ascribe to each isotropic medium a *specific impedance* which is a function of frequency. The dielectric constant will merely appear as a capacitance in the expression of the specific impedance and will always preserve its static value. This is only a formal change with respect to standard textbooks, but it is required for reasons of consistency and clarity.

In a book of this kind one cannot have a much more ambitious aim than to provide a good presentation of well-known results. However, the reader will find here and there some new minor contributions to the theory as, for example, *parageometrical optics* which was introduced and developed by the author.

The reader is assumed to have a mathematical training which

does not go beyond that usually given to students of mathematics, physics, or engineering in the first two years at the university. For this reason the volume is provided with a mathematical introduction. However, mathematics has always been presented as a means, not as an end; intuition and simplicity have often been preferred to rigor. As to the tensor notation adopted, the best reply to possible criticism cannot be but that given by a well-known English author in a similar case: Try for yourself! After a very short initial training one cannot fail to discover the great usefulness of a concise tensor notation both as a means of visualizing and memorizing many physical laws and as a tool for finding new results.

Not many words should be necessary to show the convenience of banishing from vector calculus the symbol vector times sign which indicates scalar product in some countries and vector product in others.

The present volume deals with general fundamentals rather than with particular problems, which, as is well known, would in most cases amount to mere exercises on special functions. For this reason the mathematical introduction does not contain the customary little treatise on Bessel functions and spherical functions. The student who has assimilated well the general principles will not encounter any difficulty in their application to particular cases.

The author wishes to express his gratitude to Professor Robert E. Marshak for having first suggested an English edition of the book. Most cordial thanks are due to Ernest H. Traub for having accepted the heavy task of revising the author's translation. The author is also greatly indebted to Interscience Publishers for their efficient cooperation and to the Italian publisher Zanichelli for having facilitated in many ways the realization of the present edition.

The following books were found useful for consultation by the author:

M. Born, *Optik*, Berlin, 1933.

B. Finzi and M. Pastori, *Calcolo tensoriale e applicazioni*, Bologna, 1949.

G. Giorgi, *Verso l'elettrotecnica moderna*, Milano 1949.

Geiger and Scheel, *Handbuch der Physik*, Vol. XII, *Theorien der Elektrizität*, Berlin, 1927.

W. Heitler, *Quantum Theory of Radiation*, Oxford, 1947.

N. Marcuvitz, *Waveguide Handbook*, New York, 1951.

S. A. Schelkunoff, *Electromagnetic Waves*, New York, 1948.

J. C. Slater, *Microwave Electronics*, New York, 1950.

J. A. Stratton, *Electromagnetic Theory*, New York, 1941.

W. Weizel, *Lehrbuch der theoretischen Physik*, Vol. I, Berlin, 1949.

G. Toraldo di Francia

Florence, Italy
September, 1955

CONTENTS

Mathematical Introduction

M1. Vector Calculus and Curvilinear Coordinates

Elementary Vector Algebra

§ 1. We shall assume that the reader is familiar with elementary vector calculus. Some of the formulas used in this book will be briefly summarized in order to give them the form that is most suitable for our purpose.

First of all we shall introduce the concept of the *direct triad.* Let us consider (Fig. 1M) three axes x, y, z, which for the time being

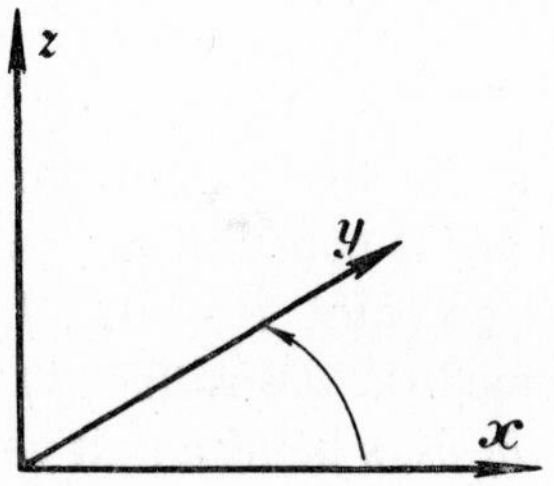

Fig. 1M

will be assumed to be orthogonal. They form a direct triad when a corkscrew advancing in the positive direction of z rotates so that x coincides with y. Through a continuous deformation of the angles (by less than 90°) one obtains a non-orthogonal direct triad.

A triad not corresponding to the above definition is an *inverse triad.*

In this book this simple rule will replace the many different rules that are usually applied, especially in electromagnetic theory, for characterizing the relative positions of three vectors.

§ 2. It is useful to remember that the three vectors $\boldsymbol{u}$, $\boldsymbol{v}$, $\boldsymbol{w}$ obeying the relation $\boldsymbol{u} \wedge \boldsymbol{v} = \boldsymbol{w}$ form a direct triad in this order. Consequently for the unit vectors $\boldsymbol{i}$, $\boldsymbol{j}$, $\boldsymbol{k}$ parallel respectively to the rectangular axes x, y, z the relation $\boldsymbol{i} \wedge \boldsymbol{j} = \boldsymbol{k}$ holds, with the others obtained by a cyclical permutation of the letters.

The following formulas are important, and their derivation is well known (a dot indicates the scalar product, and φ is the angle made by the vectors $\boldsymbol{u}$, $\boldsymbol{v}$).

$$\text{(M1-1)} \quad \begin{cases} \boldsymbol{u} \cdot \boldsymbol{v} = uv \cos \varphi = u_x v_x + u_y v_y + u_z v_z \\ \text{mod } (\boldsymbol{u} \wedge \boldsymbol{v}) = uv \sin \varphi \\ \boldsymbol{u} \wedge \boldsymbol{v} = (u_y v_z - u_z v_y)\boldsymbol{i} + \text{etc.} \\ \boldsymbol{u} \wedge \boldsymbol{v} \cdot \boldsymbol{w} = \boldsymbol{v} \wedge \boldsymbol{w} \cdot \boldsymbol{u} = \boldsymbol{w} \wedge \boldsymbol{u} \cdot \boldsymbol{v} \\ \boldsymbol{u} \wedge \boldsymbol{v} \cdot \boldsymbol{w} = \boldsymbol{u} \cdot \boldsymbol{v} \wedge \boldsymbol{w} \\ (\boldsymbol{u} \wedge \boldsymbol{v}) \wedge \boldsymbol{w} = -\boldsymbol{u}(\boldsymbol{v} \cdot \boldsymbol{w}) + \boldsymbol{v}(\boldsymbol{u} \cdot \boldsymbol{w}). \end{cases}$$

The last formula is one of the most useful and powerful formulas of vector algebra.

The Gradient

§ 3. Let $f(P)$ be a scalar function of the points P of space (†). The surfaces over which f is constant are called the *level surfaces*. Passing from point P to point $P + dP$, f increases by df. The ratio $df/\text{mod } dP$ is termed the *derivative of f in the direction* of dP. It will be indicated by $\partial f/\partial s$, $\boldsymbol{s}$ being a unit vector in that direction.

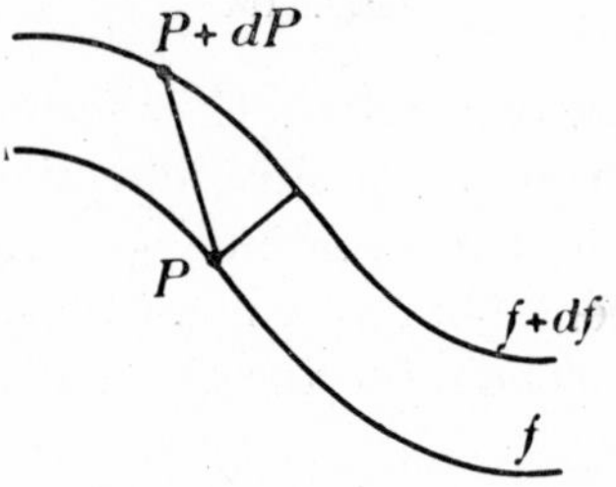

Fig. 2M

Consider now a dP corresponding to a positive df. If we maintain P fixed on the level surface f and move $P + dP$ on the level surface $f + df$, we see by inspection that the maximum of $\partial f/\partial s$

(†) All the scalar and vector functions that we shall consider will be as regular as required.

is obtained when mod dP is a minimum, i.e., when dP is normal to the level surface. A vector having the direction of this normal and the magnitude equal to this maximum of the derivative will be called the *gradient* of f and will be denoted by grad f. From Fig. 2M it follows at once that

$$\frac{\partial f}{\partial s} = \text{grad}\, f \cdot \boldsymbol{s} \tag{M1-2}$$

for any direction $\boldsymbol{s}$.

Flux and Divergence

§ 4. Let Σ be any regular surface with two sides. One of them will be called the positive side. We shall indicate by $\boldsymbol{n}(P)$ the unit vector perpendicular to the surface at P and directed from the negative to the positive side. For any vector function $\boldsymbol{v}(P)$ of the points P of space (†) the *flux* of $\boldsymbol{v}$ through the surface Σ is defined by the surface integral

$$\Phi = \iint_{\Sigma} \boldsymbol{v} \cdot \boldsymbol{n}\, \mathrm{d}\Sigma. \tag{M1-3}$$

The name is due to the evident analogy with the flow of a liquid. For the same reason the lines which are tangent to $\boldsymbol{v}$ at every point are called the *flux lines*.

Let Σ be a closed surface around the volume V, and consider the ratio Φ/V the positive normal pointing outward from Σ. If Σ contracts to a point P, the *divergence* of $\boldsymbol{v}$ at P will be defined as the limit

$$\text{div}\, \boldsymbol{v} = \lim_{V\to 0} \frac{\Phi}{V} = \lim_{V\to 0} \frac{1}{V} \oiint_{\Sigma} \boldsymbol{v} \cdot \boldsymbol{n}\, \mathrm{d}\Sigma. \tag{M1-4}$$

It is clear that the divergence is an intrinsic operator and does not depend on the choice of a particular system of coordinates. It can also be said that the divergence is the flux going out of the

(†) A *vector function* or *vector field* will be often referred to as a *vector* for the sake of convenience. The same remark applies to the *tensor fields* that will be considered later on.

unit volume. A vector whose divergence is zero will be called *solenoidal.*

Divergence Theorem

§ 5. Let the surface Σ enclose a finite volume V. We want to calculate the outgoing flux Φ. Let us divide the volume into a number of elementary cells (Fig. 3M) and consider the flux through

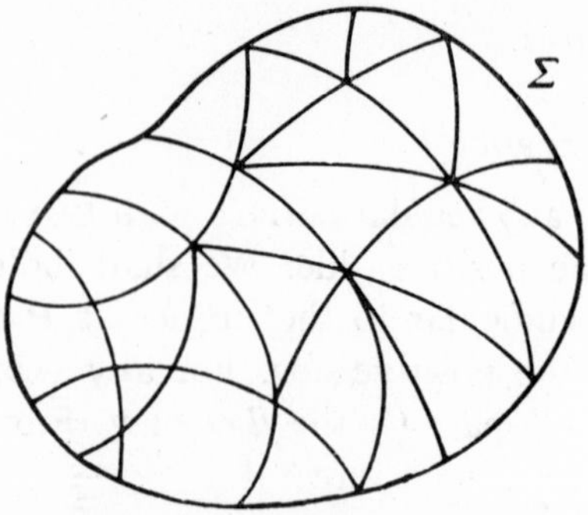

Fig. 3M

the boundary of each cell, which, by definition, is $d\Phi = \text{div}\, \boldsymbol{v} dV$. It is evident that at a common wall between two cells the flux is outward for one cell and inward for the other. If we add the outward fluxes of the two cells, the net contribution of the common wall is zero because the positive and negative terms cancel one another. Then, when the outward fluxes of all the cells are added, there will remain only the terms corresponding to those boundaries which coincide with Σ that is the total outward flux from Σ. We have

(M1-5) $$\Phi = \iiint_V \text{div}\, \boldsymbol{v} dV.$$

This is called the divergence theorem.

If $\boldsymbol{v}$ is solenoidal, its flux through any closed surface is zero. In particular, for a *flux tube* consisting of all the flux lines which pass through any bounded surface, we find that the flux is constant through every cross section.

Circulation and Curl

§ **6.** Let $\boldsymbol{l}$ be an arc of a regular line and $\boldsymbol{v}(P)$ a vector function of position. Choosing a positive direction along l and denoting an elementary arc by $\mathrm{d}\boldsymbol{l}$ (vector), the integral

$$\int_l \boldsymbol{v} \cdot \mathrm{d}\boldsymbol{l}$$

is called the *line integral* of $\boldsymbol{v}$ along l. If l is closed, the line integral will be termed the *circulation.*

Consider a plane loop l (Fig. 4M) and denote by Σ the enclosed

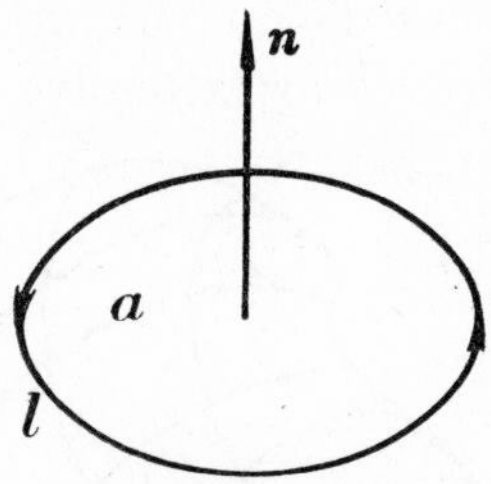

Fig. 4M

area. The positive normal of Σ will be the unit vector $\boldsymbol{n}$ whose direction is specified with respect to the positive direction of circulation by means of the corkscrew rule. Form the quotient C/Σ, where C designates the circulation of $\boldsymbol{v}$ around l.

We shall denote by $(\mathrm{curl}\ \boldsymbol{v})_n$ the limit

$$(\mathrm{curl}\ \boldsymbol{v})_n = \lim_{\Sigma \to 0} \frac{C}{\Sigma}, \qquad \text{(M1-6)}$$

which is obtained by allowing the loop to shrink to a point in the plane perpendicular to $\boldsymbol{n}$. It can be shown, as will be seen later, that there exists a vector which is called the *curl* of $\boldsymbol{v}$ and is denoted by curl $\boldsymbol{v}$, such that

$$(\mathrm{curl}\ \boldsymbol{v})_n = \boldsymbol{n} \cdot \mathrm{curl}\ \boldsymbol{v}$$

for any direction of $\boldsymbol{n}$, that is, for any orientation of the plane of l. Consequently $(\mathrm{curl}\ \boldsymbol{v})_n$ is really the component of curl $\boldsymbol{v}$ in the direction $\boldsymbol{n}$. In condensed form it may be said that the curl is the maximum circulation per unit area. A vector having zero curl is *irrotational.*

Note that a scalar quantity $f(P, Q, \ldots)$ or a vector $\boldsymbol{v}(P, Q, \ldots)$ may be functions of several points $P, Q, \ldots$ at the same time. When this happens, every differential operator must be labeled with the point with respect to which it operates. For example, we shall write $\operatorname{div}_P \boldsymbol{v}$, $\operatorname{div}_Q \boldsymbol{v}$, $\operatorname{grad}_P f$, and so forth. No subscript will be used when dealing with only one variable point.

Stokes' Theorem

§ 7. Consider any closed loop l, not necessarily plane (Fig. 5M), and any surface Σ bounded by l. Resolve Σ into many elementary

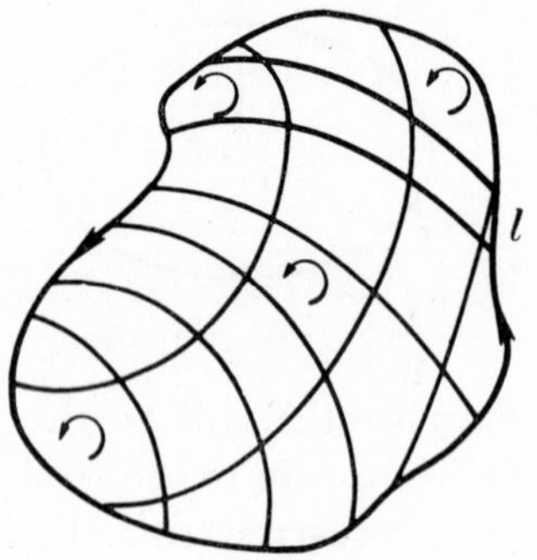

Fig. 5M

loops. For every elementary loop the circulation, according to definition (M1-6), will be

$$dC = (\operatorname{curl} \boldsymbol{v})_n \, d\Sigma = \boldsymbol{n} \cdot \operatorname{curl} \boldsymbol{v} \, d\Sigma,$$

$d\Sigma$ being the area bounded by the loop. Adding all the circulations, we note that the contributions from the boundary of any two adjacent loops cancel with one another so that we are left with only the circulation C around l. It follows (Stoke's theorem) that

$$C = \iint_\Sigma \boldsymbol{n} \cdot \operatorname{curl} \boldsymbol{v} \, d\Sigma. \tag{M1-7}$$

Note that this result is independent of the surface Σ provided that the surface is bounded by l.

Characteristic Properties of the Gradient and of the Curl

§ 8. If $f(P)$ is a uniform scalar function of position, we shall obviously have by definition of the directional derivative

$$f(B) = f(A) + \int_A^B \frac{\partial f}{\partial l}\, \mathrm{d}l = f(A) + \int_A^B \operatorname{grad} f \cdot \mathrm{d}\boldsymbol{l},$$

independently of the path followed from A to B in the integration (Fig. 6M). Consequently, if we construct a closed line with l from

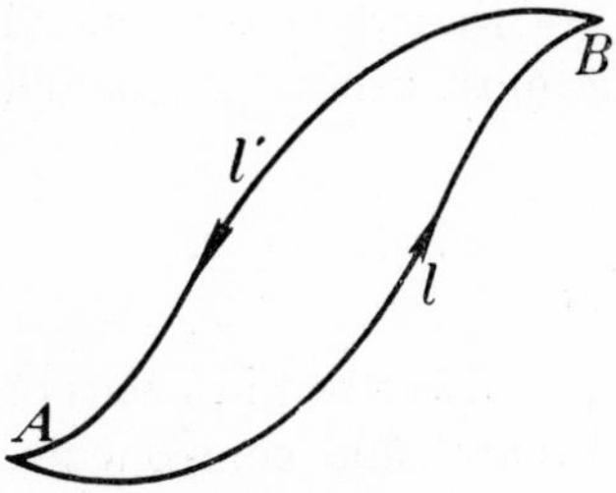

Fig. 6M

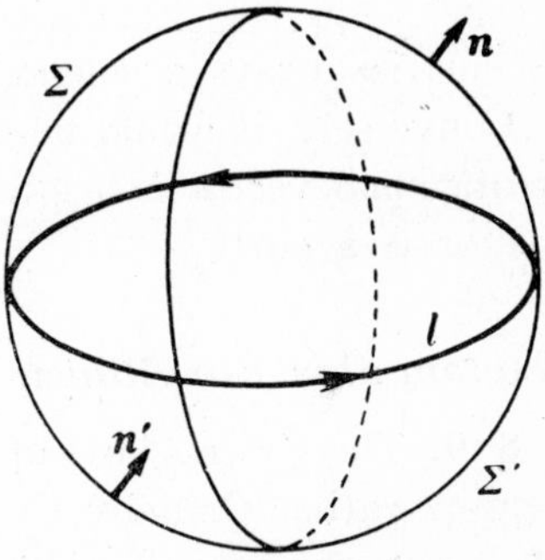

Fig. 7M

A to B and l' from B to A, the following equation must hold:

$$\oint_{l+l'} \operatorname{grad} f \cdot \mathrm{d}\boldsymbol{l} = 0.$$

Thus the circulation of grad f along any closed line is zero. It follows from (M1-7) that

(M1-8) $$\operatorname{curl} \operatorname{grad} f = 0.$$

Thus a gradient is always an irrotational vector.

Consider now two different surfaces Σ and Σ' which are bounded by the same closed line l (Fig. 7M). We already know from § 7 that

$$C = \oint_l \boldsymbol{v} \cdot \mathrm{d}\boldsymbol{l} = \iint_\Sigma \boldsymbol{n} \cdot \operatorname{curl} \boldsymbol{v}\, \mathrm{d}\Sigma = \iint_{\Sigma'} \boldsymbol{n} \cdot \operatorname{curl} \boldsymbol{v}\, \mathrm{d}\Sigma'.$$

The two surfaces Σ and Σ' considered as a whole represent a closed surface having $\boldsymbol{n}$ as outward normal and $\boldsymbol{n}'$ as inward normal. Then, when $\boldsymbol{n} = -\boldsymbol{n}'$ is superposed on Σ', the above equation gives

$$\oint\!\!\oint_{\Sigma+\Sigma'} \boldsymbol{n} \cdot \operatorname{curl} \boldsymbol{v} \, d\Sigma = 0.$$

Thus the flux of curl $\boldsymbol{v}$ across any closed surface is zero. Consequently we have, by (M1-5),

(M1-9) $$\operatorname{div} \operatorname{curl} \boldsymbol{v} = 0.$$

A curl is always a solenoidal vector.

Conversely, it would be possible to show that the most general irrotational vector is a gradient and the most general solenoidal vector is a curl.

Rectangular Curvilinear Coordinates

§ 9. The general laws of physics are best described in terms of vectors rather than by the use of coordinates and components. However, the introduction of a system of coordinates may often prove very convenient for the analytical solution of particular problems.

For this reason a brief outline of the so-called method of the coordinates will be given.

Let $f_1(P)$, $f_2(P)$, $f_3(P)$ represent three scalar functions of position. The equations

(M1-10) $$f_1(P) = u_1, \qquad f_2(P) = u_2, \qquad f_3(P) = u_3,$$

where u_1, u_2, u_3 are constant, represent three surfaces having (in general) a common point. The three numbers u_1, u_2, u_3 are then suitable for specifying this point and are called its *coordinates* (curvilinear coordinates). Any triplet of numbers u_1, u_2, u_3 will give three *coordinate surfaces* (M1-10), three *coordinate lines* as their intersections, and a point as the intersection of the three coordinate lines. We shall limit ourselves to the case where the coordinate surfaces intersect each other at right angles (*rectangular curvilinear coordinates*).

We shall call the surface $u_i = constant$ the u_i-*surface* (Fig. 8M) and the line along which only u_i is variable the u_i-*line*.

Consider the coordinate lines u_1, u_2, u_3 through a typical point $P(u_1, u_2, u_3)$ and the unit vectors $\boldsymbol{i}_1$, $\boldsymbol{i}_2$, $\boldsymbol{i}_3$ which are tangent to the lines at P and are assumed to form a direct triad. These unit vectors will have respectively the directions of $\partial P/\partial u_1$, $\partial P/\partial u_2$,

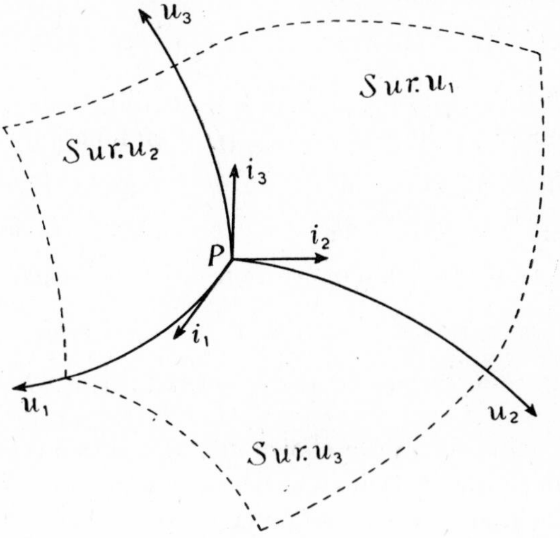

Fig. 8M

$\partial P/\partial u_3$. For an infinitely close point $P + \mathrm{d}P$, having the coordinates $u_1 + \mathrm{d}u_1$, $u_2 + \mathrm{d}u_2$, $u_3 + \mathrm{d}u_3$, we shall have

$$\mathrm{d}P = \frac{\partial P}{\partial u_1}\mathrm{d}u_1 + \frac{\partial P}{\partial u_2}\mathrm{d}u_2 + \frac{\partial P}{\partial u_3}\mathrm{d}u_3 = h_1\boldsymbol{i}_1\mathrm{d}u_1 + h_2\boldsymbol{i}_2\mathrm{d}u_2 + h_3\boldsymbol{i}_3\mathrm{d}u_3,$$

h_1, h_2, h_3 being three functions of u_1, u_2, u_3 equal respectively to the magnitude of $\partial P/\partial u_1$, $\partial P/\partial u_2$, $\partial P/\partial u_3$. Denoting by $\mathrm{d}s_1$, $\mathrm{d}s_2$, $\mathrm{d}s_3$ the elementary arcs (that is, mod $\mathrm{d}P$) along the coordinate lines, we have

(M1-11) $\quad \mathrm{d}s_1 = h_1\mathrm{d}u_1, \qquad \mathrm{d}s_2 = h_2\mathrm{d}u_2, \qquad \mathrm{d}s_3 = h_3\mathrm{d}u_3.$

The three elementary arcs determine an *elementary volume*. The faces of the elementary volume which lie on the surfaces u_1, u_2, u_3 obviously have the areas

$$d\Sigma_1 = ds_2 ds_3, \qquad d\Sigma_2 = ds_1 ds_3, \qquad d\Sigma_3 = ds_1 ds_2,$$

or

(M1-12) $$d\Sigma_1 = h_2 h_3 du_2 du_3, \quad d\Sigma_2 = h_1 h_3 du_1 du_3, \quad d\Sigma_3 = h_1 h_2 du_1 du_2.$$

The elementary volume will have the value

(M1-13) $$dV = ds_1 ds_2 ds_3 = h_1 h_2 h_3 du_1 du_2 du_3.$$

By virtue of the definition given in § 3, the directional derivatives along the coordinate lines of a scalar position function $f(P)$ will be

(M1-14) $$\frac{\partial f}{\partial i_1} = \frac{1}{h_1}\frac{\partial f}{\partial u_1}, \qquad \frac{\partial f}{\partial i_2} = \frac{1}{h_2}\frac{\partial f}{\partial u_2}, \qquad \frac{\partial f}{\partial i_3} = \frac{1}{h_3}\frac{\partial f}{\partial u_3}.$$

If $\mathbf{v}(P)$ is a vector function of position, the three scalar quantities

(M1-15) $$v_1 = \mathbf{v} \cdot \mathbf{i}_1, \qquad v_2 = \mathbf{v} \cdot \mathbf{i}_2, \qquad v_3 = \mathbf{v} \cdot \mathbf{i}_3$$

are called its *components* on the coordinate lines.

§ 10. It will shortly be shown that for any system of rectangular curvilinear coordinates the knowledge of the three functions h_1, h_2, h_3 is sufficient to obtain the expressions of the differential operators of space. It is convenient to evaluate these functions for the coordinate systems which are most useful in practice.

In the case of the Cartesian coordinates the coordinate surfaces are the planes $x =$ *const.*, $y =$ *const.*, $z =$ *const.* and the three line elements are given by

$$ds_1 = dx, \qquad ds_2 = dy, \qquad ds_3 = dz,$$

whence

(M1-16) $$h_1 = h_2 = h_3 = 1.$$

For the *cylindrical coordinates* r, φ, z the coordinate surfaces are the cylinders $r =$ *const.*, the planes $\varphi =$ *const.*, and the planes $z =$ *const.* The line elements are

$$ds_1 = dr, \qquad ds_2 = r d\varphi, \qquad ds_3 = dz,$$

whence

$$h_1 = 1, \qquad h_2 = r, \qquad h_3 = 1. \tag{M1-17}$$

For the *spherical coordinates* r, θ, φ the coordinate surfaces are the spheres $r = const.$, the cones $\theta = const$, and the planes $\varphi = const.$, The line elements are

$$ds_1 = dr, \qquad ds_2 = r\,d\theta, \qquad ds_3 = r \sin\theta\, d\varphi,$$

whence

$$h_1 = 1, \qquad h_2 = r, \qquad h_3 = r \sin\theta. \tag{M1-18}$$

Differential Operators in Curvilinear Coordinates

§ 11. From (M1-2) it follows that the components of grad f as defined by (M1-15) are respectively $\partial f/\partial i_1$, $\partial f/\partial i_2$, $\partial f/\partial i_3$. By recalling (M1-14) we have

$$\operatorname{grad} f = \frac{1}{h_1}\frac{\partial f}{\partial u_1}\boldsymbol{i}_1 + \frac{1}{h_2}\frac{\partial f}{\partial u_2}\boldsymbol{i}_2 + \frac{1}{h_3}\frac{\partial f}{\partial u_3}\boldsymbol{i}_3. \tag{M1-19}$$

Consequentely for the Cartesian, cylindrical, and spherical coordinates we obtain respectively, taking into account (M1-16, 17, 18),

$$\left\{\begin{aligned} \operatorname{grad} f &= \frac{\partial f}{\partial x}\boldsymbol{i} + \frac{\partial f}{\partial y}\boldsymbol{j} + \frac{\partial f}{\partial z}\boldsymbol{k}, \\ \operatorname{grad} f &= \frac{\partial f}{\partial r}\boldsymbol{i}_r + \frac{1}{r}\frac{\partial f}{\partial \varphi}\boldsymbol{i}_\varphi + \frac{\partial f}{\partial z}\boldsymbol{k}, \\ \operatorname{grad} f &= \frac{\partial f}{\partial r}\boldsymbol{i}_r + \frac{1}{r}\frac{\partial f}{\partial \theta}\boldsymbol{i}_\theta + \frac{1}{r\sin\theta}\frac{\partial f}{\partial \varphi}\boldsymbol{i}_\varphi. \end{aligned}\right. \tag{M1-20}$$

Let us now calculate the divergence of a vector $\boldsymbol{v}$ from the definition (M1-4) taking for the infinitesimal volume V that of the elementary cell. The outward flux from the face u_1 of the elementary volume is $d\Phi_1 = -\, v_1 d\Sigma_1 = -\, v_1 h_2 h_3 du_2 du_3$. The outward flux across the opposite face (which is displaced from u_1 to $u_1 + du_1$) is greater by $\partial(d\Phi_1)/\partial u_1 \cdot du_1$ and has the opposite sign. By adding the two fluxes the total $d\Phi_1$ is obtained:

$$d\Phi_1 = \frac{\partial(h_2 h_3 v_1)}{\partial u_1} du_1 du_2 du_3.$$

By adding then the fluxes of the other two pairs of opposite faces we have

$$d\Phi = \left[\frac{\partial}{\partial u_1}(h_2 h_3 v_1) + \frac{\partial}{\partial u_2}(h_3 h_1 v_2) + \frac{\partial}{\partial u_3}(h_1 h_2 v_3)\right] du_1 du_2 du_3.$$

Finally, dividing by the elementary volume (M1-13) we obtain the divergence

$$\text{(M1-21)}\quad \operatorname{div} \boldsymbol{v} = \frac{1}{h_1 h_2 h_3}\left[\frac{\partial}{\partial u_1}(h_2 h_3 v_1) + \frac{\partial}{\partial u_2}(h_3 h_1 v_2) + \frac{\partial}{\partial u_3}(h_1 h_2 v_3)\right].$$

In the three systems of coordinates we shall have

$$\text{(M1-22)}\quad \begin{cases} \operatorname{div} \boldsymbol{v} = \dfrac{\partial v_x}{\partial x} + \dfrac{\partial v_y}{\partial y} + \dfrac{\partial v_z}{\partial z}, \\[2ex] \operatorname{div} \boldsymbol{v} = \dfrac{1}{r}\dfrac{\partial}{\partial r}(r v_r) + \dfrac{1}{r}\dfrac{\partial v_\theta}{\partial \theta} + \dfrac{\partial v_z}{\partial z}, \\[2ex] \operatorname{div} \boldsymbol{v} = \dfrac{1}{r^2}\dfrac{\partial}{\partial r}(r^2 v_r) + \dfrac{1}{r \sin\theta}\dfrac{\partial}{\partial \theta}(\sin\theta\, v_\theta) + \dfrac{1}{r\sin\theta}\dfrac{\partial v_\varphi}{\partial \varphi}. \end{cases}$$

Let us now calculate the circulation around the boundary of the u_1-face (Fig. 8M) of the elementary cell ($\boldsymbol{i}_1$, $\boldsymbol{i}_2$, $\boldsymbol{i}_3$ are a direct triad). The line integral along the side u_2 is $dC_2 = \boldsymbol{v} \cdot \boldsymbol{i}_2 ds_2 = v_2 h_2 du_2$. The line integral along the opposite side is increased by $\partial(dC_2)/\partial u_3 du_3$ and has the sign reversed. Upon adding the contributions of the two sides we have

$$dC_2 = -\frac{\partial(h_2 v_2)}{\partial u_3} du_2 du_3.$$

Adding the contribution of the other two sides and dividing by the elementary area $ds_2 ds_3 = h_2 h_3 du_2 du_3$, we obtain by (M1-6)

$$(\operatorname{curl} \boldsymbol{v})_1 = \frac{1}{h_2 h_3}\left[\frac{\partial(h_3 v_3)}{\partial u_2} - \frac{\partial(h_2 v_2)}{\partial u_3}\right];$$

hence

(M1-23)
$$\operatorname{curl} \boldsymbol{v} = \frac{1}{h_2 h_3}\left[\frac{\partial(h_3 v_3)}{\partial u_2} - \frac{\partial(h_2 v_2)}{\partial u_3}\right]\boldsymbol{i}_1 + \\ + \frac{1}{h_3 h_1}\left[\frac{\partial(h_1 v_1)}{\partial u_3} - \frac{\partial(h_3 v_3)}{\partial u_1}\right]\boldsymbol{i}_2 + \frac{1}{h_1 h_2}\left[\frac{\partial(h_2 v_2)}{\partial u_1} - \frac{\partial(h_1 v_1)}{\partial u_2}\right]\boldsymbol{i}_3.$$

In the three particular systems we have

(M1-24)
$$\begin{cases} \operatorname{curl} \boldsymbol{v} = \left(\dfrac{\partial v_z}{\partial y} - \dfrac{\partial v_y}{\partial z}\right)\boldsymbol{i} + \left(\dfrac{\partial v_x}{\partial z} - \dfrac{\partial v_z}{\partial x}\right)\boldsymbol{j} + \left(\dfrac{\partial v_y}{\partial x} - \dfrac{\partial v_x}{\partial y}\right)\boldsymbol{k}, \\ \operatorname{curl} \boldsymbol{v} = \left(\dfrac{1}{r}\dfrac{\partial v_z}{\partial \theta} - \dfrac{\partial v_\theta}{\partial z}\right)\boldsymbol{i}_r + \left(\dfrac{\partial v_r}{\partial z} - \dfrac{\partial v_z}{\partial r}\right)\boldsymbol{i}_\theta + \\ \qquad\qquad + \left(\dfrac{1}{r}\dfrac{\partial (r v_\theta)}{\partial r} - \dfrac{1}{r}\dfrac{\partial v_r}{\partial \theta}\right)\boldsymbol{k}, \\ \operatorname{curl} \boldsymbol{v} = \dfrac{1}{r \sin\theta}\left(\dfrac{\partial}{\partial \theta}(v_\varphi \sin\theta) - \dfrac{\partial v_\theta}{\partial \varphi}\right)\boldsymbol{i}_r + \\ \qquad + \dfrac{1}{r}\left(\dfrac{1}{\sin\theta}\dfrac{\partial v_r}{\partial \varphi} - \dfrac{\partial}{\partial r}(r v_\varphi)\right)\boldsymbol{i}_\theta + \dfrac{1}{r}\left(\dfrac{\partial}{\partial r}(r v_\theta) - \dfrac{\partial v_r}{\partial \theta}\right)\boldsymbol{i}_\varphi. \end{cases}$$

The Symbolic Vector $\boldsymbol{\nabla}$

§ 12. In order to find most readily the relations connecting the differential vector operators, it is often useful to introduce the symbolic vector $\boldsymbol{\nabla}$, defined by its Cartesian components, as follows:

$$\boldsymbol{\nabla} = \boldsymbol{i}\frac{\partial}{\partial x} + \boldsymbol{j}\frac{\partial}{\partial y} + \boldsymbol{k}\frac{\partial}{\partial z}.$$

It is easily seen that, carrying out the formal operations, we have

$$\boldsymbol{\nabla} f = \operatorname{grad} f, \qquad \boldsymbol{\nabla} \cdot v = \operatorname{div} \boldsymbol{v}, \qquad \boldsymbol{\nabla} \wedge \boldsymbol{v} = \operatorname{curl} \boldsymbol{v}.$$

Note, incidentally, that the third equation shows that curl $\boldsymbol{v}$ is really a vector.

By means of the vector $\boldsymbol{\nabla}$ we obtain at once, for example,

$$\operatorname{curl} \operatorname{grad} f = \boldsymbol{\nabla} \wedge \boldsymbol{\nabla} f = 0, \qquad \operatorname{div} \operatorname{curl} \boldsymbol{v} = \boldsymbol{\nabla} \,.\, \boldsymbol{\nabla} \wedge \boldsymbol{v} = 0,$$

by virtue of a known property of the vector and mixed products.

Great care is recommended when using the vector $\boldsymbol{\nabla}$ in order not to forget its character of a *differential operator*. It cannot be commuted with the quantity to which it is applied; and when applied to a product it must act on each factor, like ordinary derivation. Keeping this precaution in mind, the following useful relations can be easily obtained:

(M1-25) $\quad \text{grad}\, fg = \boldsymbol{\nabla} fg = g\boldsymbol{\nabla} f + f\boldsymbol{\nabla} g = g \,\text{grad}\, f + f \,\text{grad}\, g,$

(M1-26) $\quad \text{grad}\, g(f) = \boldsymbol{\nabla} g(f) = g'(f)\boldsymbol{\nabla} f = g'(f)\, \text{grad}\, f,$

(M1-27) $\quad \text{div}\, f\boldsymbol{v} = \boldsymbol{\nabla} \cdot f\boldsymbol{v} = \boldsymbol{\nabla} f \cdot \boldsymbol{v} + f\boldsymbol{\nabla} \cdot \boldsymbol{v} = \boldsymbol{v} \cdot \text{grad}\, f + f \,\text{div}\, \boldsymbol{v},$

(M1-28) $$\text{div}\,(\boldsymbol{u} \wedge \boldsymbol{v}) = \boldsymbol{\nabla} \cdot \boldsymbol{u} \wedge \boldsymbol{v} = \begin{cases} \boldsymbol{\nabla} \wedge \boldsymbol{u} \cdot \boldsymbol{v} \\ -\boldsymbol{\nabla} \wedge \boldsymbol{v} \cdot \boldsymbol{u} \end{cases} = \boldsymbol{v} \cdot \text{curl}\, \boldsymbol{u} - \boldsymbol{u} \cdot \text{curl}\, \boldsymbol{v}$$

(M1-29) $$\text{curl}\, f\boldsymbol{v} = \boldsymbol{\nabla} \wedge f\boldsymbol{v} = \boldsymbol{\nabla} f \wedge \boldsymbol{v} + f\boldsymbol{\nabla} \wedge \boldsymbol{v} = \text{grad}\, f \wedge \boldsymbol{v} + f \,\text{curl}\, \boldsymbol{v},$$

(M1-30) $$\text{curl curl}\, \boldsymbol{v} = \boldsymbol{\nabla} \wedge (\boldsymbol{\nabla} \wedge \boldsymbol{v}) = \boldsymbol{\nabla}(\boldsymbol{\nabla} \cdot \boldsymbol{v}) - (\boldsymbol{\nabla} \cdot \boldsymbol{\nabla})\boldsymbol{v} = \text{grad div}\, \boldsymbol{v} - \nabla^2 \boldsymbol{v}.$$

In the same manner many other relations could be obtained, but there is no purpose in developing them.

Sometimes it is convenient to apply $\boldsymbol{\nabla}$ to the quantity which precedes it. In this case we shall write $\overleftarrow{\boldsymbol{\nabla}}$. For example, $\boldsymbol{v} \cdot \overleftarrow{\boldsymbol{\nabla}} = \text{div}\, \boldsymbol{v}$.

Laplacian Operator

§ 13. The operator ∇^2, which was introduced in the last equation, expressed in Cartesian coordinates is

(M1-31) $$\nabla^2 = \frac{\partial^2}{\partial x^2} + \frac{\partial^2}{\partial y^2} + \frac{\partial^2}{\partial z^2}.$$

It is known as the *Laplacian* operator and it is a *scalar* linear operator of the second order.

When ∇^2 is applied to a scalar, it is obviously equal to div grad. By (M1-21, 19) we have

$$\text{(M1-32)}\quad \nabla^2 f = \frac{1}{h_1 h_2 h_3}\left[\frac{\partial}{\partial u_1}\left(\frac{h_2 h_3}{h_1}\frac{\partial f}{\partial u_1}\right) + \frac{\partial}{\partial u_2}\left(\frac{h_3 h_1}{h_2}\frac{\partial f}{\partial u_2}\right) + \frac{\partial}{\partial u_3}\left(\frac{h_1 h_2}{h_3}\frac{\partial f}{\partial u_3}\right)\right],$$

and in cylindrical and spherical coordinates respectively

$$\text{(M1-33)}\quad \begin{cases} \nabla^2 f = \dfrac{1}{r}\dfrac{\partial}{\partial r}\left(r\dfrac{\partial f}{\partial r}\right) + \dfrac{1}{r^2}\dfrac{\partial^2 f}{\partial \theta^2} + \dfrac{\partial^2 f}{\partial z^2}, \\ \nabla^2 f = \dfrac{1}{r^2}\dfrac{\partial}{\partial r}\left(r^2\dfrac{\partial f}{\partial r}\right) + \dfrac{1}{r^2 \sin\theta}\dfrac{\partial}{\partial \theta}\left(\sin\theta\dfrac{\partial f}{\partial \theta}\right) + \dfrac{1}{r^2 \sin^2\theta}\dfrac{\partial^2 f}{\partial \varphi^2}. \end{cases}$$

If ∇^2 is to be applied to a vector, we write the vector by means of its Cartesian components. Since the unit vectors of the Cartesian axes are constant, ∇^2 may be applied to each component separately, obtaining $\nabla^2 \boldsymbol{v} = (\nabla^2 v_x)\boldsymbol{i} + (\nabla^2 v_y)\boldsymbol{j} + (\nabla^2 v_z)\boldsymbol{k}$. Here ∇^2 acts on scalar quantities and (M1-31, 32, 33) may be applied.

Green's Formulas

§ 14. Equation (M1-27) yields

$$\operatorname{div}(f \operatorname{grad} g) = \operatorname{grad} f \cdot \operatorname{grad} g + f\nabla^2 g,$$

and by the divergence theorem (M1-5) we have

$$\text{(M1-34)}\quad \iiint\limits_V f\nabla^2 g \, dV = -\iiint\limits_V \operatorname{grad} f \cdot \operatorname{grad} g \, dV + \oint\!\!\oint\limits_\Sigma f\frac{\partial g}{\partial n}\, d\Sigma.$$

Interchanging f and g and subtracting the resulting equation from (M1-34), we find

$$\text{(M1-35)}\quad \iiint\limits_V (f\nabla^2 g - g\nabla^2 f)\, dV = \oint\!\!\oint\limits_\Sigma \left(f\frac{\partial g}{\partial n} - g\frac{\partial f}{\partial n}\right) d\Sigma.$$

The last two equations are known as *Green's formulas*.

A vector analog of these formulas can be found in the following way. From (M1-28) we have

$$\operatorname{div}(\boldsymbol{u} \wedge \operatorname{curl} \boldsymbol{v}) = \operatorname{curl} \boldsymbol{u} \cdot \operatorname{curl} \boldsymbol{v} - \boldsymbol{u} \cdot \operatorname{curl}\operatorname{curl} \boldsymbol{v},$$

and by the divergence theorem (M1-5)

(M1-36) $$\iiint(\text{curl}\,\boldsymbol{u}\cdot\text{curl}\,\boldsymbol{v}-\boldsymbol{u}\cdot\text{curl curl}\,\boldsymbol{v})dV=\oiint_{\Sigma}\boldsymbol{u}\wedge\text{curl}\,\boldsymbol{v}\cdot\boldsymbol{n}d\Sigma$$

Upon interchanging $\boldsymbol{u}$ and $\boldsymbol{v}$ and subtracting the resulting equation from (M1-36) we obtain

(M1-37) $$\iiint_{V}(\boldsymbol{v}\cdot\text{curl curl}\,\boldsymbol{u}-\boldsymbol{u}\cdot\text{curl curl}\,\boldsymbol{v})dV=$$
$$=\oiint_{\Sigma}(\boldsymbol{u}\wedge\text{curl}\,\boldsymbol{v}-\boldsymbol{v}\wedge\text{curl}\,\boldsymbol{u})\cdot\boldsymbol{n}\,d\Sigma.$$

Equations (M1-36, 37) represent the desired formulas.

M2. **Elements of Tensor Calculus**

Vectors in n-Dimensional Space

§ 1. In elementary physics one considers vectors in three-dimensional space. The generalization to an Euclidean n-dimensional space presents no difficulties other than the impossibility of visualizing geometrical entities.

In an Euclidean n-dimensional space we shall consider n mutually orthogonal unit vectors $\boldsymbol{i}_1, \boldsymbol{i}_2, \ldots, \boldsymbol{i}_n$ (*fundamental unit vectors*). Any vector of this space will be expressed by

$$\boldsymbol{v}=v_1\boldsymbol{i}_1+v_2\boldsymbol{i}_2+\ldots+v_n\boldsymbol{i}_n=\Sigma v_k\boldsymbol{i}_k.$$

We shall also write

(M2-1) $$\boldsymbol{v}=v_k\boldsymbol{i}_k,$$

with the convention that the occurrence of the same subscript twice in a product implies summation over the values of that subscript from 1 to n. This convention will be adopted throughout this volume unless the contrary is stated. The quantities v_k are called the *components* of the vector.

For the sum and the scalar product the same rules will hold as in the three-dimensional case. Hence it follows that $v_k = \boldsymbol{v} \cdot \boldsymbol{i}_k$ and $\boldsymbol{u} \cdot \boldsymbol{v} = u_k v_k$.

Orthogonal Transformations

§ **2.** Let us investigate the manner in which the components vary when passing from the reference system $\boldsymbol{i}_1, \ldots \boldsymbol{i}_n$ to a *new* orthogonal system $\boldsymbol{i}'_1 \ldots \boldsymbol{i}'_n$. We shall have

$$\boldsymbol{v} = v'_k \boldsymbol{i}'_k = v_k \boldsymbol{i}_k. \tag{M2-2}$$

Forming the scalar product of both sides and $\boldsymbol{i}'_1$ and taking into account that $\boldsymbol{i}'_k \cdot \boldsymbol{i}'_j = \delta_{kj}$ we obtain (†)

$$v'_j = v_k(\boldsymbol{i}'_j \cdot \boldsymbol{i}'_k), \tag{M2-3}$$

or, introducing the direction cosines $\alpha_{jk} = \boldsymbol{i}'_j \cdot \boldsymbol{i}'_k$ of the $\boldsymbol{i}'$ with respect to the $\boldsymbol{i}$,

$$v'_j = \alpha_{jk} v_k. \tag{M2-4}$$

We shall state that a vector is defined when n numbers v_k are given subject to the transformation (M2-4) for changes in the orthogonal system of references.

Interchanging the quantities with primes and without primes and remembering the definition of α_{jk} it is evident that from (M2-4) the inverse transformation follows:

$$v_j = \alpha_{kj} v'_k. \tag{M2-5}$$

§ **3.** The quantities α_{jk} form a matrix with n rows and n columns. These quantities are not completely arbitrary, for they must be ≤ 1 and in addition are subject to certain conditions that will be derived.

(†) As is well known, δ_{kj} (*Kronecker's symbol*) equals 1 or zero according to whether $k = j$ or $k \neq j$.

Let us express $\boldsymbol{i}'_j$ by means of its components as was done for $\boldsymbol{v}$ in (M2-1):

$$\boldsymbol{i}'_j = \alpha_{jk}\boldsymbol{i}_k.$$

By making the scalar product with $\boldsymbol{i}'_l$ we have

$$\boldsymbol{i}'_j \cdot \boldsymbol{i}'_l = \alpha_{jk}\boldsymbol{i}'_l \cdot \boldsymbol{i}_k = \alpha_{jk}\alpha_{lk},$$

whence

(M2-6) $$\alpha_{jk}\alpha_{lk} = \delta_{jl}.$$

Since it is immaterial which is the old and which is the new reference system, it will obviously follow that $\alpha_{kj}\alpha_{kl} = \delta_{jl}$. The quantities α_{jk} subject to the conditions (M2-6) define an *orthogonal transformation* in n-dimensional space. The *determinant* of the transformation is

$$\varDelta = \begin{vmatrix} \alpha_{11} & \cdots & \alpha_{1n} \\ \cdot & \cdots & \cdot \\ \cdot & \cdots & \cdot \\ \alpha_{n1} & \cdots & \alpha_{nn} \end{vmatrix}.$$

Multiplying $\varDelta$ by itself, we obtain (†)

$$\varDelta^2 = \begin{vmatrix} \alpha_{1k}\alpha_{1k} & \alpha_{1k}\alpha_{2k} & \cdots & \alpha_{1k}\alpha_{nk} \\ \alpha_{2k}\alpha_{1k} & \alpha_{2k}\alpha_{2k} & \cdots & \alpha_{2k}\alpha_{nk} \\ \cdot & \cdot & \cdots & \cdot \\ \cdot & \cdot & \cdots & \cdot \\ \alpha_{nk}\alpha_{1k} & \alpha_{nk}\alpha_{2k} & \cdots & \alpha_{nk}\alpha_{nk} \end{vmatrix} = \begin{vmatrix} \delta_{11} & \cdots & \delta_{1n} \\ \cdot & \cdots & \cdot \\ \cdot & \cdots & \cdot \\ \delta_{n1} & \cdots & \delta_{nn} \end{vmatrix} = 1.$$

Hence $\varDelta = \pm 1$. The fundamental systems $\boldsymbol{i}_k$ and $\boldsymbol{i}'_k$ are said to be congruent if they can be superimposed on one another by means of a continuous and rigid movement. During this movement the variation of $\varDelta$ must be continuous and, since at the end we have $\varDelta = 1$, the same value will hold throughout the process. Hence for any two congruent systems we shall have

(M2-7) $$\varDelta = 1.$$

We shall be concerned solely with this case.

(†) Note that the subscript n which appears twice will not imply summation in this case.

Variance and Invariance

§ **4.** Physics distinguishes between *variant* and *invariant* scalar quantities. The invariant quantities do not vary when the fundamental system is changed (in particular, by means of an orthogonal transformation), whereas the variant quantities vary according to well-determined laws. For example, the temperature at a point is invariant, while the component of a force is variant, as may be seen from (M2-4).

The scalar product of two fixed vectors is an invariant. Indeed by (M2-5, 6) we have

$$\boldsymbol{u} \cdot \boldsymbol{v} = u_j v_j = \alpha_{kj} u'_k \alpha_{lj} v'_l = \delta_{kl} u'_k v'_l = u'_k v'_k.$$

A set of n numbers varying according to (M2-4, 5) represents a vector. The Cartesian coordinates of a point have exactly that type of variance. Consequently, they represent a vector (position vector of the point). Indeed for a fixed origin we have

(M2-8) $$x_k = \alpha_{jk} x'_j.$$

The square of the distance $(P - O)^2 = x_j x_j$ of a point P from the origin O is invariant (invariance of the scalar product).

The partial derivatives of a scalar f with respect to the Cartesian coordinates transform as follows (extending the summation convention to this case):

$$\frac{\partial f}{\partial x'_j} = \frac{\partial f}{\partial x_k} \frac{\partial x_k}{\partial x'_j} = \alpha_{jk} \frac{\partial f}{\partial x_k}.$$

This law of transformation is identical with that of the components of a vector. Consequently grad f and $\boldsymbol{\nabla}$ defined by means of the Cartesian components are really vectors, even in an n-dimensional space.

If one defines div $\boldsymbol{v} = \boldsymbol{\nabla} \cdot \boldsymbol{v}$ it follows by the invariance of the scalar product that the divergence of a vector is an invariant. Of course, the Laplacian $\nabla^2 f = \boldsymbol{\nabla} \cdot \boldsymbol{\nabla} f =$ div grad f is also an invariant (†).

(†) In the three-dimensional case it follows also that $\boldsymbol{\nabla} \wedge \boldsymbol{v} =$ curl $\boldsymbol{v}$ is a true vector.

Tensors

§ 5. Not all the quantities that appear in physics are scalars (associated with no direction) or vectors (associated with one direction). There are also more complex quantities, which in a typical case are associated with two or more directions.

Consider, for example, the internal stress of a continuous material body. For any surface element (defined by the direction of its normal) the force acting upon it (and therefore a second direction) must be specified. As is well known, the stress is completely defined by specifying the $\boldsymbol{i}_1$, $\boldsymbol{i}_2$, $\boldsymbol{i}_3$ components of the forces acting on each one of the surface elements perpendicular to $\boldsymbol{i}_1$, $\boldsymbol{i}_2$, $\boldsymbol{i}_3$ respectively. Any one of the nine quantities Φ_{jk} thus defined is associated with a pair $\boldsymbol{i}_j\boldsymbol{i}_k$ of fundamental unit vectors, whereas each component of a vector is associated with only one unit vector. It is natural, therefore, to assume as a fundamental system of reference the nine pairs $\boldsymbol{i}_j\boldsymbol{i}_k$ which are called the fundamental *dyads*. The Φ_{jk} are the *components* with respect to the fundamental dyads of an intrinsic entity which is termed a *tensor*.

By analogy with (M2-1) we shall write

$$\mathbf{\Phi} = \Phi_{jk}\boldsymbol{i}_j\boldsymbol{i}_k, \tag{M2-9}$$

implying summation over the subscripts j and k.

For obvious reasons, $\mathbf{\Phi}$ will be said to be a tensor of the second rank, while a vector is a tensor of the first rank and a scalar is a tensor of rank zero. With an easy generalization one can speak of m-th rank tensors (referred to fundamental *triads*, *tetrads*, and so on, instead of dyads) and of tensors in n-dimensional space. A second rank tensor in n-dimensional space will have n^2 components, n^2 being also the number of the fundamental dyads. In this chapter, unless stated to the contrary, we shall refer only to second rank tensors for the sake of convenience. But of course our considerations can be extended to the tensors of any rank.

§ 6. We shall picture the dyad $\boldsymbol{i}_j\boldsymbol{i}_k$ as a product (neither scalar nor vector product, of course) possessing all but the commutative properties of ordinary algebra.

Since α_{jk} is the component of $\boldsymbol{i}_k$ with respect to $\boldsymbol{i}'_j$, we can write

$$\boldsymbol{i}_k = \alpha_{jk}\boldsymbol{i}'_j .$$

Hence the transformation formula for the fundamental dyads will be

$$\boldsymbol{i}_k\boldsymbol{i}_m = \alpha_{jk}\boldsymbol{i}'_j\alpha_{lm}\boldsymbol{i}'_l = \alpha_{jk}\alpha_{lm}\boldsymbol{i}'_j\boldsymbol{i}'_l .$$

From this we derive for a second rank tensor $\boldsymbol{T}$

$$\boldsymbol{T} = T_{km}\boldsymbol{i}_k\boldsymbol{i}_m = T_{km}\alpha_{jk}\alpha_{lm}\boldsymbol{i}'_j\boldsymbol{i}'_l = T'_{jl}\boldsymbol{i}'_j\boldsymbol{i}'_l ,$$

with

(M2-10) $$T'_{jl} = \alpha_{jk}\alpha_{lm}T_{km}.$$

This equation represents the law of variance for the components of a tensor and is an obvious generalization of (M2-4). A physical quantity represented by n^2 numbers will be said to be a tensor if and only if these numbers are subject to the transformation law (M2-10). For example, this is actually the case for the stress tensor $\boldsymbol{\Phi}$ (as one can easily derive from the Cauchy relation $\boldsymbol{\Phi}_n = n_k\boldsymbol{\Phi}_k$).

A tensor $\boldsymbol{T}$ is said to be symmetrical when $T_{km} = T_{mk}$ and anti-symmetrical when $T_{km} = -T_{mk}$. It is evident from (M2-10) that the properties of symmetry and anti-symmetry are preserved in an orthogonal transformation; they are invariant properties. If $\boldsymbol{T}$ is anti-symmetrical, all the components with equal subscripts are zero.

The determinant

$$\det \boldsymbol{T} = \begin{vmatrix} T_{11} & \dots & T_{1n} \\ \dots & \dots & \dots \\ T_{n1} & \dots & T_{nn} \end{vmatrix}$$

of the components of a tensor is invariant to an orthogonal transformation. To show this let us multiply it by the determinant Δ of the transformation, which is unity. We shall obtain a new determinant of the same rank with the elements given by $p_{lk} = \alpha_{lm}T_{km}$. If we multiply again by Δ we shall obtain a determinant whose elements are $q_{jl} = \alpha_{jk}p_{lk} = \alpha_{jk}\alpha_{lm}T_{km}$ or T'_{jl} by (M2-10). Thus det $\boldsymbol{T}$ is an invariant.

The tensor

(M2-11) $$\boldsymbol{U} = \boldsymbol{i}_k \boldsymbol{i}_k,$$

whose components are $U_{lk} = \delta_{lk}$ is called the *fundamental tensor.* It is easy to show that its components have the same values in any system of reference. Indeed by (M2-10, 6) we obtain

$$U'_{jl} = \alpha_{jk}\alpha_{lm} U_{km} = \alpha_{jk}\alpha_{lm}\delta_{km} = \alpha_{jk}\alpha_{lk} = \delta_{jl}.$$

Finally the name dyad will be extended to the product of any two vectors $\boldsymbol{uv}$ obtained with a formal application of the laws of algebra:

$$\boldsymbol{uv} = u_j \boldsymbol{i}_j v_k \boldsymbol{i}_k = u_j v_k \boldsymbol{i}_j \boldsymbol{i}_k.$$

The components of $u_j v_k$ transform just like the components of a tensor, as one sees by applying the transformation formulas of the vectors.

Scalar Products

§ 7. With a view to generalizing the scalar product, we shall by definition let $\boldsymbol{i}_k \boldsymbol{i}_l \cdot \boldsymbol{i}_m = \boldsymbol{i}_k(\boldsymbol{i}_l \cdot \boldsymbol{i}_m) = \delta_{lm}\boldsymbol{i}_k$ and $\boldsymbol{i}_k \cdot \boldsymbol{i}_l \boldsymbol{i}_m = (\boldsymbol{i}_k \cdot \boldsymbol{i}_l)\boldsymbol{i}_m = \delta_{kl}\boldsymbol{i}_m$. Then we obtain for a tensor $\boldsymbol{T}$ and a vector $\boldsymbol{v}$ the two *scalar products*

(M2-12) $$\begin{cases} \boldsymbol{T} \cdot \boldsymbol{v} = (T_{kl}\boldsymbol{i}_k \boldsymbol{i}_l) \cdot (v_m \boldsymbol{i}_m) = T_{kl} v_m \boldsymbol{i}_k \boldsymbol{i}_l \cdot \boldsymbol{i}_m = \\ \qquad = T_{kl} v_m \delta_{lm} \boldsymbol{i}_k = T_{kl} v_l \boldsymbol{i}_k, \\ \boldsymbol{v} \cdot \boldsymbol{T} = (v_k \boldsymbol{i}_k) \cdot (T_{lm} \boldsymbol{i}_l \boldsymbol{i}_m) = v_k T_{lm} \boldsymbol{i}_k \cdot \boldsymbol{i}_l \boldsymbol{i}_m = \\ \qquad = v_k T_{lm} \delta_{kl} \boldsymbol{i}_m = v_k T_{km} \boldsymbol{i}_m. \end{cases}$$

The results of these products are vectors (because their components present the required type of variance, as it would be easy to show) and in general $\boldsymbol{T} \cdot \boldsymbol{v} \neq \boldsymbol{v} \cdot \boldsymbol{T}$.

The condition $\boldsymbol{T} \cdot \boldsymbol{v} = \boldsymbol{v} \cdot \boldsymbol{T}$ is characteristic of symmetrical tensors, as is evident.

It can be proved that the definitions of the scalar products given for the fundamental dyads are valid for any dyad. By writing all the expressions in components one readily finds the useful formulas

(M2-13) $$\boldsymbol{uv} \cdot \boldsymbol{w} = \boldsymbol{u}(\boldsymbol{v} \cdot \boldsymbol{w}) = \boldsymbol{w} \cdot \boldsymbol{vu}; \quad \boldsymbol{u} \cdot \boldsymbol{vw} = (\boldsymbol{u} \cdot \boldsymbol{v})\boldsymbol{w} = \boldsymbol{wv} \cdot \boldsymbol{u}.$$

For any vector $\boldsymbol{v}$ we shall have

$$\boldsymbol{v} \cdot \boldsymbol{U} = \boldsymbol{U} \cdot \boldsymbol{v} = \boldsymbol{v}, \tag{M2-14}$$

a characteristic relation of the fundamental tensor.

One may notice that by means of the dyads the double vector product becomes

$$(\boldsymbol{u} \wedge \boldsymbol{v}) \wedge \boldsymbol{w} = \boldsymbol{w} \wedge (\boldsymbol{v} \wedge \boldsymbol{u}) = \boldsymbol{w} \cdot (\boldsymbol{uv} - \boldsymbol{vu}). \tag{M2-15}$$

In tensor calculus it is also possible to give a meaning to the double scalar product. It is possible to form the scalar product of a tensor and a vector, and then to form the scalar product of the result and a second vector. We shall make the convention that the double scalar product may be written in either of the two following ways:

$$(\boldsymbol{T} \cdot \boldsymbol{u}) \cdot \boldsymbol{v} = \boldsymbol{T} : \boldsymbol{uv}, \tag{M2-16}$$

The right side will be termed the double scalar product of $\boldsymbol{T}$ and the dyad $\boldsymbol{uv}$. One can esaily prove that by this convention the necessary and sufficient condition for $\boldsymbol{T}$ to be symmetrical is that for any dyad $\boldsymbol{uv}$ the relation

$$\boldsymbol{T} : (\boldsymbol{uv} - \boldsymbol{vu}) = 0. \tag{M2-17}$$

will hold.

One can extend the definitions of simple and double scalar products to two tensors $\boldsymbol{T}$ and $\boldsymbol{Z}$:

$$\boldsymbol{T} \cdot \boldsymbol{Z} = T_{jk} Z_{kl} \boldsymbol{i}_j \boldsymbol{i}_l, \tag{M2-18}$$

$$\boldsymbol{T} : \boldsymbol{Z} = T_{jk} Z_{kj}. \tag{M2-19}$$

Finally notice the relation

$$\boldsymbol{Z} \cdot (\boldsymbol{T} \cdot \boldsymbol{v}) = (\boldsymbol{Z} \cdot \boldsymbol{T}) \cdot \boldsymbol{v}, \tag{M2-20}$$

whose proof offers no difficulty.

Inverse of a Tensor

§ 8. The equation

(M2-21) $$\boldsymbol{v} = \boldsymbol{T} \cdot \boldsymbol{u},$$

states that the components of $\boldsymbol{v}$ are linear combinations of those of $\boldsymbol{u}$ and it is equivalent to a system of n scalar equations. Now if det $\boldsymbol{T} \neq 0$ this system can be solved for the components of $\boldsymbol{u}$, which will be expressed as linear combinations of the components of $\boldsymbol{v}$. As a consequence there will exist a tensor $\boldsymbol{T}^{-1}$, such that

(M2-22) $$\boldsymbol{u} = \boldsymbol{T}^{-1} \cdot \boldsymbol{v}.$$

The tensor $\boldsymbol{T}^{-1}$ will be called the *inverse* of $\boldsymbol{T}$ because one passes from (M2-21) to (M2-22) by carrying out, as it were, a division by $\boldsymbol{T}$. Introducing into (M2-22) the expression (M2-21) of $\boldsymbol{v}$ and remembering (M2-20), one obtains

(M2-23) $$\boldsymbol{u} = \boldsymbol{T}^{-1} \cdot (\boldsymbol{T} \cdot \boldsymbol{u}) = (\boldsymbol{T}^{-1} \cdot \boldsymbol{T}) \cdot \boldsymbol{u},$$

whence by (M2-14)

(M2-24) $$\boldsymbol{T}^{-1} \cdot \boldsymbol{T} = \boldsymbol{U}.$$

In a similar way one obtains $\boldsymbol{T} \cdot \boldsymbol{T}^{-1} = \boldsymbol{U}$. These relations can be assumed as a definition of the inverse tensor.

If $\boldsymbol{T}$ is symmetrical, (M2-23) may be written

$$\boldsymbol{u} = \boldsymbol{T}^{-1} \cdot (\boldsymbol{u} \cdot \boldsymbol{T}) = (\boldsymbol{T}^{-1} \cdot \boldsymbol{u}) \cdot \boldsymbol{T},$$

and forming the scalar product of each side with $\boldsymbol{T}^{-1}$ on the right, we get

$$\boldsymbol{u} \cdot \boldsymbol{T}^{-1} = \boldsymbol{T}^{-1} \cdot \boldsymbol{u}.$$

Thus $\boldsymbol{T}^{-1}$ is symmetrical, too.

Divergence of a Tensor

§ 9. Corresponding to the two scalar products of a tensor and a vector there are two different ways to define the *divergence* of a tensor $\boldsymbol{T}$. One can take either the expression $\boldsymbol{\nabla} \cdot \boldsymbol{T}$ or the expression $\boldsymbol{T} \cdot \overleftarrow{\boldsymbol{\nabla}}$ (the arrow indicating that $\boldsymbol{\nabla}$ operates on the preceding quantity). We shall choose the second form putting

(M2-25) $$\operatorname{div} \boldsymbol{T} = \boldsymbol{T} \cdot \overleftarrow{\nabla} = \frac{\partial T_{kl}}{\partial x_l} \boldsymbol{i}_k .$$

Note that div $\boldsymbol{T}$ is a vector.

Let us go back for a moment to the three-dimensional space and let Σ be a closed surface with the outward normal $\boldsymbol{n}$. The vector

$$\boldsymbol{\Phi} = \oint\!\!\oint_{\Sigma} \boldsymbol{T} \cdot \boldsymbol{n} \mathrm{d}\Sigma$$

will be called the outward *flux* of $\boldsymbol{T}$ across Σ.

By the first equation (M2-12) and the divergence theorem (M1-5) we shall have

(M2-26) $$\boldsymbol{\Phi} = \oint\!\!\oint_{\Sigma} T_{kl} n_l \boldsymbol{i}_k \mathrm{d}\Sigma = \boldsymbol{i}_k \oint\!\!\oint_{\Sigma} (T_{kl} \boldsymbol{i}_l) \cdot \boldsymbol{n} \mathrm{d}\Sigma =$$

$$= \boldsymbol{i}_k \iiint_V \operatorname{div} (T_{kl} \boldsymbol{i}_l) \mathrm{d}V = \iiint_V \frac{\partial T_{kl}}{\partial x_l} \boldsymbol{i}_k \mathrm{d}V = \iiint_V \operatorname{div} \boldsymbol{T} \mathrm{d}V.$$

This is the divergence theorem for a tensor. As is seen, div $\boldsymbol{T}$ may be defined as the limit of Φ/V for $V \to 0$.

Gradient of a Vector

§ 10. The symbolic vector ∇ can very well be the component of a dyad, the Cartesian components being defined in the usual way. Thus, given the vector $\boldsymbol{v}$ we have

(M2-27) $$\begin{cases} \nabla \boldsymbol{v} = \dfrac{\partial v_l}{\partial x_k} \boldsymbol{i}_k \boldsymbol{i}_l , \\ \boldsymbol{v} \overleftarrow{\nabla} = \dfrac{\partial v_k}{\partial x_l} \boldsymbol{i}_k \boldsymbol{i}_l = \operatorname{grad} \boldsymbol{v}. \end{cases}$$

The second of these dyads will be called the *gradient* of the vector $\boldsymbol{v}$. We see at once that for an infinitesimal displacement dP the increment of $\boldsymbol{v}$ will be d$\boldsymbol{v}$ = (grad $\boldsymbol{v}$) · dP.

Remembering the rules for the application of ∇ to a product we find the relation

$$\text{(M2-28)} \qquad \text{grad}\,(f\boldsymbol{v}) = f\,\text{grad}\,\boldsymbol{v} + \boldsymbol{v}\,\text{grad}\,f,$$

f being a scalar and $\boldsymbol{v}$ a vector. The last term is a dyad.

In the same way by (M2-13) we obtain

$$\text{(M2-29)} \quad \text{grad}\,(\boldsymbol{u}\cdot\boldsymbol{v}) = \begin{Bmatrix} \text{grad}\,(\boldsymbol{u}\cdot\boldsymbol{v}) \\ \text{grad}\,(\boldsymbol{v}\cdot\boldsymbol{u}) \end{Bmatrix} = \boldsymbol{u}\cdot\text{grad}\,\boldsymbol{v} + \boldsymbol{v}\cdot\text{grad}\,\boldsymbol{u}.$$

From the expansion (M2-15) of the double vector product taking into account (M2-13), one may derive

$$\boldsymbol{a} \wedge (\boldsymbol{b} \wedge \boldsymbol{c}) = \boldsymbol{a}\cdot\boldsymbol{cb} - \boldsymbol{cb}\cdot\boldsymbol{a},$$

whence it follows that

$$\text{(M2-30)} \quad \boldsymbol{u} \wedge \text{curl}\,\boldsymbol{v} = \boldsymbol{u} \wedge (\nabla \wedge \boldsymbol{v}) = \boldsymbol{u}\cdot\text{grad}\,\boldsymbol{v} - (\text{grad}\,\boldsymbol{v})\cdot\boldsymbol{u}.$$

We are now in a position to evaluate the curl of a vector product. We must remember that when ∇ is applied to a product we must take care that it operate on each factor separately. Since the double vector product may be written in either of the two ways

$$\boldsymbol{a} \wedge (\boldsymbol{b} \wedge \boldsymbol{c}) = \begin{cases} \boldsymbol{b}(\boldsymbol{a}\cdot\boldsymbol{c}) - \boldsymbol{c}(\boldsymbol{a}\cdot\boldsymbol{b}), \\ (\boldsymbol{ba})\cdot\boldsymbol{c} - (\boldsymbol{ca})\cdot\boldsymbol{b}, \end{cases}$$

we derive

$$\text{(M2-31)} \quad \text{curl}\,(\boldsymbol{u} \wedge \boldsymbol{v}) = \nabla \wedge (\boldsymbol{u} \wedge \boldsymbol{v}) = \\ = \boldsymbol{u}\,\text{div}\,\boldsymbol{v} - \boldsymbol{v}\,\text{div}\,\boldsymbol{u} + (\text{grad}\,\boldsymbol{u})\cdot\boldsymbol{v} - (\text{grad}\,\boldsymbol{v})\cdot\boldsymbol{u}.$$

Finally since $\boldsymbol{ab}\cdot\boldsymbol{c}$ may be written either as $\boldsymbol{a}(\boldsymbol{b}\cdot\boldsymbol{c})$ or as $\boldsymbol{ac}\cdot\boldsymbol{b}$ it is an easy matter to obtain the divergence of a dyad:

$$\text{(M2-32)} \quad \text{div}\,(\boldsymbol{uv}) = \boldsymbol{uv}\cdot\overleftarrow{\nabla} = \boldsymbol{u}(\boldsymbol{v}\cdot\overleftarrow{\nabla}) + (\boldsymbol{u}\overleftarrow{\nabla})\cdot\boldsymbol{v} = \\ = \boldsymbol{u}\,\text{div}\,\boldsymbol{v} + (\text{grad}\,\boldsymbol{u})\cdot\boldsymbol{v}.$$

Another useful formula can be obtained from (M2-32, 29, 30):

$$\text{(M2-33)} \quad \text{div}\,(\boldsymbol{uu}) - \frac{1}{2}\,\text{grad}\,(\boldsymbol{u}\cdot\boldsymbol{u}) = \boldsymbol{u}\,\text{div}\,\boldsymbol{u} - \boldsymbol{u} \wedge \text{curl}\,\boldsymbol{u}.$$

Consider now the tensor grad grad $f(P)$ where $f(P)$ represents a function of position on a plane. As grad $f = (\partial f/\partial x_k)\boldsymbol{i}_k$, we shall have by the definition (M2-27)

$$\text{grad grad } f = \frac{\partial^2 f}{\partial x_k \partial x_l} \boldsymbol{i}_k \boldsymbol{i}_l .$$

Hence we readily find

$$\text{(M2-34)} \qquad \det \text{grad grad } f = \frac{\partial^2 f}{\partial x^2}\frac{\partial^2 f}{\partial y^2} - \left(\frac{\partial^2 f}{\partial x\, \partial y}\right)^2 ,$$

that is to say that the determinant of grad grad f is the Hessian determinant of f with respect to x and y. It is invariant with respect to an orthogonal transformation.

Differential Properties of the Position Vector

§ 11. It is of interest to investigate the properties of the vector $\boldsymbol{r}(P, Q) = Q - P$ which will be termed the position vector of Q with respect to P. Let $\boldsymbol{s} = \boldsymbol{r}/r$ be the corresponding unit vector. In components we have

$$\text{(M2-35)} \qquad \boldsymbol{r} = (x_k^Q - x_k^P)\, \boldsymbol{i}_k .$$

By a simple geometrical consideration we deduce

$$\text{(M2-36)} \qquad \text{grad}_Q\, r = \boldsymbol{s} = -\,\text{grad}_P\, r$$

Furthermore from (M2-35)

$$\text{(M23-7)} \qquad \text{div}_Q\, \boldsymbol{r} = \frac{\partial r_k}{\partial x_k^Q} = 3 = -\,\text{div}_P\, \boldsymbol{r},$$

$$\text{(M2-38)} \quad \text{grad}_Q\, \boldsymbol{r} = \frac{\partial r_k}{\partial x_l^Q} \boldsymbol{i}_k \boldsymbol{i}_l = \delta_{kl} \boldsymbol{i}_k \boldsymbol{i}_l = \boldsymbol{U} = -\,\text{grad}_P\, \boldsymbol{r},$$

$\boldsymbol{U}$ being the fundamental tensor.

For the unit vector $\boldsymbol{s}$ we obtain by (M2-37, 38, 28)

$$\text{(M2-39)} \quad \text{div}_Q\, \boldsymbol{s} = \text{div}_Q \frac{\boldsymbol{r}}{r} = \frac{1}{r}\,\text{div}_Q\, \boldsymbol{r} + \boldsymbol{r} \cdot \text{grad}_Q \frac{1}{r} =$$

$$= \frac{3}{r} - \boldsymbol{r} \cdot \frac{\boldsymbol{s}}{r^2} = \frac{3}{r} - \frac{\boldsymbol{s} \cdot \boldsymbol{s}}{r} = \frac{2}{r} = -\,\text{div}_P\, \boldsymbol{s},$$

$$\text{(M2-40)} \quad \operatorname{grad}_Q \boldsymbol{s} = \operatorname{grad}_Q \frac{\boldsymbol{r}}{r} = \frac{1}{r} \operatorname{grad}_Q \boldsymbol{r} + $$

$$+ \boldsymbol{r} \operatorname{grad}_Q \frac{1}{r} = \frac{1}{r} (\boldsymbol{U} - \boldsymbol{ss}) = - \operatorname{grad}_P \boldsymbol{s}.$$

Finally it will be noticed that for a function $G(r)$ we have

$$\text{(M2-41)} \quad \operatorname{grad}_Q G(r) = G'(r) \operatorname{grad}_Q r = G'(r)\boldsymbol{s} = - \operatorname{grad}_P G(r).$$

Ricci's Tensor

§ 12. Thus far, only tensors of rank 2 or less than 2 have been considered. Now we must make an exception for *Ricci's tensor* $\boldsymbol{\epsilon}$. Its rank is equal to the number n of the dimensions of the space in which it is considered. The components $\varepsilon_{k_1 k_2 \ldots k_n}$ of Ricci's tensor are zero every time that two of the subscripts $k_1 k_2 \ldots k_n$ are equal; the other components are ± 1 according to whether the permutation $k_1 k_2 \ldots k_n$ is even or odd with respect to the fundamental permutation $1, 2, \ldots, n$.

The tensor character of $\boldsymbol{\epsilon}$ results from the fact that

$$\varepsilon'_{j_1 j_2 \ldots j_n} = \alpha_{j_1 k_1} \alpha_{j_2 k_2} \ldots \alpha_{j_n k_n} \varepsilon_{k_1 k_2 \ldots k_n}$$

is the determinant of the α (i.e., equal to 1) if $j_1 j_2 \ldots j_n$ is an even permutation, while it is the determinant with the reversed sign (i.e., equal to -1), if $j_1 j_2 \ldots j_n$ is an odd permutation.

In three-dimensional space we obviously have

$$\varepsilon_{k_1 k_2 k_3} = \boldsymbol{i}_{k_1} \cdot \boldsymbol{i}_{k_2} \wedge \boldsymbol{i}_{k_3}.$$

If $\boldsymbol{u}$ and $\boldsymbol{v}$ are vectors we have

$$\varepsilon_{k_1 k_2 k_3} u_{k_3} v_{k_2} = \boldsymbol{i}_{k_1} \cdot v_{k_2} \boldsymbol{i}_{k_2} \wedge u_{k_3} \boldsymbol{i}_{k_3} = \boldsymbol{i}_{k_1} \cdot \boldsymbol{v} \wedge \boldsymbol{u},$$

that is, the k_1-th component of $\boldsymbol{v} \wedge \boldsymbol{u}$. We shall then write

$$\boldsymbol{\epsilon} : \boldsymbol{uv} = (\boldsymbol{\epsilon} \cdot \boldsymbol{u}) \cdot \boldsymbol{v} = \boldsymbol{v} \wedge \boldsymbol{u},$$

whereby also

$$\text{(M2-42)} \qquad \operatorname{curl} \boldsymbol{u} = \boldsymbol{\nabla} \wedge \boldsymbol{u} = \boldsymbol{\epsilon} : \boldsymbol{u}\overleftarrow{\boldsymbol{\nabla}} = \boldsymbol{\epsilon} : \operatorname{grad} \boldsymbol{u}.$$

This definition of the curl may be extended to a space with more than three dimensions.

Similarly the definition can be extended to the tensors. For example, given a second rank tensor $\boldsymbol{T}$ we shall write

(M2-43) $$\text{curl}\ \boldsymbol{T} = \boldsymbol{\epsilon} \vdots \boldsymbol{T}\overleftarrow{\nabla}.$$

In a four-dimensional space curl $\boldsymbol{T}$ is a vector and its k_1-th component is

(M2-44) $$(\text{curl}\ \boldsymbol{T})_{k_1} = \varepsilon_{k_1k_2k_3k_4}\partial T_{k_4k_3}/\partial x_{k_2}.$$

For instance,

$$(\text{curl}\ \boldsymbol{T})_1 = \varepsilon_{1234}\frac{\partial T_{43}}{\partial x_2} + \varepsilon_{1243}\frac{\partial T_{34}}{\partial x_2} + \varepsilon_{1342}\frac{\partial T_{24}}{\partial x_3} + \varepsilon_{1324}\frac{\partial T_{42}}{\partial x_3} + \varepsilon_{1423}\frac{\partial T_{32}}{\partial x_4} +$$
$$+ \varepsilon_{1432}\frac{\partial T_{23}}{\partial x_4} = \frac{\partial T_{43}}{\partial x_2} - \frac{\partial T_{34}}{\partial x_2} + \frac{\partial T_{24}}{\partial x_3} - \frac{\partial T_{42}}{\partial x_3} + \frac{\partial T_{32}}{\partial x_4} - \frac{\partial T_{23}}{\partial x_4}.$$

If $\boldsymbol{T}$ is an anti-symmetrical tensor the foregoing equation reduces to

(M2-45) $$(\text{curl}\ \boldsymbol{T})_1 = 2\left(\frac{\partial T_{43}}{\partial x_2} + \frac{\partial T_{24}}{\partial x_3} + \frac{\partial T_{32}}{\partial x_4}\right).$$

M3. Fourier Series and Integrals

Fourier Series

§ 1. Consider a real or complex periodic function $f(x)$ of the real variable x with the periodicity a. In textbooks on analysis (to which we refer the reader for the exact proofs) it is shown that, subject to some general conditions which are always satisfied in the application to physical problems, $f(x)$ can be represented by a *Fourier series*:

(M3-1) $$f(x) = \sum_{-\infty\, n}^{+\infty} A_n \exp\left(2ni\pi\frac{x}{a}\right).$$

We shall limit ourselves to showing that once the existence of such a series is admitted, we can calculate the coefficients A_n. We have only to multiply both sides by exp $(-2mi\pi x/a)$ and to integrate from 0 to a. If the right side is integrated term by term we obtain a vanishing contribution for all n's different from m. It is customary to say that the exponential functions considered form a system of *orthogonal functions.*

We are left with the contribution of the term $m = n$, which is aA_m. In conclusion we obtain

$$A_m = \frac{1}{a}\int_0^a f(x') \exp\left(-2mi\pi\frac{x'}{a}\right) dx'. \tag{M3-2}$$

Obviously the origin of the integration could be different from zero, provided that the integration is over an entire period.

This procedure can be applied also to the functions of several variables. Let $f(x, y)$ be a periodical function both with respect to x (period a) and with respect to y (period b). As a function of x it may be written, as seen above, in the form

$$f(x, y) = \sum_{-\infty}^{+\infty}{}_n A_n \exp\left(2ni\pi\frac{x}{a}\right), \tag{M3-3}$$

with

$$A_n = \frac{1}{a}\int_0^a f(x', y) \exp\left(-2ni\pi\frac{x'}{a}\right) dx'. \tag{M3-4}$$

Then A_n is a periodic function of y with periodicity b, so that we may set

$$A_n = \sum_{-\infty}^{+\infty}{}_m A_{nm} \exp\left(2mi\pi\frac{y}{b}\right), \tag{M3-5}$$

with

$$A_{nm} = \frac{1}{b}\int_0^b A_n \exp\left(-2mi\pi\frac{y'}{b}\right) dy'. \tag{M3-6}$$

Upon substitution of (M3-5) into (M3-3) we obtain

$$f(x, y) = \sum_{-\infty}^{+\infty}{}_n \sum_{-\infty}^{+\infty}{}_m A_{nm} \exp\left(2ni\pi\frac{x}{a} + 2mi\pi\frac{y}{b}\right).$$

The coefficients A_{nm} of this double Fourier series are calculated by substituting (M3-4) into (M3-6) with the result

$$A_{nm} = \frac{1}{ab} \int_0^a \int_0^b f(x', y') \exp\left(-2ni\pi\frac{x'}{a} - 2mi\pi\frac{y'}{b}\right) dx' dy'.$$

One should proceed in a similar way in the case of three or more variables.

If we interpret x, y and x', y' as the Cartesian coordinates of the two points P and P' respectively on a plane surface Σ and denote by $\mathbf{v}_{nm}$ a vector parallel to Σ and having the components $2n\pi/a$ and $2m\pi/b$ the last two formulas become

$$\text{(M3-7)} \qquad f(P) = \sum_{-\infty}^{+\infty}{}_n \sum_{-\infty}^{+\infty}{}_m A_{nm}[i\mathbf{v}_{nm} \cdot (P - O)],$$

$$\text{(M3-8)} \qquad A_{nm} = \frac{1}{ab} \iint_{\Sigma} f(P') \exp[-i\mathbf{v}_{nm} \cdot (P' - O)]\, d\Sigma_{P'},$$

the integration being extended over the area Σ of a rectangle ab.

Fourier Integral

§ 2. Substituting (M3-2) into (M3-1) we have

$$f(x) = \sum_{-\infty}^{+\infty}{}_n \exp\left(2ni\pi\frac{x}{a}\right) \frac{1}{a} \int_{-a/2}^{+a/2} f(x') \exp\left(-2ni\pi\frac{x'}{a}\right) dx'.$$

Let us now put $2n\pi/a = \omega$. Upon varying the integral number n, the quantity ω will assume a series of discrete values equispaced by $\Delta\omega = 2\pi/a$. The foregoing equation may then be written

$$f(x) = \sum_{-\infty}^{+\infty} \exp(i\omega x) \frac{\Delta\omega}{2\pi} \int_{-a/2}^{+a/2} f(x') \exp(-i\omega x')\, dx'.$$

If a goes to infinity ω tends to become a continuous variable, $\Delta\omega$ being its differential, and the sum becomes an integral. Thus we arrive at

(M3-9) $$f(x) = \frac{1}{2\pi}\int_{-\infty}^{+\infty} \exp(i\omega x)\,d\omega \int_{-\infty}^{+\infty} f(x')\exp(-i\omega x')\,dx'.$$

It follows that a function $f(x)$ defined from $-\infty$ to $+\infty$ may be represented by the *Fourier integral*

(M3-10) $$f(x) = \int_{-\infty}^{+\infty} A(\omega)\exp(i\omega x)\,d\omega,$$

with

(M3-11) $$A(\omega) = \frac{1}{2\pi}\int_{-\infty}^{+\infty} f(x')\exp(-i\omega x')\,dx'.$$

An exact investigation would show that this representation is allowed whenever $f(x)$ is subject to certain general conditions which are always satisfied in the physical problems to be considered.

With a procedure similar to that followed for the double Fourier series we find for a function of two variables $f(x, y)$

(M3-12) $$f(x, y) = \int_{-\infty}^{+\infty}\int_{-\infty}^{+\infty} A(\omega, \psi)\exp(i\omega x + i\psi y)\,d\omega\,d\psi,$$

where

(M3-13) $$A(\omega, \psi) = \frac{1}{4\pi^2}\int_{-\infty}^{+\infty}\int_{-\infty}^{+\infty} f(x', y')\exp(-i\omega x' - i\psi y')\,dx'dy'.$$

These formulas represent the double Fourier integral.

If we picture ω and ψ as the rectangular components of a vector $\mathbf{v}$ parallel to Σ, we may write

(M3-14) $$f(P) = \int_{-\infty}^{+\infty}\int_{-\infty}^{+\infty} A(\mathbf{v})\exp[i\mathbf{v}\cdot(P-O)]\,dv_x\,dv_y,$$

with

(M3-15) $$A(\mathbf{v}) = \frac{1}{4\pi^2}\iint_{\Sigma} f(P')\exp[-i\mathbf{v}\cdot(P'-O)]\,d\Sigma_{P'},$$

v_x, v_y representing the components of $\mathbf{v}$ on Σ.

Dirac's Function

§ 3. Dirac's function δ is not an actual function in the true sense of the word and is termed an *improper function.* In some way it represents a function and a limit at the same time.

First consider a function δ of the variable x which vanishes everywhere except in a small interval about $x = 0$, where it assumes such great values as to have

$$\int_a^b \delta(x)\, dx = 1, \tag{M3-16}$$

with $a < 0 < b$. Then let the interval where $\delta \neq 0$ shrink to the point $x = 0$, always maintaining the condition (M3-16).

In the limit $\delta(x)$ will be defined as a function which vanishes for $x \neq 0$ and is subject to the condition (M3-16). This formulation may appear absurd from the mathematical standpoint. However, no inconsistency arises if one remembers that an operation of limit is to be understood. The function δ is always employed in expressions which must be integrated and in almost all cases the limit of the integral exists.

It is customary to express the properties of δ by means of equations. The meaning of such equations is that if the left side appears under the sign of integration it can be replaced by the right side, obtaining the same value for the integral (provided the integral is over a domain which includes the origin of x; this will always be understood in material that follows).

§ 4. It is now easy to establish the following property of δ:

$$\int_a^b f(x)\, \delta(x)\, dx = f(0), \tag{M3-17}$$

which is valid for any function $f(x)$. Outside an infinitesimal domain about zero we have $\delta(x) = 0$. Inside the domain $f(x)$ has a practically constant value $f(0)$. Hence by (M3-16) we deduce (M3-17).

If we shift the origin of x to the point x' we get

(M3-18) $$\int_a^b f(x)\,\delta(x-x')\mathrm{d}x = f(x').$$

This equation may be written in the form

(M3-19) $$f(x)\delta(x-x') = f(x')\delta(x-x').$$

Indeed, by integrating both sides one obtains (M3-18).

By comparing (M3-18) with (M3-9) one directly gets the expression of δ as a Fourier integral (x and x' are interchanged)

(M3-20) $$\delta(x-x') = \frac{1}{2\pi}\int_{-\infty}^{+\infty}\int_{-\infty}^{+\infty} \exp\,[i\omega(x'-x)]\,\mathrm{d}\omega.$$

§ 5. Another interesting property is obtained by the following partial integration:

$$\int_a^b f(x)\,\delta'(x)\,\mathrm{d}x = [f(x)\,\delta(x)]_a^b - \int_a^b f'(x)\,\delta(x)\,\mathrm{d}x.$$

Since $\delta(a) = \delta(b) = 0$ it follows that

(M3-21) $$f(x)\,\delta'(x) = -\,f'(x)\,\delta(x).$$

With the same procedure we find

(M3-22) $$f(x)\,\delta''(x) = f''(x)\,\delta(x).$$

§ 6. With an easy generalization we shall consider the Dirac function of space defined as

(M3-23) $$\delta(P-P') = \delta(x-x')\delta(y-y')\delta(z-z'),$$

$P(x, y, z)$, $P'(x', y', z')$ being any two points. We have obviously

(M3-24) $$\iiint_V f(P)\,\delta(P-P')\,\mathrm{d}V = f(P').$$

provided the integration is over a volume V containing P'.

M4. The Principle of Stationary Phase

The Fresnel Integral

§ 1. The integral

$$F = \int_{-\infty}^{+\infty} \exp(ix^2)\,dx \tag{M4-1}$$

is known as the complete Fresnel integral. In order to evaluate it we put

$$F(s) = \int_{-\infty}^{+\infty} \exp[(i-s)x^2]\,dx, \tag{M4-2}$$

with s positive. Hence $F = \lim F(s)$ for $s \to 0$.

From (M4-2) we have

$$F^2(s) = \int_{-\infty}^{+\infty} \exp[(i-s)x^2]\,dx \int_{-\infty}^{+\infty} \exp[(i-s)y^2]\,dy =$$

$$= \int_{-\infty}^{+\infty}\int_{-\infty}^{+\infty} \exp[(i-s)(x^2+y^2)]\,dx\,dy.$$

With a change of variables $x = \varrho\cos\theta$, $y = \varrho\sin\theta$, the last integral becomes

$$F^2(s) = \int_0^{2\pi} d\theta \int_0^{\infty} \exp[(i-s)\varrho^2]\varrho\,d\varrho = \pi\int_0^{\infty} \exp[(i-s)z]\,dz = -\frac{\pi}{i-s}$$

whence $F(s) = \sqrt{-\pi/(i-s)}$. For the determination of the sign one must assume for a moment that s takes such a great value that i is negligible in (M4-2); it is evident that in that case the integral would be positive, whence for the square root we must choose the value having a positive real part. By making s vanishingly small we finally obtain the value of F

$$F = \sqrt{i\pi}.$$

With a change of the variable of integration we have also the more general formula

$$\int_{-\infty}^{+\infty} \exp(i\alpha x^2)\,dx = \sqrt{\frac{i\pi}{\alpha}}, \tag{M4-3}$$

α being a real constant.

The Principle of Stationary Phase

§ 2. Consider the integral

$$I(k) = \int_a^b g(x) \exp[ikf(x)]dx, \tag{M4-4}$$

where $f(x)$, $g(x)$ represent two known functions of x which are sufficiently regular and a, b, k three real numbers. We want to investigate the behavior of $I(k)$ for a very large k.

To begin let us assume that the interval a—b contains no zeros of the derivative $f'(x)$. Then, taking f as integration variable, the integral (M4-4) becomes

$$I(k) = \int_{f(a)}^{f(b)} \frac{g(x)}{f'(x)} \exp[ikf]\,df, \tag{M4-5}$$

where, of course, x is to be expressed as a function of f by an inversion of the function $f(x)$. Hence we may put $g(x)/f'(x) = \varphi(f)$, obtaining

$$I(k) = \int_{f(a)}^{f(b)} \varphi(f) \exp[ikf]\,df.$$

By a partial integration we get

$$I(k) = \frac{1}{ik}\int_{f(a)}^{f(b)} \varphi(f)d[\exp(ikf)] = \frac{1}{ik}\{\varphi[f(b)]\exp[ikf(b)] -$$

$$- \varphi[f(a)]\exp[ikf(a)]\} - \frac{1}{ik}\int_{f(a)}^{f(b)} \varphi'(f)\exp(ikf)\,df.$$

By successive partial integrations we shall obviously get a term in

k^{-2}, then a term in k^{-3}, and so on. We can derive the conclusion that for increasing values of k the function $I(k)$ vanishes, at least as k^{-1}.

§ **3.** Suppose now that $f'(x)$ has a zero x_0 within the interval a—b. Let this zero be of the first order so that $f''(x_0) \neq 0$. The substitution (M4-5) is now impossible. We shall write instead

$$I(k) = \int_a^b g(x_0) \exp [ikf(x)] \mathrm{d}x + \int_a^b [g(x) - g(x_0)] \exp [ikf(x)] \mathrm{d}x.$$

In the second integral the difference $g(x) - g(x_0)$ has a zero of at least the first order at $x = x_0$; the function $[g(x) - g(x_0)]/f'(x)$ is regular at $x = x_0$, and by the same reasoning (†) applied to (M4-5) we conclude that the second integral vanishes at least as k^{-1} when $k \to \infty$. As for the first integral, by a Taylor series expansion of $f(x)$ about x_0 and the substitution $(x - x_0)\sqrt{k} = \xi$ we get

$$g(x_0)\int_a^b \exp\left\{ik\left[f(x) + \frac{1}{2}f''(x_0)(x-x_0)^2 + \frac{1}{6}f'''(x_0)(x-x_0)^3 + \dots\right]\right\}\mathrm{d}x =$$

$$= g(x_0) \exp [ikf(x_0)] \int_{(a-x_0)\sqrt{k}}^{(b-x_0)\sqrt{k}} \exp\left\{i\left[\frac{1}{2}f''(x_0)\xi^2 + \frac{1}{6\sqrt{k}}f'''(x_0)\xi^3 + \dots\right]\right\}\frac{\mathrm{d}\xi}{\sqrt{k}}.$$

When $k \to \infty$ the limits of the integration become $-\infty$ and $+\infty$ and all the terms but the first in the argument of the exponential become negligible. We are left with an integral of the type (M4-3) and finally obtain

$$\text{(M4-6)} \qquad I(k) = g(x_0)\sqrt{\frac{2i\pi}{kf''(x_0)}} \exp [ikf(x_0)] + O(1/k),$$

where $O(1/k)$ stands for terms which vanish at least as $1/k$.

(†) In the present case x is not a single-valued function of f in the interval $a - b$. This difficulty is obviously overcome by dividing the interval into the two intervals $a - x_0$ and $x_0 - b$ where $f(x)$ can be uniquely inverted.

Thus the principal part of $I(k)$ is of the order of $1/\sqrt{k}$ and depends solely on the behavior of $f(x)$ and $g(x)$ at x_0. If we call $f(x)$ the *phase* we derive the principle of the *stationary phase*. This principle states that when k is very large the major contribution to the value of $I(k)$ comes from the region where the phase is stationary.

§ **4.** The above result may be extended to the case of two variables. Consider the integral

$$\text{(M4-7)} \qquad I(k) = \iint_{\Sigma} g(P) \exp\,[ikf(P)]\, \mathrm{d}\Sigma,$$

where k is very large and f, g are now two position functions defined in a convex and simply connected region Σ of a plane. Introducing the Cartesian coordinates x, y of P we may put (M4-7) in the form

$$I(k) = \int_a^b \mathrm{d}y \int_{c(y)}^{d(y)} g(x, y) \exp\,[ikf(x, y)]\, \mathrm{d}x.$$

Let us assume now that, for each value of y, $\partial f/\partial x$ presents a single zero $x_0(y)$ within the interval $c(y) \mapsto d(y)$ with $\partial^2 f/\partial x^2 \neq 0$. Equation (M4-6) allows us to evaluate the principal part of the second integral. Thus we obtain

$$\text{(M4-8)} \quad I(k) = \int_a^b g[x_0(y), y] \sqrt{\frac{2i\pi}{kf''_{xx}[x_0(y), y]}} \exp\{ikf[x_0(y), y]\}\mathrm{d}y.$$

In order to apply the principle of the stationary phase to the remaining integral one must construct the derivative with respect to y of the argument of the exponential and put it equal to zero; thus

$$\left[\frac{\partial f}{\partial y} + \frac{\partial f}{\partial x}\frac{\mathrm{d}x_0}{\mathrm{d}y}\right]_{x=x_0} = 0.$$

But, at $x = x_0(y)$, $\partial f/\partial x$ vanishes by hypothesis. We are left with $\partial f/\partial y = 0$. Suppose then that inside Σ there is one and only one point $P_0(x_0, y_0)$ where both first derivatives of f vanish so that

(M4-9) $$(\text{grad } f)_{P=P_0} = 0.$$

If we want to apply the principle of the stationary phase to (M4-8) we must evaluate the second derivative of $f[x_0(y), y]$ with respect to y. Since $\partial f/\partial x = 0$ such second derivative has the expression

(M4-10) $$\left[\frac{\partial^2 f}{\partial y^2} + 2\frac{\partial^2 f}{\partial x\, \partial y}\frac{\mathrm{d}x_0}{\mathrm{d}y} + \frac{\partial^2 f}{\partial x^2}\left(\frac{\mathrm{d}x_0}{\mathrm{d}y}\right)^2\right]_{\substack{x=x_0\\ y=y_0}}.$$

We can orient the axes x, y in such a manner that $\mathrm{d}x_0/\mathrm{d}y = 0$ at $y = y_0$. To this end we must set x, y parallel to the lines of curvature at P_0 of the surface $z = f(P)$ where z is the coordinate normal to the plane of Σ. Thus the expression (M4-10) reduces simply to $\partial^2 f/\partial y^2$.

We can now apply the principle of the stationary phase to (M4-8), obtaining

$$I(k) \to g(x_0, y_0)\frac{2i\pi}{k\sqrt{f''_{xx}(x_0, y_0)\, f''_{yy}(x_0, y_0)}} \exp\,[ikf(x_0, y_0)].$$

Note that also $\partial^2 f/\partial x \partial y$ vanishes at P_0 because of the orientation given to the axes x, y. Hence the quantity under the radical is nothing but the Hessian determinant of f with respect to x and y. Then remembering (M4-34) we shall write

(M4-11) $$I(k) \to g(P_0)\frac{2i\pi}{k\sqrt{\det \text{grad grad } f(P_0)}} \exp\,[ikf(P_0)],$$

where any reference to particular coordinates has disappeared; the determinant of a tensor is an invariant.

CHAPTER 1

The Rationalized Giorgi System

Mechanical Units

§ 1. The system of units that Giorgi proposed in 1901 and the International Electrotechnical Commission officially adopted in 1935 is particularly convenient for the presentation of the laws of electromagnetism, independently of the difficult and awkward constructions of the CGS system. However for didactic reasons we shall illustrate its connection with the CGS system of units for electricity and magnetism whose formulas are assumed to be familiar to the reader.

The fundamental mechanical quantities of the Giorgi system are length, mass, and time, and their units are the *meter*, the *kilogram*, and the *second* respectively (MKS system).

The units of the other mechanical quantities are derived in much the same way as for the CGS system. Thus the unit of velocity is the *meter/second* and the unit of acceleration the *meter/second*^{2}.

A unitary force will confer to the mass of a *kilogram* the unit acceleration; such a force is called the *newton*. From the equation $F = ma$ we derive *newtons* = *meter* · *kilograms/second*^{2}; hence *newtons* = 10^2 *centimeters* · 10^3 *grams/second*^{2} = 10^5 *centimeter* · *grams/second*^{2} = 10^5 *dynes*. The weight of one *kilogram* is 980,000 *dynes* or 9.8 *newtons*.

Unitary amount of work is performed by a force of one *newton* when its point of application is displaced through one *meter* in the direction of the force. By the relation $L = Fs$, where L represents work, F the force and s the displacement, the unit of work is the *newton* · *meter* = 10^5 *dynes* · 10^2 *centimeters* = 10^7 *ergs* or one *joule*.

The unit of power is the *joule/second* or the *watt*.

Thus the practical units of mechanics turn out to belong naturally to the MKS system.

Convenience of a Four-Unit System

§ **2.** The construction of the classical absolute systems of units for electricity and magnetism is based on the two Coulomb formulas (**s** designates a unit vector in the direction of the position vector **r**)

$$\boldsymbol{F} = k_1 \frac{QQ'}{r^2}\,\boldsymbol{s}, \qquad \boldsymbol{F} = k_2 \frac{MM'}{r^2}\,\boldsymbol{s},$$

which express the interaction between two electric or magnetic point charges and the elementary Laplace law

$$\mathrm{d}\boldsymbol{F} = k_3 M \frac{\mathrm{d}\boldsymbol{l} \wedge \boldsymbol{s}}{r^2},$$

(Fig. 1) representing the interaction between a current element and a magnetic charge (†). These laws are derived from experience.

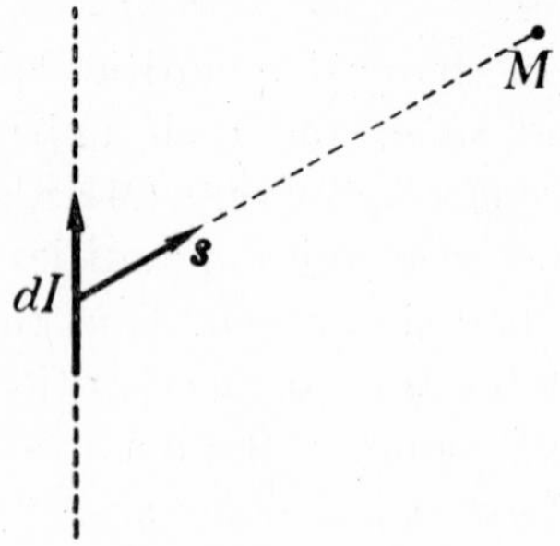

Fig. 1

But it is impossible to determine experimentally the values of the three constants k_1, k_2, k_3, which depend upon the units. The so-called absolute CGS system is constructed by arbitrarily fixing the values and the dimensions of any two of these constants *in a vacuum*.

In the CGS *electrostatic* system k_1 and k_3 are put equal to 1 (pure numbers). As a consequence the dimensions of k_2 turn out to be

(†) If d**F** designates the force exerted by the current element on the magnetic charge, **s** is directed as in the figure, namely from d**l** to M. Conversely, if d**F** represents the force exerted by the magnetic field upon the current element, **s** will be directed from M to d**l**.

those of velocity squared. Putting $k_2 = c^2$, it is found experimentally with considerable accuracy that $c = 2{,}998 \cdot 10^{10}$ *centimeters/second.*

In the CGS *electromagnetic* system one puts $k_2 = k_3 = 1$ and there follows $k_1 = c^2$.

Finally there is the CGS *mixed* system, or Gaussian system, where one assumes $k_1 = k_2 = 1$ and there follows $k_3 = 1/c$.

§ 3. It is hopeless to attempt to construct by the above classical methods a truly absolute system, or a system whose fundamental formulas do not contain any dimensional constants derived from experience. Most of the difficulty arises from the absurd attempt to derive all the electrical quantities from the mechanical quantities. This may be the source of considerable misunderstanding, such as when a capacitance is reduced to a length with both quantities measured in *centimeters.*

The definition of the fundamental quantities and of the units is only a matter of convenience. And it is not always convenient to use the connection (physical law) between two different quantities for reducing the dimensions of one to those of the other. For example, from the law of universal gravitation written in the form $F = mm'/r^2$ one might derive $a = F/m = m'/r^2$ and then express the mass solely in terms of length and time by defining the unitary mass as a mass which, when placed 1 *centimeter* from an identical mass, is caused to acquire the acceleration of 1 *centimeter/second*^{2}. As is well known, this is not done because it is not convenient, and it is better in mechanics to maintain three independent fundamental quantities. As a consequence the law of the universal gravitation must be written with a suitable dimensional coefficient.

It was emphasized by Giorgi that much the same situation holds for the Coulomb law. It is not *convenient* to use this law for expressing the electrical quantities in terms of the mechanical quantities. It is better instead to consider electricity as a physical entity irreducible to mechanical phenomena and to choose an electrical quantity as a *fourth fundamental quantity* added to the three mechanical quantities. Thus Coulomb's law, like the law of the universal gravitation, will show a dimensional coefficient to be determined by experiment.

Electric Units

§ 4. Since we must select a fundamental unit of electricity it will obviously be convenient to choose one of the practical units which have been adopted for their convenience.

As unit of electrical charge we shall take the *coulomb*, defined as 1/10 of the CGS electromagnetic unit or as $10c$ CGS electrostatic units (†).

The unit of current will be the *coulomb/second* or the *ampere*; also this unit is 10^{-1} CGS electromagnetic units or $10c$ CGS electrostatic units. We have a unitary difference of potential between two points when the passage of one *coulomb* corresponds to the work of one *joule*. This is the well-known definition of the *volt*. From the formula $V = L/Q$, which connects the voltage V, the work L, and the charge Q, one obtains *volts* = *joules/coulomb*; hence 1 *volt* = $10^7/10^{-1} = 10^8$ CGS electromagnetic units and 1 *volt* = $10^7/(10c) = 10^6/c$ CGS electrostatic units.

The force acting on the unit positive charge will be called the *electric field strength* and will be denoted by $\boldsymbol{E}$. Evidently this force will be unitary when, acting on a *coulomb*, it produces a mechanical force of a *newton*. It follows from the relation $\boldsymbol{E} = \boldsymbol{F}/Q$ that the unit of electric field strength is the *newton/coulomb* = *joule/(coulomb · meter)* = *volt/meter*; no special name has been given to this quantity which is called simply the *volt/meter*. This unit is equal to $10^8/10^2 = 10^6$ CGS electromagnetic units and to $(10^6/c)/10^2 = 10^4/c$ CGS electrostatic units.

The unitary capacitance will be possessed by a capacity requiring one *volt* to be charged with one *coulomb*. This unit is called the *farad*. From the formula $C = Q/V$ we deduce 1 *farad* = 1 *coulomb/volt*, whence 1 *farad* = $10^{-1}/10^8 = 10^{-9}$ CGS electro-

(†) Hereafter c is expressed in *meters/second*. Consequently its value is $c = 2{,}998 \times 10^8$.

magnetic units and 1 *farad* $= 10c/(10^6/c) = c^2 10^{-5}$ CGS electrostatic units (*centimeters*).

The unitary resistance is that of a conductor where one *volt* produces a current of one *ampere*. This unit is called the *ohm*. By the relation $R = V/I$ one can derive 1 *ohm* = 1 *volt*/*ampere*, whence 1 *ohm* $= 10^8/10^{-1} = 10^9$ CGS electromagnetic units and 1 *ohm* $= (10^6/c)/10c = 10^5/c^2$ CGS electrostatic units.

Thus all the practical units belong to the Giorgi system.

§ 5. We shall write Coulomb's electrostatic law for an isotropic and homogeneous dielectric in the form

$$\mathbf{F} = \frac{QQ'}{4\pi\varepsilon r^2}\,\mathbf{s}, \tag{1-1}$$

where ε represents the above mentioned dimensional coefficient and is termed the *dielectric constant* of the medium (we shall later see the reason for the factor 4π).

Since F is measured in *newtons*, Q in *coulombs*, and r in *meters*, it is seen by inspection that ε will have the dimensions of *coulombs*²/(*newton* · *meter*²) = *coulombs*²/(*joule* · *meter*) = *coulombs*/(*volt* · *meter*) = *farads*/*meter*.

It is of interest to know the value ε_0 of ε for a vacuum. To this end remember that in the CGS electrostatic system Coulomb's law for empty space reads $F = QQ'/r^2$; if F is in *newtons*, Q, Q' in *coulombs*, and r in *meters*, this formula becomes (†) $10^5 F = 10^2 c^2 QQ'/10^4 r^2$, or $F = (QQ'/4\pi r^2)/(10^7/4\pi c)^2$ so that by comparing this equation with (1-1) we get

$$\varepsilon_0 = \frac{10^7}{4\pi c^2} = 8.854 \cdot 10^{-12} \quad \textit{farads/meter}.$$

Note that the quantity we referred to as the dielectric constant is not identical with the quantity of the same name in the classical CGS electrostatic system. The latter is given by the ratio $\varepsilon/\varepsilon_0 = \varepsilon_r$,

(†) The following rule will often prove very useful in this book: if a physical law is expressed by the equation $f(x, y, z \ldots) = 0$ and the unit of any quantity concerned, say of y, is multiplied by a, the equation transforms into $f(x, ay, z, \ldots) = 0$.

which in the Giorgi system is termed the *relative dielectric constant* and is obviously a pure number.

The vector $\boldsymbol{D}$ defined for an isotropic dielectric by

$$\boldsymbol{D} = \varepsilon \boldsymbol{E} \tag{1-2}$$

is termed the *electric induction* or *electric displacement*. Its unit is clearly the (*farad/meter*) × (*volt/meter*) = *coulomb/meter*^{2}. In empty space it is $\boldsymbol{D} = \varepsilon_0 \boldsymbol{E}$. In the CGS electrostatic system one would write instead $\boldsymbol{D} = \boldsymbol{E}$; and by adopting for $\boldsymbol{E}$ the Giorgi unit, equal to $10^4/c$ CGS electrostatic units, this relation transforms into $c10^{-4}\boldsymbol{D} = \boldsymbol{E}$, or multiplying by ε_0, $\varepsilon_0 c 10^{-4}\boldsymbol{D} = \varepsilon_0 \boldsymbol{E}$. To proceed from this to the relation in the Giorgi system one has to multiply the unit of $\boldsymbol{D}$ by $1/\varepsilon_0 c \cdot 10^{-4} = 4\pi c \cdot 10^{-3}$. Hence the *coulomb/meter*^{2} equals $4\pi c \cdot 10^{-3}$ CGS electrostatic units. In the CGS electromagnetic system the dielectric constant of empty space is $1/c^2$, whence, expressing c in *meters/second*, we have $\boldsymbol{D} = \boldsymbol{E}/(c^2 \cdot 10^4)$. By a procedure identical with that just applied we find *coulomb/meter*^{2} $= 4\pi \cdot 10^{-5}$ CGS electromagnetic units.

The flux of the vector $\boldsymbol{D}$ across a given surface is called the *electric flux* and is denoted by Ψ. The unit of Ψ is the (*coulomb/meter*^{2}) × *meter*^{2} = *coulomb*. Clearly this unit is equal to $4\pi c \cdot 10^{-3} \cdot 10^4 = 4\pi c\, 10$ CGS electrostatic units and to $4\pi \cdot 10^{-5} \cdot 10^4 = 4\pi \cdot 10^{-1}$ CGS electromagnetic units.

Magnetic Units

§ 6. In the elementary Laplace law we shall put $k_3 = 1/4\pi$, writing (Fig. 1)

$$\mathrm{d}\boldsymbol{F} = M \frac{\mathrm{d}\boldsymbol{I} \wedge \boldsymbol{s}}{4\pi r^2}. \tag{1-3}$$

Here M represents the magnetic charge and the unit vector $\boldsymbol{s}$ is directed from the acting element (M or $\mathrm{d}\boldsymbol{I}$) to the element which is acted upon ($\mathrm{d}\boldsymbol{I}$ or M). By current element $\mathrm{d}\boldsymbol{I}$ is meant a vector oriented in the direction of the current and having the magnitude $I\,\mathrm{d}l$ equal to the product of the current and the length of the wire element considered. The unit of M, as it follows from (1-3), will be the *newton · meter²/(ampere · meter) = joule/ampere = volt · second.* This unit is known as the *weber.* Since in the CGS electrostatic and CGS electromagnetic systems the Laplace law is written as (1-3) without the factor 4π in the denominator, it can easily be proved by the usual procedure that the *weber* $= 10^8/4\pi$ CGS electromagnetic units or $10^6/4\pi c$ CGS electrostatic units of magnetic charge.

Let us now write the magnetic Coulomb law in the form

$$\mathbf{F} = \frac{MM'}{4\pi\mu r^2}\,\mathbf{s}, \tag{1-4}$$

where μ denotes the *magnetic permeability* of the homogeneous medium considered. Obviously μ will be measured in *volts² · second²/(newton · meter²) = volts² · second²/(joule · meter) = volt · second²/(coulomb · meter) = volt · second/(ampere · meter) = henrys/meter.* The unit *volt · second/ampere* is called the *henry.*

The permeability μ_0 of the vacuum may be evaluated by recalling that in the CGS electromagnetic system (1-4) is $F = MM'/r^2$. The above procedure enables one to calculate

$$\mu_0 = 4\pi \cdot 10^{-7} = 1.257 \cdot 10^{-6} \qquad \textit{henrys/meter}.$$

What is called the magnetic permeability in the CGS electromagnetic system will be termed in the Giorgi system the *relative magnetic permeability* of the medium considered, and is given by the quotient $\mu/\mu_0 = \mu_r$.

The force acting upon a positive unit magnetic charge is known as *magnetic force* and is denoted by $\mathbf{H}$. By the relation $\mathbf{H} = \mathbf{F}/M$ we find that the unit of $\mathbf{H}$ is the *newton/weber = newton/(volt · second) = newton · coulomb/(joule · second) = ampere/meter.* By writing the same relation in the CGS systems and passing to the Giorgi units for F and M one readily finds *amperes/meter* $= 4\pi \cdot 10^{-3}$ CGS electromagnetic units (*oersteds*) and $4\pi c \cdot 10^{-1}$ CGS electrostatic units of magnetic force.

It is important to consider the vector $\mathbf{B}$ defined by

$$\mathbf{B} = \mu\mathbf{H} \tag{1-5}$$

and called the *magnetic induction* or the *density of magnetic flux.*

Its unit is the (*henry/meter*) $\times$ (*ampere/meter*) = *volt · second/meter*^{2} = *weber/meter*^{2}. In the vacuum we have $\boldsymbol{B} = \mu_0 \boldsymbol{H}$ instead of $\boldsymbol{B} = \boldsymbol{H}$ as in the CGS electromagnetic system. As a consequence the Giorgi unit equals 10^4 CGS electromagnetic units (*gauss*). In the CGS electrostatic system the magnetic permeability of a vacuum is $1/c^2$ so that, expressing c in *meters/second*, $\boldsymbol{B} = \boldsymbol{H}/(c^2 \cdot 10^4)$, we find by the same procedure that the *weber/meter*^{2} = $10^2/c$ CGS electrostatic units.

The flux Φ of $\boldsymbol{B}$ across a surface is called the *magnetic flux* and its unit is the *weber*. This unit equals 10^8 CGS electromagnetic units (*maxwells*) and $10^6/c$ CGS electrostatic units of magnetic flux.

Conversion Table, Giorgi/CGS

§ 7. The following conversion table gives the ratios Giorgi/CGS and allows an easy transformation of the formulas of the electromagnetic theory expressed with the CGS systems into those expressed with the Giorgi system. A purely *numerical* meaning is to be attributed to these ratios because the physical quantities in the two systems are not homogeneous since they have different dimensions.

	Q, coulombs	I, amperes	V, volts	R, ohms	C, farads	L, henrys
Giorgi/CGS (es)	$10c$	$10c$	$10^6/c$	$10^5/c^2$	$c^2/10^5$	$10^5/c^2$
Giorgi/CGS (em)	$1/10$	$1/10$	10^8	10^9	$1/10^9$	10^9

	E, $\frac{\text{volts}}{\text{meter}}$	D, $\frac{\text{coulombs}}{\text{meter}^2}$	Ψ, coulombs	H, $\frac{\text{amperes}}{\text{meter}}$	B, $\frac{\text{webers}}{\text{meter}^2}$	Φ, webers
Giorgi/CGS (es)	$10^4/c$	$4\pi c/10^3$	$4\pi c \cdot 10$	$4\pi c/10$	$10^2/c$	$10^6/c$
Giorgi/CGS (em)	10^6	$4\pi/10^5$	$4\pi \cdot 10$	$4\pi/10^3$	10^4	10^8

The unit of magnetic charge is not considered in the table because, as is well known, the magnetic charge is a fiction and as a rule does not appear in the formulas which express a real physical situation.

The unit of inductance which is included in the table will be presented below.

Some Electromagnetic Formulas

§ 8. Let us see now the form assumed in the Giorgi system by some of the main formulas that are well known in the CGS system. To this end we shall apply the conversion ratios of the foregoing table.

A capacitor consisting of two plane parallel plates of area Σ at a distance d apart, embedded in a dielectric of dielectric constant ε has in the CGS electrostatic system the capacitance $C = \varepsilon_r \Sigma / 4\pi d$; hence we find in the Giorgi system

$$C = \varepsilon \frac{\Sigma}{d} \qquad \textit{farads} \tag{1-6}$$

having made the substitution $\varepsilon_r = \varepsilon/\varepsilon_0 = 4\pi c^2 \varepsilon \cdot 10^{-7}$.

A conducting sphere of radius r placed at an infinite distance from all other conductors has the capacitance $C = \varepsilon_r r$ and in the Giorgi system

$$C = 4\pi\varepsilon r \qquad \textit{farads.} \tag{1-7}$$

From (1-6) we may easily derive the electric field strength in the vicinity of a conductor charged with a surface density $Q/\Sigma =$ $= \sigma$ *coulombs/meter*^{2}. Between the two plates we have $E = V/d =$ $Q/Cd = (Q/\Sigma)/(Cd/\Sigma)$, whence

$$E = \frac{\sigma}{\varepsilon} \qquad \textit{volts/meter,} \tag{1-8}$$

instead of $E = 4\pi\sigma/\varepsilon$ as in the CGS electrostatic system. There follows $D = \sigma$ *coulombs/meter*^{2}. This shows that it is rational to measure D in *coulombs/meter*^{2}.

The Biot and Savart law (Fig. 2) $H = 2I/r$ CGS electromagnetic units assumes now the form

$$H = \frac{I}{2\pi r} \qquad \textit{amperes/meter.} \tag{1-9}$$

For an infinite solenoid with n turns per unit length we have in the CGS electromagnetic system $H = 4\pi nI$ and in the Giorgi system

(1-10) $$H = nI \qquad \textit{amperes/meter}.$$

This may show the reason why H is measured in *amperes/meter* (†).

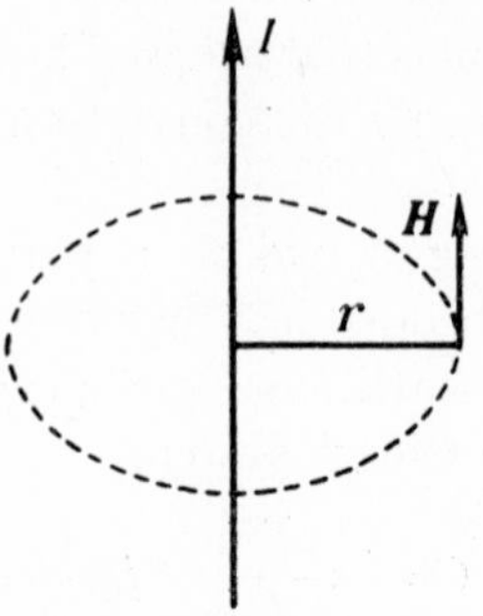

Fig. 2

By (1-3), noting that (1-4, 5) give $\boldsymbol{Ms}/4\pi r^2 = \boldsymbol{B}$, we obtain for the force exerted by the magnetic field upon a current element:

(1-11) $$\mathrm{d}\boldsymbol{F} = \mathrm{d}\boldsymbol{I} \wedge \boldsymbol{B} \qquad \textit{newtons}$$

By combining the last formula with the Biot and Savart law we find that two infinite and parallel straight wires carrying the currents I, I' respectively exert on one another a force

(1-12) $$F = \mu \frac{II'}{2\pi r} \qquad \textit{newtons/meter},$$

per unit length. This force is attractive or repulsive according to whether the currents have the same or opposite directions.

The law of electromagnetic induction, which gives the electromotive force produced in a loop by a variation of the magnetic flux through it,

(1-13) $$V = -\frac{\partial \Phi}{\partial t} \qquad \textit{volts},$$

(†) For obvious reasons the term *ampere · turns/meter* is sometimes used.

preserves in the Giorgi system the same form as in the CGS electromagnetic system.

A closed loop carrying a current gives rise to a magnetic field and the magnetic flux across the same loop is proportional to the current

$$\Phi = LI \qquad \textit{webers}. \tag{1-14}$$

This equation has the same form in the CGS electromagnetic system. *Inductance* (†) L is measured in *henrys* = *webers/ampere*. By (1-14) and the conversion ratios of the table we readily obtain that a *henry* equals 10^9 CGS electromagnetic units and $10^5/c^2$ CGS electrostatic units.

The inductance of a solenoid having N turns over a length l and a cross section Σ is in CGS electromagnetic units $L = 4\pi\mu_r N^2 \Sigma/l$ and in Giorgi units

$$L = \mu N^2 \frac{\Sigma}{l} \qquad \textit{henrys}, \tag{1-15}$$

having made the substitution $\mu_r = \mu/\mu_0 = 10^7\mu/4\pi$.

By combining (1-13) and (1-14) we obtain the relation

$$V = -L\frac{dI}{dt} \qquad \textit{volts}, \tag{1-16}$$

giving the counter-electromotive force produced by a variation of the current.

It is now evident that all the laws that are usually expressed in practical units, as for instance Ohm's law, the Joule effect, the connection between the mechanical power, the voltage and the current, maintain their familiar form.

We want to recall in particular the expressions of the energies stored in a capacitor of capacitance C and in a coil of inductance L, respectively,

$$U_C = \frac{1}{2}\frac{Q^2}{C} \quad \textit{joules}, \qquad U_L = \frac{1}{2}LI^2 \quad \textit{joules}, \tag{1-17}$$

(†) More precisely one should speak of *self-inductance*; but ordinarily no confusion can arise by using simply the term *inductance*.

where Q designates the charge of the capacitor and I the current flowing in the coil.

History of the Units of Electricity and Magnetism

§ 9. The conception of the absolute systems of units was introduced by Gauss and successively developed by Weber (after 1840) on the basis of the *millimeter, milligram, second.* But these did not yet represent complete systems of units comprising all the quantities of physics.

The need for a complete and officially established system arose mainly because of the applications of electricity. In order to define such a system the *British Association for the Advancement of Science* appointed a Committee whose work ended in 1873 with the adoption of the CGS system. This was from the very outset a double system: electrostatic and electromagnetic. Furthermore the size of its units was unacceptable for practical purposes. The well-known practical units, defined as multiples of the CGS electromagnetic units were proposed to meet the needs of the applications (1881). Maxwell showed that the practical units could form an absolute system together with the *terrestrial quadrant,* the mass of 10^{-11} *grams* and the *second*; but obviously the size of the first two units was absurd.

Another point was emphasized by Heaviside (1890). In the formulas of the classical CGS system there often appears a factor 4π when one is dealing with neither circles not spheres. This is the case, for instance, for the capacitance of a parallel plate capacitor, for the electric field strength in the vicinity of a conductor, for the formula connecting the electric field strength, the induction, and the polarization, for the corresponding magnetic formula, and so on. Conversely, the factor 4π does not appear in the capacitance of a sphere where its presence might be logical. This fact was called the *irrationality* of the classical system. In order to bring about a rationalization Heaviside proposed to multiply the different practical units either by $\sqrt{4\pi}$ or by $1/\sqrt{4\pi}$.

It was pointed out by Giorgi that all the difficulties could be overcome at the same time by giving up the absurd requirement to reduce the electromagnetic units to those of mechanics. Giorgi remarked that the only necessary connection is that electric power be measured in *watts* like mechanical power. Consequently one may retain the *volt* and the *ampere* as well as all the other practical units. At the end of a chain of relations we find the Coulomb formulas which in the old system were assumed as the starting point. Since the electric units have been defined arbitrarily it will not be possible to put the dielectric constant and the magnetic permeability of a vacuum equal to unity. On the contrary their values must be derived by experiment. In other words the physical constants of empty space must be *measured* instead of being given fixed and arbitrary values.

The system proposed by Giorgi at the Italian Electrotechnical Association in 1901 was adopted only very slowly, although several scientific authorities supported it from the start. It was officially adopted in 1935 by the *International Electrotechnical Commission* under the name of *Giorgi System.* The question of the rationalization was left undecided. Following the example of most modern authors we shall adopt in the present book the rationalized Giorgi System, as one may see from the formulas (1-6, 7, 8, 10).

The fourth (electric) unit is left undetermined. At the present time this is still a difficult question. Since the appearance of the practical units it has been necessary to set up some standards in order to avoid very difficult absolute measurements. Thus the *legal units* were adopted (1881 and 1889). As was to be expected, progress in the accuracy of absolute measurements showed a discrepancy between these units and the theoretical units. Then the *international units* were developed (1893—1910); but, of course, a perfect agreement with the theoretical units is impossible. Giorgi pointed out that this fact should not have great importance, because the standard of an independent unit can be chosen arbitrarily, no matter how much it deviates from its initial definition. In the same way it is irrelevant that the standard *meter* and *kilogram* at Sèvres are different respectively from 1/40,000,000 of the terrestrial meridian and from the mass of a cubic *decimeter* of distilled water. Progress in absolute measurements should only mean a higher accuracy in the measurement of the physical constants of space (ε_0, μ_0).

Nevertheless, owing to several practical reasons and perhaps also to the old prejudice that only the CGS systems are absolute, the International Commission of Weights and Measures in 1938 restated the *theoretical* definitions of the electrical units. The resolution (which became valid only in 1948 because of the war) defines the *ampere* as the current which when flowing in each of two parallel straight wires placed one *meter* apart in vacuum gives rise to a force of mutual attraction of $2 \cdot 10^{-7}$ *newtons/meter*. By virtue of (1-12) this amounts to the same as setting $\mu_0 = 4\pi \cdot 10^{-7}$. As to the standards, their values are to be brought as close as possible to the theoretical definition.

CHAPTER 2

Basic Properties of the Electromagnetic Field

Gauss' Theorem

§ **1.** From Coulomb's law (1-1) one derives for a point charge Q embedded in an isotropic dielectric

$$\boldsymbol{D} = \frac{Q}{4\pi r^2}\,\boldsymbol{s},$$

$\boldsymbol{s}$ being a unit vector in the direction of the vector $\boldsymbol{r}$ which goes from the charge to the point under investigation. Let $\mathrm{d}\Sigma$ be a surface element through the latter point, the positive normal $\boldsymbol{n}$ being on the same side as $\boldsymbol{s}$. The electric flux $\mathrm{d}\Psi$ across the surface will be given by $\boldsymbol{D}\cdot\boldsymbol{n}\mathrm{d}\Sigma$. But $\boldsymbol{s}\cdot\boldsymbol{n}\mathrm{d}\Sigma/r^2$ equals the solid angle $\mathrm{d}\Omega$ subtended by $\mathrm{d}\Sigma$ from the point charge. We shall write

$$\mathrm{d}\Psi = Q\,\frac{\mathrm{d}\Omega}{4\pi}.$$

In the case of a closed surface around Q the integral of $\mathrm{d}\Omega$ is the complete solid angle 4π, so that the outward flux through the surface is

$$\Psi = Q \qquad \textit{coulombs}.$$

This is *Gauss' theorem*, which is generalized to the case when the surface Σ encloses several charges:

$$\Psi = \Sigma_i Q_i \qquad \textit{coulombs}. \tag{2-1}$$

For a charge located outside Σ, the solid angle vanishes, because it is composed of two equal parts with opposite signs; thus the external charges do not contribute to Ψ.

Gauss's theorem supplies a new justification for Ψ being measured in *coulombs*.

If the charges instead of being concentrated are distributed with the density $\varrho(P)$ *coulombs/meter*^{3}, Gauss' theorem will assume the form

$$\Psi = \iiint_V \varrho(P) \mathrm{d}V, \tag{2-2}$$

the integral being over the volume V enclosed by Σ. If V becomes vanishingly small, we obtain by definition of divergence (M1-4)

$$\operatorname{div} \boldsymbol{D} = \varrho \qquad \textit{coulombs/meter}^3. \tag{2-3}$$

Since there are no true magnetic charges the flux Φ of the magnetic field across a closed surface will always be given by

$$\Phi = 0, \tag{2-4}$$

so that the equation corresponding to (2-3) will be

$$\operatorname{div} \boldsymbol{B} = 0. \tag{2-5}$$

The vector $\boldsymbol{B}$ is solenoidal.

Equation of Continuity

§ **2.** Electric current consists of a motion of charges. At a point of the field where a charge density ϱ moves with the velocity $\mathbf{v}$ (*meters/second*) there exists a *current density* $\boldsymbol{J}$ given by

$$\boldsymbol{J} = \varrho \mathbf{v} \qquad \textit{amperes/meter}^2. \tag{2-6}$$

The magnitude of $\boldsymbol{J}$ is equal to the charge which crosses a unit surface normal to $\mathbf{v}$ in a *second*. The *intensity* I of the current across any surface is equal to the flux of $\boldsymbol{J}$ across the same surface.

No physical experiment has ever revealed a creation or annihilation of the electric charge (in the algebraic sense, that is, not taking into account the creation or annihilation of two equal and opposite charges, which is possible in nuclear physics). Consequently the outward flux I of $\boldsymbol{J}$ across a closed surface is equal to the decrement of the inner charges per unit time. We shall have

$$I = -\frac{\partial}{\partial t} \iiint_V \varrho \mathrm{d}V = -\iiint_V \frac{\partial \varrho}{\partial t} \mathrm{d}V, \tag{2-7}$$

the interchange of the derivation and the integration being allowed because the surface of V is fixed. If the volume V is very small we obtain by the definition of the divergence

$$\text{div}\,\boldsymbol{J} + \frac{\partial \varrho}{\partial t} = 0. \tag{2-8}$$

This is termed the *equation of continuity* of electricity.

It follows that in the stationary case ($\partial/\partial t = 0$) $\boldsymbol{J}$ is solenoidal and the flux is constant all along a tube of flux; one can speak of the intensity I flowing in the tube. But in the general case one has to specify the particular cross section of the tube to which the flux I is referred.

Conduction Current

§ 3. It is customary to distinguish between *convection* and *conduction* currents. A convection current consists of the motion of a charged body. A conduction current is caused by electrons which move inside a material body (usually a metal) or by ions which move inside an electrolyte or an ionized gas. We are mainly concerned with the electronic conduction.

It is found experimentally that inside a normal conductor the density of current is proportional to the electric field strength:

$$\boldsymbol{J} = \gamma \boldsymbol{E} \qquad \textit{amperes/meter}^2. \tag{2-9}$$

The constant γ, which depends upon the medium, is called *conductivity* and is measured in (*amperes/meter*^{2})/(*volts/meter*) = = 1/(*ohm* · *meters*) = *mhos/meter* (†).

We shall show how, from (2-9), there follows Ohm's law in the familiar form. Let l be the length of a wire and Σ its cross section. The difference of potential between the two ends or *electromotive force* acting upon the wire is (by definition)

$$V = \int_l \boldsymbol{E} \cdot \mathrm{d}\boldsymbol{l} \qquad \textit{volts}. \tag{2-10}$$

As is well known, if the wire is not too long and the electromotive

(†) The reciprocal of the *ohm* is designated by *mho*.

force is not subject to very sudden variations, the intensity I is very nearly constant along the wire (it is exactly constant in the stationary case; see §2). Therefore we shall have $\Sigma \boldsymbol{J} \cdot \mathrm{d}\boldsymbol{l} = I\mathrm{d}l$ with a constant I. By substituting in this equation the value (2-9) of $\boldsymbol{J}$, we have $\Sigma\gamma \boldsymbol{E} \cdot \mathrm{d}\boldsymbol{l} = I\mathrm{d}l$, so that (2-10) becomes

$$V = I \int_l \frac{\mathrm{d}l}{\gamma \Sigma(l)}.$$

Putting

$$R = \int_l \frac{\mathrm{d}l}{\gamma \Sigma(l)} \qquad \textit{ohms}, \tag{2-11}$$

there follows Ohm's law. We see that γ is the reciprocal of resistivity (measured in *ohm · meters*).

The difference between conductors and dielectrics is only a quantitative one, because γ does not vanish in any material body. However, the ratio of the value $6 \cdot 10^7$ *mhos/meter* which it assumes for the best conductors (silver, copper) and the value of about 10^{-15} which is shown by paraffin is so enormous that in practice the differences appear to be qualitative.

§ 4. Inside a conductor the force exerted by the field upon the charge contained in a unit volume is $\varrho \boldsymbol{E}$. During the time $\mathrm{d}t$ the charge moves by $\mathbf{v}\mathrm{d}t$ so that the work done by the field is $\varrho \boldsymbol{E} \cdot \mathbf{v}\mathrm{d}t$. But $\varrho \mathbf{v} = \boldsymbol{J}$ and by (2-9) we find that

$$W = \boldsymbol{E} \cdot \boldsymbol{J} = \gamma E^2 \qquad \textit{watts/meter}^3 \tag{2-12}$$

represents the power dissipated by the field in the unit volume because of the conductivity. It is well known that this power gives rise to generation of heat and (2-12) represents Joule's effect in a specific form.

Relaxation Time

§ 5. Let us now consider a homogeneous medium of dielectric constant ε and conductivity γ. By (2-8, 9) we have

$$\gamma \operatorname{div} \boldsymbol{E} + \frac{\partial \varrho}{\partial t} = 0,$$

while (2-3) and (1-2) yield

$$\varepsilon \operatorname{div} \boldsymbol{E} = \varrho.$$

By dividing the first equation by the second we get

$$\frac{\partial}{\partial t} \log \varrho = -\frac{\gamma}{\varepsilon},$$

and integrating from 0 to t

$$\varrho = \varrho_0(P) \exp\left(-\frac{\gamma}{\varepsilon} t\right), \tag{2-13}$$

where $\varrho_0(P)$ designates the initial ($t = 0$) distribution of the charge density. We conclude that the field everywhere causes a dissipation of the charge with an exponential law.

By putting

$$\frac{\varepsilon}{\gamma} = \tau \qquad \textit{seconds}, \tag{2-14}$$

(2-13) becomes

$$\varrho = \varrho_0(P) \exp\left(-\frac{t}{\tau}\right).$$

Thus τ represents the time needed for the charge to reduce to $1/e$ of its initial value; it is called the *relaxation time*.

In metallic conductors τ is extremely small. It is not easy to measure the ε of a metal, but for an approximate evaluation we may put $\varepsilon = \varepsilon_0$. We find then that, for the best conductors ($\gamma \cong 6 \cdot 10^7$), τ is of the order of 10^{-19} *seconds*. We derive the conclusion that in practice no charge can exist inside a conductor (†). As soon as a charge is introduced, it passes immediately to the surface. The well-known fact follows also that in a static condition the electric field inside a conductor vanishes.

In a good dielectric τ is very large. In paraffin, for instance, its order of magnitude is 10^4 *seconds*.

(†) One must always bear in mind the *algebraic* definition of the charge. Otherwise one might fail to understand how an electric current, or a motion of charges, can exist inside a conductor. Only the electrons move and at every point of the conductor there are as many fixed protons as needed to neutralize the electronic charges.

Impressed Voltages and Currents

§ 6. In the foregoing sections we have investigated the motion of the charges caused by field forces. There are several devices, which generically will be called *generators*, where the charges are set into motion by different causes (mechanical, chemical, and so on). The corresponding current is then called an *impressed* current. Inside the generator the separation of the positive and negative charges which produces the current gives rise also to an electric force which opposes such separation. The corresponding voltage must be overcome by the peculiar forces of the generator. Everything occurs as though the generator created an electromotive force, equal and opposite to that voltage. This is called the impressed electromotive force.

For example, in a voltaic cell the contact forces pull opposite charges onto the two metallic plates. This gives rise to an electric field and, consequently, to an electromotive force inside the cell, which must be overcome by the contact forces. The charges appear to be acted upon, as it were, by an opposite electromotive force, that is, by the impressed electromotive force.

The qualification of *impressed* is often extended to those electromotive forces and currents which are not generated by the field under investigation and may be considered as its sources.

We shall revert later (6-§6) to the important conception of impressed current. For the time being we note that the work done by the forces which impress the current is equal and opposite to that done by the field forces. Hence if $\boldsymbol{J}^i$ designates the impressed current, the power expended for its generation is, by (2-12),

$$W^i = -\boldsymbol{E}\cdot\boldsymbol{J}^i \tag{2-15}$$

per unit volume. This will be called the impressed power.

Ampère's Relation

§ 7. By analogy with electromotive force, it is customary to define *magnetomotive force* along a given line as the line integral of the vector $\boldsymbol{H}$. Denoting magnetomotive force by U we have

$$U = \int_l \boldsymbol{H} \cdot \mathrm{d}\boldsymbol{l} \qquad \textit{amperes.} \tag{2-16}$$

The unit of magnetomotive force is evidently the *ampere.* If the field is produced by the current I flowing in a straight infinite wire and the line l is a circle lying on a plane perpendicular to the wire and with its center on the wire, the Biot and Savart law (1-9) yields the magnetomotive force

$$\int \boldsymbol{H} \cdot \mathrm{d}\boldsymbol{l} = I. \tag{2-17}$$

This formula holds under very general conditions. It applies also when the line is not a circle and the wire is curved. By making use of the analogy between a closed electric circuit and a magnetic plate one can conclude in the well-known manner that (2-17) gives in all cases the expression of the magnetomotive force acting around a line linked to the current I (Ampère's relation).

Displacement Current

§ **8.** No ambiguity can arise from the definition of a current linked with a given line when the current flows around a closed

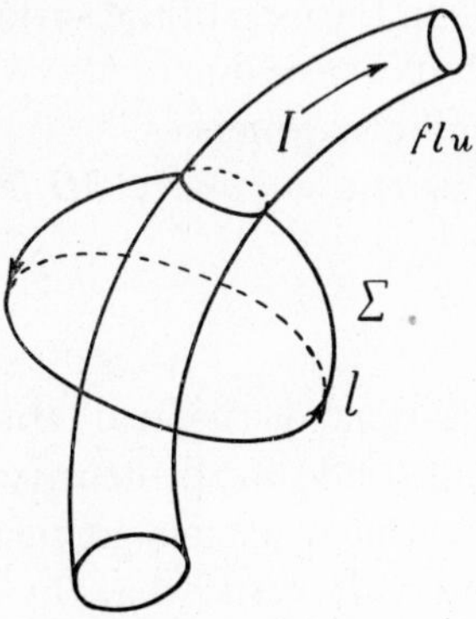

Fig. 3

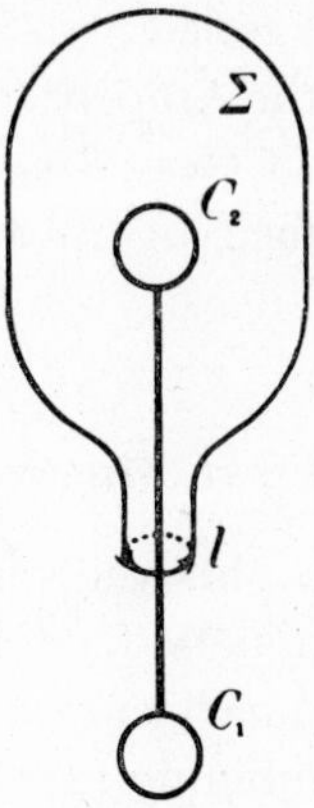

Fig. 4

circuit, or more precisely when its distribution is solenoidal. In this case the flux of $\boldsymbol{J}$ across any surface Σ bounded by l (Fig. 3) is constant, in other words, does not depend on the particular shape of Σ. This flux represents the current I.

The situation is more complicated when the circuit is open. Let us consider, for example, a steady flow of charges (*I coulombs per second*) from a conductor C_1 (Fig. 4) to a conductor C_2 along a thin and very long wire. One would assume that for a line l infinitely close to the wire Ampère's law should be valid also in tnis case. If we choose as Σ a surface intersecting the wire, we actually obtain a flux of $\boldsymbol{J}$ equal to I. But if Σ is chosen as in the figure, the flux vanishes.

The way out of this difficulty was proposed by Maxwell. We note that, unlike the flux of $\boldsymbol{J}$, the electric flux Ψ across Σ does not vanish. By virtue of Gauss' theorem (2-1) the electric flux is equal to the charge contained in C_2 so that its increment per unit time is exactly I. Thus we have

$$\frac{\partial \Psi}{\partial t} = I \qquad \textit{amperes}. \tag{2-18}$$

The left side is known as the electric *displacement current.* Let us assume that its effects, as far as the production of magnetomotive force is concerned, are identical with those of the ordinary current. Then the Ampère relation will hold also in the case of the surface Σ of Fig. 4. Actually the validity of this hypothesis due to Maxwell is confirmed by its many and important consequences.

The density of the displacement current is clearly $\partial \boldsymbol{D}/\partial t$.

The First Maxwell Equation

§ 9. Maxwell's hypothesis postulates that for the evaluation of the magnetic field at every point one must add to the density $\boldsymbol{J}$ of the ordinary current the density $\partial \boldsymbol{D}/\partial t$ of the displacement current. By combining (2-3) with (2-8) one may easily verify that the total density of current thus obtained is solenoidal. Indeed we have

$$\operatorname{div}\left(\boldsymbol{J} + \frac{\partial \boldsymbol{D}}{\partial t}\right) = 0.$$

The Ampère relation can now be written with full generality as follows:

$$U = I \qquad \textit{amperes,} \tag{2-19}$$

U representing the magnetomotive force acting around a closed line and I the *total* electric current across any surface bounded by that line. The sense of the circulation is *direct* with respect to the flow of the current (rule of the corkscrew).

The relation (2-19) is called the *first Maxwell equation,* written in the form of a *circuit relation.*

If we apply (2-19) to an infinitesimal plane loop of normal $\boldsymbol{n}$ and remember the definition of the curl (M1-§6) we readily find

$$(\text{curl}\,\boldsymbol{H})_n = \left(\frac{\partial \boldsymbol{D}}{\partial t} + \boldsymbol{J}\right) \cdot \boldsymbol{n},$$

whence obviously

$$\text{curl}\,\boldsymbol{H} = \frac{\partial \boldsymbol{D}}{\partial t} + \boldsymbol{J}. \tag{2-20}$$

This is the differential form assumed by the first Maxwell equation. It is evident that in order to pass from (2-19) to (2-20) one must assume that $\boldsymbol{H}$ be continuous and differentiable.

The current density $\boldsymbol{J}$ on the right side stands for the sum of the convection, conduction, and impressed currents.

The Second Maxwell Equation

§ 10. There are no real magnetic charges in nature and consequently there are no magnetic currents of convection nor conduction. However, following the analogy with the electric case, one can define the magnetic displacement current as the derivative with respect to time of the magnetic flux across a given surface. Denoting this current by K, we shall write

$$\frac{\partial \Phi}{\partial t} = K \qquad \textit{volts.} \tag{2-21}$$

The unit is clearly the *weber/second* = *volt.*

The density of the magnetic displacement current is $\partial \boldsymbol{B}/\partial t$. Taking the derivative of (2-5) with respect to time, one sees by inspection that the magnetic current is always solenoidal.

The law of electromagnetic induction (1-13) can be written simply as

$$V = -K \qquad \textit{volts}, \tag{2-22}$$

where V represents the electromotive force arising in a closed circuit around the magnetic current K. The negative sign means that the sense of rotation of V is *inverse* with respect to the direction of K (opposite to the corkscrew rule).

The relation (2-22) is the *second Maxwell equation* in the form of a circuit relation.

With an argument perfectly similar to that of the previous section we may find, in the case that $\boldsymbol{E}$ is differentiable,

$$\text{curl}\, \boldsymbol{E} = -\frac{\partial \boldsymbol{B}}{\partial t}, \tag{2-23}$$

i.e., the second Maxwell equation in differential form.

It is important to note that *the Maxwell equations are linear.* As a consequence when they are also homogeneous, that is to say when no impressed current is present, the sum of two solutions is a new solution.

As to the inhomogeneous case we may say that, if an impressed current $\boldsymbol{J}_1^i$ gives rise to a field $\boldsymbol{E}_1$, $\boldsymbol{H}_1$ and an impressed current $\boldsymbol{J}_2^i$ gives rise to a field $\boldsymbol{E}_2$, $\boldsymbol{H}_2$, the impressed current $\boldsymbol{J}_1^i + \boldsymbol{J}_2^i$ will give rise to the field $\boldsymbol{E}_1 + \boldsymbol{E}_2$, $\boldsymbol{H}_1 + \boldsymbol{H}_2$. Physically this means that two electromagnetic fields of different origin can overlap without disturbing one another (*principle of superposition*).

Polarization of the Medium

§ 11. From the Maxwell equations it is easy to derive a physical interpretation of the fact that generally speaking the dielectric constant and the magnetic permeability of a material substance differ from those of empty space.

If we put

$$D = \varepsilon_0 E + P_e, \tag{2-24}$$

(2-20) may be written

$$\text{curl } \boldsymbol{H} = \frac{\partial \varepsilon_0 \boldsymbol{E}}{\partial t} + \frac{\partial \boldsymbol{P}_e}{\partial t} + \boldsymbol{J}.$$

This is the same equation that we should have in free space, except for the addition of the term $\partial \boldsymbol{P}_e/\partial t$ to the ordinary current $\boldsymbol{J}$. The interpretation of this fact is the following. A neutral piece of matter is composed of an enormous number of positive and negative particles in equilibrium. In a dielectric these particles are strongly but not completely bound to their normal positions. An electric force of external origin can effect some slight displacements; the restoring force is of the elastic type. From a macroscopic point of view we may imagine that inside the dielectric two clouds of electricity are superimposed with the densities $+ \varrho$ and $- \varrho$ respectively; under the action of the field the two clouds undergo a shift $\mathrm{d}\boldsymbol{l}$ with respect to one another. The dielectric is said to be *polarized*. The vector $\boldsymbol{P}_e = \varrho \mathrm{d}\boldsymbol{l}$ is called the *intensity of polarization*. It is easy to see that $\boldsymbol{P}_e$ represents the electric moment of the unit volume (†).

Without loosing in generality we may suppose that the cloud $- \varrho$ is fixed, while the cloud $+ \varrho$ moves with the velocity $\boldsymbol{v}$. Then by (2-6) we obtain $\partial \boldsymbol{P}_e/\partial t = \varrho \boldsymbol{v} = \boldsymbol{J}$. Thus we verify that owing to the polarization a new current density $\partial \boldsymbol{P}_e/\partial t$ is added to the ordinary current. Note that, by virtue of (2-24), $\boldsymbol{P}_e$ has the same dimensions as $\boldsymbol{D}$ and is measured in *coulombs/meter*^{2}.

It may be remarked that (2-3) can be written as

$$\text{div } \varepsilon_0 \boldsymbol{E} = \varrho - \text{div } \boldsymbol{P}_e.$$

Thus owing to polarization there arises a distribution of charge of density $-$ div $\boldsymbol{P}_e$ which is added to the ordinary charge ϱ. Also

(†) It will be recalled that the electric moment of two equal and opposite charges is a vector whose magnitude equals the product of the absolute value of either charge and their distance apart and is directed from the negative to the positive charge.

this fact can be justified, but we omit the argument for the sake of brevity.

In a normal isotropic dielectric, experiment shows that $\boldsymbol{P}_e$ is proportional to $\boldsymbol{E}$:

$$\boldsymbol{P}_e = \chi \boldsymbol{E}. \tag{2-25}$$

The constant χ is called the *electric susceptivity* and is measured in *farads/meter*. From (2-24, 25) we may derive

$$\varepsilon = \varepsilon_0 + \chi \qquad \textit{farads/meter}. \tag{2-26}$$

Since χ is always positive, ε is always greater than ε_0.

§ 12. By a similar argument, starting from (2-23) one can define the *magnetic polarization* $\boldsymbol{P}_m$ by

$$\boldsymbol{B} = \mu_0 \boldsymbol{H} + \boldsymbol{P}_m. \tag{2-27}$$

The derivative of $\boldsymbol{P}_m$ with respect to the time corresponds to a fictitious magnetic current which is not so readily interpreted as the electric one due to the absence of real magnetic charges. Here we have rather to deal with a dipolar magnetic moment which varies with time. From the macroscopic standpoint an investigation of the microscopic cause of this magnetic moment may be dispensed with.

We may put

$$\boldsymbol{P}_m = \varkappa \boldsymbol{H}, \tag{2-28}$$

whence

$$\mu = \mu_0 + \varkappa \qquad \textit{henrys/meter}. \tag{2-29}$$

The *magnetic susceptivity* $\varkappa$ is really constant in *paramagnetic* and *diamagnetic* substances. In a paramagnetic substance it is positive ($\mu > \mu_0$) and in a diamagnetic substance it is negative ($\mu < \mu_0$). But in both cases the susceptivity is so small that generally speaking one can neglect it, putting $\mu = \mu_0$. In a *ferromagnetic* substance $\varkappa$ is not constant (†) and attains very high positive values (μ/μ_0 may be of the order of thousands or even more).

(†) It depends on the value of the magnetic force at the time considered and on the values that it has assumed in the past (*hysteresis*).

Energy of the Field

§ 13. Let us consider (Fig. 5) an infinite plane distribution of electricity of surface density σ embedded in a homogeneous dielectric. The electric field that will arise will be symmetrical and perpendicular to the plane. Let us enclose a portion of the plane with a cylindrical box having its bases parallel to the plane. The area of either base will be Σ. The total flux across the wall vanishes.

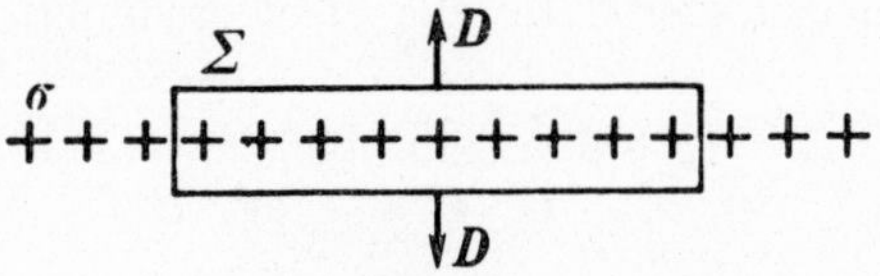

Fig. 5

The flux going out through the bases will be $\Sigma\sigma$ according to Gauss' theorem. To each base there corresponds a flux $\Psi = \Sigma\sigma/2$, so that (†)

$$D = \sigma/2, \tag{2-30}$$

independent of the point considered.

Between two parallel plane distributions of density $+\sigma$ and $-\sigma$ respectively we shall have a field $D = \sigma$. Each one will be acted upon by a force per unit surface which according to (2-30) is $F = (\sigma/2\varepsilon)\sigma = \boldsymbol{E} \cdot \boldsymbol{D}/2$ if by $\boldsymbol{E}$ and $\boldsymbol{D}$ we understand the field created by both distributions, or the field actually existing between them. The work necessary to remove the two distributions one *meter* from one another, will also be represented by $\boldsymbol{E} \cdot \boldsymbol{D}/2$ per *meter*^{2}. In the premaxwellian conception this work was converted into a *potential energy* of the charges. After Maxwell, it is assumed instead that the energy is stored and remains *localized* in the field with the density

(†) This result is not inconsistent with (1-8), which gives $D = \sigma$ at the surface of a *conductor*. In that case besides the field generated by the distribution σ one has to consider the field due to other charges either on the same conductor or on external bodies, which are necessary in order to maintain the charge σ at the point considered.

$$U_e = \frac{1}{2} \boldsymbol{E} \cdot \boldsymbol{D} = \frac{1}{2} \varepsilon E^2 \qquad \textit{joules/meter}^3 \tag{2-31}$$

holding also for an inhomogeneous dielectric.

By a similar argument one is led to assume that a magnetic field stores the energy

$$U_m = \frac{1}{2} \boldsymbol{H} \cdot \boldsymbol{B} = \frac{1}{2} \mu H^2 \qquad \textit{joules/meter}^3. \tag{2-32}$$

The total energy stored by the electromagnetic field has the density

$$U = \frac{1}{2} \boldsymbol{E} \cdot \boldsymbol{D} + \frac{1}{2} \boldsymbol{H} \cdot \boldsymbol{B}. \tag{2-33}$$

It is of interest to note that the principle of superposition which is valid for the field vectors does not hold for the energy. The superposition of the fields $\boldsymbol{E}_1$, $\boldsymbol{D}_1$ and $\boldsymbol{E}_2$, $\boldsymbol{D}_2$ gives rise to the field $\boldsymbol{E}_1 + \boldsymbol{E}_2$, $\boldsymbol{D}_1 + \boldsymbol{D}_2$, hence to the energy density

$$\frac{1}{2} (\boldsymbol{E}_1 + \boldsymbol{E}_2) \cdot (\boldsymbol{D}_1 + \boldsymbol{D}_2) \neq \frac{1}{2} \boldsymbol{E}_1 \cdot \boldsymbol{D}_1 + \frac{1}{2} \boldsymbol{E}_2 \cdot \boldsymbol{D}_2.$$

The energy of the resultant field is different in general from the sum of the energies of the two separate fields. It is customary to say that there is an *interference* between the two fields.

The basic equations and hypotheses of the present chapter are fully confirmed by the consequences that will be developed in the following chapters and by their agreement with experience.

CHAPTER 3

Propagation of the Electromagnetic Field

Surfaces of Discontinuity

§ 1. In order to proceed from the circuit relations (2-19, 22) to the differential Maxwell equations (2-20, 23) one has to assume that the field quantites are continuous and differentiable. Hence the circuit relations are more general than the differential equations. They govern also the case when the field presents a surface of discontinuity, as will be shown shortly.

§ 2. Let us consider the field inside a medium, not necessarily homogeneous or continuous.

Let Σ be a surface of discontinuity of the field, which has a fixed shape and a fixed position in space. For the sake of generality we shall assume that on Σ there is a surface distribution of current.

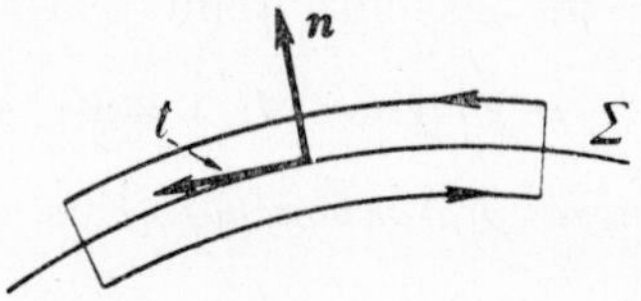

Fig. 6

By analogy with the case of the space current density $\boldsymbol{J}$ we shall define the surface current by means of its density $\boldsymbol{\iota} = \sigma \boldsymbol{v}$, σ designating the surface density of charge, which moves with the velocity $\boldsymbol{v}$ (tangent to the surface). The unit of $\boldsymbol{\iota}$ is obviously the *ampere/meter*.

Denote by $\boldsymbol{n}$ the normal to the surface (Fig. 6) and by $\boldsymbol{t}$ the tangent to the intersection with the plane of the figure. The normal to this plane directed to the reader will be $\boldsymbol{k} = \boldsymbol{n} \wedge \boldsymbol{t}$. The side on which $\boldsymbol{n}$ is drawn will be called the positive side of Σ.

Consider now an infinitesimal rectangle like that represented in the figure. Let the two sides parallel to Σ have an infinitesimal length dl of the first order, and those perpendicular to Σ be infinitesimals of the second order. The magnetomotive force acting along this circuit, apart from infinitesimals of the second order, will be $\boldsymbol{t} \cdot (\boldsymbol{H}^+ - \boldsymbol{H}^-)dl$, where $\boldsymbol{H}^+$ and $\boldsymbol{H}^-$ denote the values of $\boldsymbol{H}$ on the positive and on the negative side of Σ respectively. On the other hand the current passing through the rectangle will be $\boldsymbol{\iota} \cdot \boldsymbol{k}dl$. The first circuit relation (2-19) then yields

$$\boldsymbol{t} \cdot (\boldsymbol{H}^+ - \boldsymbol{H}^-) = \boldsymbol{k} \cdot \boldsymbol{\iota}.$$

By writing $\boldsymbol{k} \wedge \boldsymbol{n}$ in place of $\boldsymbol{t}$ on the left side one obtains $\boldsymbol{k} \wedge \boldsymbol{n} \cdot (\boldsymbol{H}^+ - \boldsymbol{H}^-) = \boldsymbol{k} \cdot \boldsymbol{\iota}$ or $\boldsymbol{k} \cdot \boldsymbol{n} \wedge (\boldsymbol{H}^+ - \boldsymbol{H}^-) = \boldsymbol{k} \cdot \boldsymbol{\iota}$. Since $\boldsymbol{k}$ may have any direction tangent to Σ, we finally obtain

$$\boldsymbol{n} \wedge (\boldsymbol{H}^+ - \boldsymbol{H}^-) = \boldsymbol{\iota}. \tag{3-1}$$

This is the fundamental equation governing the possible discontinuity of $\boldsymbol{H}$ across Σ. When $\boldsymbol{\iota} = 0$, in particular one derives that *the tangential component of* $\boldsymbol{H}$ *is continuous across* Σ.

Since there are no real magnetic currents a perfectly similar argument based on the second circuit relation leads to

$$\boldsymbol{n} \wedge (\boldsymbol{E}^+ - \boldsymbol{E}^-) = 0. \tag{3-2}$$

Consequently *the tangential component of* $\boldsymbol{E}$ *is continuous across any surface* Σ.

§ 3. Let us now consider a cylindrical box like that of (Fig. 5) with its two bases on either side of Σ and having a height which is negligible with respect to the base dimensions. The outward electric flux will be $\boldsymbol{n} \cdot (\boldsymbol{D}^+ - \boldsymbol{D}^-)a$ if a represents the area of the bases and the charge contained in the box will be σa. Gauss' theorem (2-1) then gives

$$\boldsymbol{n} \cdot (\boldsymbol{D}^+ - \boldsymbol{D}^-) = \sigma. \tag{3-3}$$

This equation governs the possible discontinuity of $\boldsymbol{D}$ across Σ. When $\sigma = 0$, *the normal component of* $\boldsymbol{D}$ *is continuous across* Σ.

In a similar manner one finds for the magnetic flux

$$\boldsymbol{n} \cdot (\boldsymbol{B}^+ - \boldsymbol{B}^-) = 0. \tag{3-4}$$

As a consequence *the normal component of* $\boldsymbol{B}$ *is continuous across any surface* Σ.

Propagation of Discontinuities

§ 4. Let us apply the foregoing results to the case of a continuous dielectric in the absence of electric charges and currents. No fixed surface of discontinuity for the field can exist in this case, as it follows by considering (3-1, 2, 3, 4). However we shall see that a moving surface of discontinuity can exist; in other words, the discontinuities of the field, once they arise (†), must be propagated.

The normal components of $\boldsymbol{D}$ and $\boldsymbol{B}$, and consequently of $\boldsymbol{E}$ and $\boldsymbol{H}$ (continuous dielectric) cannot in any case be discontinuous. Then we turn our attention to the tangential components.

For simplicity we shall assume $\boldsymbol{E}^+ = \boldsymbol{H}^+ = 0$. That is to say, the field $\boldsymbol{E}^- = \boldsymbol{E}$ and $\boldsymbol{H}^- = \boldsymbol{H}$ exists only on the negative side of Σ, and vanishes on the positive side. Therefore, $\boldsymbol{E}$ and $\boldsymbol{H}$ must be tangent to Σ; we shall have $\boldsymbol{E} \cdot \boldsymbol{n} = \boldsymbol{H} \cdot \boldsymbol{n} = 0$. The velocity of propagation of Σ will be represented by $v\boldsymbol{n}$.

We refer to the infinitesimal rectangle of Fig. 6. Along its boundary the total magnetomotive force will be $-\,\boldsymbol{t} \cdot \boldsymbol{H} \mathrm{d}l$. On the other hand, since Σ is moving, the electric flux across the rectangle will increase with the time rate $\partial\Psi/\partial t = v\,\mathrm{d}l\,\boldsymbol{D} \cdot \boldsymbol{k}$. The first circuit relation will give ($\boldsymbol{D} = \varepsilon\boldsymbol{E}$)

$$-\,\boldsymbol{t} \cdot \boldsymbol{H} = v\varepsilon\boldsymbol{E} \cdot \boldsymbol{k}.$$

Upon substitution of $\boldsymbol{k} \wedge \boldsymbol{n}$ for $\boldsymbol{t}$ in the left side, we obtain, as already seen in 3-§2 in a similar case,

$$-\,\boldsymbol{n} \wedge \boldsymbol{H} = v\varepsilon\boldsymbol{E}. \tag{3-5}$$

(†) In reality they might not be true discontinuities. They will rather be sudden variations, which in the limit would become discontinuities in the mathematical sense.

Again by applying the second circuit relation to the same rectangle one finds

$$\boldsymbol{n} \wedge \boldsymbol{E} = v\mu \boldsymbol{H}. \tag{3-6}$$

The last two equations are very remarkable. They state that ***E* and *H* are mutually perpendicular and normal to the direction of propagation of the field.** Furthermore ***E*, *H*, *n*** *form in this order a direct triad*, when v is positive, that is when Σ moves in the direction of $\boldsymbol{n}$.

Let us now introduce into (3-5) the value of $\boldsymbol{H}$ taken from (3-6); we have

$$-\boldsymbol{n} \wedge (\boldsymbol{n} \wedge \boldsymbol{E}) = v^2 \varepsilon\mu \boldsymbol{E},$$

and by developing the double vector product ($\boldsymbol{E} \cdot \boldsymbol{n} = 0$), we find

$$v = \frac{1}{\sqrt{\varepsilon\mu}}. \tag{3-7}$$

By forming the vector product of (3-5) and $\boldsymbol{H}$ and of (3-6) and $\boldsymbol{E}$ we obtain, after carrying out the double vector products,

$$\boldsymbol{n}H^2 = v\varepsilon \boldsymbol{E} \wedge \boldsymbol{H},$$

$$-\boldsymbol{n}E^2 = v\mu \boldsymbol{H} \wedge \boldsymbol{E}.$$

These equations involve four parallel vectors and may be divided by one another, yielding

$$\frac{H^2}{E^2} = \frac{\varepsilon}{\mu},$$

or

$$\sqrt{\mu}H = \sqrt{\varepsilon}E. \tag{3-8}$$

§ 5. The formulas worked out in the previous section are important. An interesting consequence is that, if the electromagnetic field is initially limited in a portion of the dielectric bounded by the surface Σ and vanishes everywhere outside, there takes place a propagation with the velocity $1/\sqrt{\varepsilon\mu}$. The field will eventually reach every point of the dielectric. In free space it is $\varepsilon_0 = 10^7/4\pi c^2$,

$\mu_0 = 4\pi \cdot 10^{-7}$, whence $v = c$. The coincidence of the value of c derived by electromagnetic measurements with the value of the velocity of light in vacuum represented the first evidence of the electromagnetic nature of light. The value of c is $2.998 \cdot 10^8 \cong 3 \cdot 10^8$ *meters/second.*

In a general dielectric we should have instead $v = 1/\sqrt{\varepsilon_r \varepsilon_0 \mu_r \mu_0} = c/\sqrt{\varepsilon_r \mu_r}$. This is in general at variance with the experience. We shall come back to this question in a later chapter. For the time being we shall accept the above conclusion as it is.

No limitation to the generality has been caused by the assumption that the field vanishes on the positive side of Σ. Indeed we can always superimpose upon the field just considered any arbitrary and continuous field (by the principle of superposition); the net result is a field which does not vanish on either side of Σ, and presents a discontinuity of its tangential components across Σ. This is the most general case of a physically admissible field presenting discontinuities. Our formulas are still valid in this case provided one understands by $\boldsymbol{E}$ and $\boldsymbol{H}$ the jump of the electric and magnetic forces respectively across Σ.

Characteristic Surfaces

§ **6.** The surface Σ is called the *wave front.* With the progress of time Σ moves and generates a family of surfaces. The lines orthogonal to this family are called *rays.* Rays are the lines of flux of the vectors $\boldsymbol{n}$.

In a homogeneous medium the rays are straight lines. To show

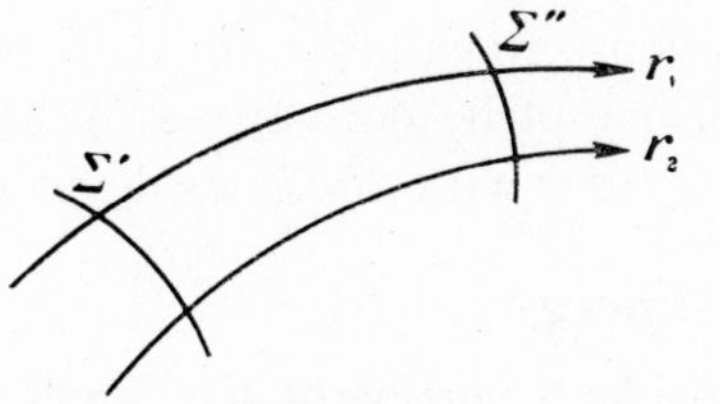

Fig. 7

this let us consider two rays r_1, r_2 close to one another (Fig. 7) and two successive positions Σ', Σ'' of Σ. If the rays were curved, as in the figure, Σ would run a longer distance along r_1 than r_2. And this is absurd if the medium is homogeneous, because the velocities along both rays are equal.

The vectors $\boldsymbol{E}$ and $\boldsymbol{H}$ are tangent to the wave front, hence normal to the ray. The electromagnetic field is *transverse*. The values of $\boldsymbol{E}$ and $\boldsymbol{H}$ are not arbitrary, being connected by (3-8). Besides, the two vectors are mutually perpendicular.

Let the equation of the family of the wave fronts be $f(P, t) = 0$; by solving this equation with respect to t it will always be possible to put it in the form

$$\varphi(P) = ct. \tag{3-9}$$

If dP represents an infinitesimal shift in the direction perpendicular to the surface $\varphi = constant$ through P, by the definition of gradient (M1-§3) we get mod grad $\varphi = \mathrm{d}\varphi/\mathrm{mod}\ \mathrm{d}P = \mathrm{d}\varphi/v\mathrm{d}t$. Differentiation of (3-9) gives $\mathrm{d}\varphi = c\mathrm{d}t$, whence finally

$$(\mathrm{grad}\ \varphi)^2 = \left(\frac{c}{v}\right)^2. \tag{3-10}$$

We have thus found a partial differential equation for φ.

The meaning of this equation is of a more general character than one might think. The solutions of a differential system like that formed by the Maxwell equations can admit discontinuities in their derivatives of any order only along well-determined surfaces, known as *characteristic surfaces*. Equation (3-10) is just the differential equation of the characteristic surfaces (3-9) of the Maxwell equations. An electromagnetic field which vanishes everywhere outside Σ and has non-zero values inside must present on Σ at least a discontinuity of one of its derivatives (of any order) and consequently is propagated with the laws developed above.

Propagation of Energy

§ 7. Let us consider a portion of Σ so small as to be practically plane. We assume that on one side of Σ the field vanishes. On the other side, if we limit ourselves to a very small region, $\boldsymbol{E}$ and $\boldsymbol{H}$ may be considered as constant; according to the previous investigation they will be parallel to Σ and mutually perpendicular. The quotient of E by H is given by (3-8).

Across any surface parallel to Σ there will occur a flow of energy. The flux density, or the flow of energy per unit area, will be equal to the energy density of the field (2-33) multiplied by the velocity of propagation of Σ. If we call this flux density W we shall have

$$W = \frac{1}{2\sqrt{\varepsilon\mu}}(\boldsymbol{E}\cdot\boldsymbol{D} + \boldsymbol{H}\cdot\boldsymbol{B}) = \frac{1}{2}\left(\sqrt{\frac{\varepsilon}{\mu}}\,E^2 + \sqrt{\frac{\mu}{\varepsilon}}\,H^2\right),$$

and by taking into account (3-8)

$$W = EH.$$

This result, in conjunction with the properties of the field discussed in the foregoing sections, shows that the energy flux is identical with the flux of the vector

$$\boldsymbol{S} = \boldsymbol{E} \wedge \boldsymbol{H}, \tag{3-11}$$

which is called the *Poynting vector*. This vector is parallel to $\boldsymbol{n}$, or to the ray.

This result can be generalized as we shall show directly.

§ 8. Let us consider any continuous medium, possibly a conductor. In the Maxwell differential equations (2-20, 23) we shall separate the conduction current $\boldsymbol{E}$ from the impressed current $\boldsymbol{J}$, assuming that no convection currents are present other than impressed (†). We shall write

$$\begin{cases} \text{curl}\,\boldsymbol{H} = \varepsilon\dfrac{\partial \boldsymbol{E}}{\partial t} + \gamma\boldsymbol{E} + \boldsymbol{J}^i \\ \text{curl}\,\boldsymbol{E} = -\mu\dfrac{\partial \boldsymbol{H}}{\partial t}. \end{cases} \tag{3-12}$$

By multiplying scalarly the second equation by $\boldsymbol{H}$ and the first by

(†) In the future this assumption will always be made.

$\boldsymbol{E}$ and subtracting we get

$$\boldsymbol{H} \cdot \operatorname{curl} \boldsymbol{E} - \boldsymbol{E} \cdot \operatorname{curl} \boldsymbol{H} = -\mu \boldsymbol{H} \cdot \frac{\partial \boldsymbol{H}}{\partial t} - \varepsilon \boldsymbol{E} \cdot \frac{\partial \boldsymbol{E}}{\partial t} - \gamma E^2 - \boldsymbol{E} \cdot \boldsymbol{J}^i.$$

By taking into account (M1-28) and (3-11) and rearranging the terms we arrive at

$$(3\text{-}13) \qquad -\boldsymbol{E} \cdot \boldsymbol{J}^i = \gamma E^2 + \frac{\partial}{\partial t}\left(\frac{1}{2}\varepsilon E^2 + \frac{1}{2}\mu H^2\right) + \operatorname{div} \boldsymbol{S}.$$

This equation expresses an energy balance. The left side by (2-15) represents the power expended per unit volume by the impressed electromotive forces in order to maintain the impressed current against the field. On the right side the first term represents the power dissipated into heat in the unit volume (Joule effect). The second term represents the time rate of increase of the energy stored in the unit volume. The third term is the outward flux of $\boldsymbol{S}$ from the unit volume. This shows that we are allowed to interpret $\boldsymbol{S}$ as the flux density of the electromagnetic energy.

One should note that the localization of the field energy according to (2-33) and the representation of its flux by $\boldsymbol{S}$ present some arbitrariness and do not lend themselves to an experimental proof. For instance one might add to $\boldsymbol{S}$ an arbitrary solenoidal vector without disturbing the energy balance (3-13).

However in their applications the above formulas prove very useful and give results in perfect agreement with the experience.

Momentum of the Field

§ **9.** A unit cube where the current density $\boldsymbol{J}$ enters through one face and goes out through the opposite one is obviously equivalent to a current element $\mathrm{d}I = I\,\mathrm{d}\boldsymbol{l} = \boldsymbol{J}$. This current element when embedded in a magnetic field is subject to the force $\boldsymbol{J} \wedge \boldsymbol{B}$, as it follows from (1-11). The total force acting on the unit volume will be

$$(3\text{-}14) \qquad \boldsymbol{F} = \varrho \boldsymbol{E} + \boldsymbol{J} \wedge \boldsymbol{B} \qquad \textit{newtons/meter}^3.$$

We shall assume that the medium is homogeneous and that the

charges are free to move inside it. Then $\boldsymbol{F}$ will be equal to the time derivative of the momentum of the charges contained in a unit volume. If we denote this momentum by $\boldsymbol{Q}$, we get

$$\frac{\partial \boldsymbol{Q}}{\partial t} = \varrho \boldsymbol{E} + \boldsymbol{J} \wedge \boldsymbol{B}. \tag{3-15}$$

Substituting into this equation the value of ϱ given by (2-3) and the value of $\boldsymbol{J}$ given by (2-20), we obtain

$$\frac{\partial \boldsymbol{Q}}{\partial t} = \boldsymbol{E} \operatorname{div} \boldsymbol{D} - \boldsymbol{B} \wedge \operatorname{curl} \boldsymbol{H} - \frac{\partial \boldsymbol{D}}{\partial t} \wedge \boldsymbol{B}. \tag{3-16}$$

On the other hand, introducing the Poynting vector $\boldsymbol{S} = \boldsymbol{E} \wedge \boldsymbol{H}$ and the velocity of propagation $v = 1/\sqrt{\varepsilon\mu}$, we have by (2-23)

$$\frac{\partial}{\partial t}\left(\frac{\boldsymbol{S}}{v^2}\right) = \frac{\partial}{\partial t}(\boldsymbol{D} \wedge \boldsymbol{B}) = \frac{\partial \boldsymbol{D}}{\partial t} \wedge \boldsymbol{B} + \boldsymbol{D} \wedge \frac{\partial \boldsymbol{B}}{\partial t} = \frac{\partial \boldsymbol{D}}{\partial t} \wedge \boldsymbol{B} - \boldsymbol{D} \wedge \operatorname{curl} \boldsymbol{E}.$$

Substitution into the last term of (3-16) gives

$$\frac{\partial \boldsymbol{Q}}{\partial t} = \boldsymbol{E} \operatorname{div} \boldsymbol{D} - \boldsymbol{B} \wedge \operatorname{curl} \boldsymbol{H} - \boldsymbol{D} \wedge \operatorname{curl} \boldsymbol{E} - \frac{\partial}{\partial t}\left(\frac{\boldsymbol{S}}{v^2}\right). \tag{3-17}$$

Let us now consider the *Maxwell tensor* $\boldsymbol{T}$ defined as

$$\boldsymbol{T} = \boldsymbol{ED} + \boldsymbol{HB} - U\boldsymbol{U}, \tag{3-18}$$

where $\boldsymbol{ED}$ and $\boldsymbol{HB}$ are dyads (see M2-§6), $\boldsymbol{U}$ is the fundamental tensor (ibid.) and $U = \boldsymbol{E} \cdot \boldsymbol{D}/2 + \boldsymbol{H} \cdot \boldsymbol{B}/2$ is the density of the electromagnetic energy. Let us calculate the divergence of this tensor:

$$\operatorname{div} \boldsymbol{T} = \operatorname{div} (\boldsymbol{ED} + \boldsymbol{HB}) - U \operatorname{div} \boldsymbol{U} - (\operatorname{grad} U) \cdot \boldsymbol{U}.$$

Since $\boldsymbol{U}$ is constant in space, we may write by (M2-14)

$$\operatorname{div} \boldsymbol{T} = \operatorname{div} (\boldsymbol{ED} + \boldsymbol{HB}) - \operatorname{grad} U =$$

$$= \varepsilon\left[\operatorname{div} (\boldsymbol{EE}) - \frac{1}{2} \operatorname{grad} (\boldsymbol{E} \cdot \boldsymbol{E})\right] + \mu\left[\operatorname{div} (\boldsymbol{HH}) - \frac{1}{2} \operatorname{grad} (\boldsymbol{H} \cdot \boldsymbol{H})\right].$$

Next, by utilizing (M2-33), we get

$$\operatorname{div} \boldsymbol{T} = \boldsymbol{E} \operatorname{div} \boldsymbol{D} - \boldsymbol{D} \wedge \operatorname{curl} \boldsymbol{E} - \boldsymbol{B} \wedge \operatorname{curl} \boldsymbol{H},$$

and substituting into (3-17)

$$\frac{\partial \boldsymbol{Q}}{\partial t} + \frac{\partial}{\partial t}\left(\frac{\boldsymbol{S}}{v^2}\right) = \operatorname{div} \boldsymbol{T}. \tag{3-19}$$

The last equation expresses a momentum balance, as it can easily be shown with the following argument. Suppose that the field has non-vanishing values only inside a finite volume V, surrounded at a distance by the surface Σ. By integrating (3-19) and remembering (M2-26), we obtain

$$\frac{\mathrm{d}}{\mathrm{d}t} \iiint_V \left(\boldsymbol{Q} + \frac{\boldsymbol{S}}{v^2}\right) \mathrm{d}V = \oiint_\Sigma \boldsymbol{T} \cdot \boldsymbol{n} \mathrm{d}\Sigma, \tag{3-20}$$

and since $\boldsymbol{T}$ vanishes on Σ it follows that

$$\iiint_V \left(\boldsymbol{Q} + \frac{\boldsymbol{S}}{v^2}\right) \mathrm{d}V = \text{constant.}$$

Hence we see that if the principle of the conservation of momentum is to be respected, we must attribute to the field a *momentum density* $\boldsymbol{g}$ given by

$$\boldsymbol{g} = \frac{\boldsymbol{S}}{v^2} = \boldsymbol{D} \wedge \boldsymbol{B}. \tag{3-21}$$

In this way the momentum lost at any time by the charges will be acquired by the field and vice versa, so that the total momentum will be a constant.

From the relation $S = Uv$ and from (3-21) we also derive the connection

$$g = \frac{U}{v},$$

between the momentum and the energy of the field.

§ 10. It is of interest to see the interpretation that is given to the right side of (3-20) when its value is different from zero. It is evident that it might represent a mechanical force giving to the charges and to the field the momentum of the left side. Accordingly, when it was still believed that electromagnetic phenomena could be interpreted merely in terms of mechanics, $\boldsymbol{T}$ was thought of as a stress tensor. This is possible because, as is well known from the mechanics of continuous bodies, the specific stress acting upon a surface element normal to $\boldsymbol{n}$ is precisely (Cauchy's theorem)

$$\boldsymbol{\Phi}_n = \boldsymbol{\Phi}_k n_k = \Phi_{jk} n_k \boldsymbol{i}_j = \boldsymbol{\Phi} \cdot \boldsymbol{n},$$

having denoted by $\boldsymbol{\Phi}$ the stress tensor, by Φ_{jk} its components, and by $\boldsymbol{\Phi}_k = \Phi_{jk} \boldsymbol{i}_j$ the three principal stresses. Putting $\boldsymbol{T} = -\boldsymbol{\Phi}$, we see that the right side of (3-20) exactly represents the total force acting from outside upon Σ.

However, nowadays no importance is attached to this mechanical interpretation. The meaning of $\boldsymbol{T}$ is instead similar to that of the Poynting vector. The Poynting vector represents the flux density of the energy; $-\boldsymbol{T}$ instead is the *flux density of momentum.* Hence $\boldsymbol{T} \cdot \boldsymbol{n} \mathrm{d}\Sigma$ gives the momentum flowing across the surface $\mathrm{d}\Sigma$ in the unit time, towards the interior of Σ. The balance expressed by (3-20) is then evident.

History of the Electromagnetic Field

§ 11. At the time when the study of electricity and the first quantitative studies on magnetism appeared, science was under the influence of Newton's gigantic work. It was quite natural that all the experimental data gathered during the eighteenth century were eventually summarized in Coulomb's law (1785) which is perfectly similar to the law of universal gravitation.

The consequences of the Coulomb law were developed by the far reaching investigations of great mathematicians, such as Poisson (1811), Green (1828) and others. These were substantially static theories where space was considered as absolutely empty of physical properties and represented only a geometrical frame for the charges. Each charge acted upon the others directly at a distance, without any intermediary. A fundamental notion was that of potential and the corresponding energy was believed to be located in the charges.

It took a long time before the notion of electric current was established with some clarity, even after the cell was discovered by Volta (1799). Oersted, when announcing his discovery of the action of the current on a magnetic needle (1820), still spoke of an *electric conflict*, as though the positive and negative charges were fighting each other and their collision disturbed the needle. However, this discovery was of exceptional importance and through the work of Arago and Ampère very soon it yielded its fruits. The concept of the electric current, which was now established with precision, came, so to speak, to the foreground. Ampère stated the identity of the magnetic field produced by a current with that produced by a magnet, discovered the electrodynamic interactions of two currents and formulated his famous hypothesis that a magnetized body contains in its interior many tiny and circular currents.

A new sensational discovery was that of electromagnetic induction, announced by Faraday in 1831. Faraday was the son of a poor blacksmith and lacked the mathematical education of his great contemporaries. But he was able to overcome this handicap by means of a wonderful physical intuition. In some ways this was a fortunate situation because he was led to create an extremely original picture of electricity and magnetism, which later had a profound influence on Maxwell's investigations. Faraday attributed a real physical existence to the lines of electric and magnetic flux, understood the role of the polarization of the dielectric separating two charged conductors and led the way to the disappearance of action at a distance, as was conceived by earlier scientists.

The notion of field prevails completely in the great work of Maxwell (*Treatise on Electricity and Magnetism*, 1873). An electric or magnetic field occupying a certain region of space does not represent a mathematical fiction, being instead a physical reality because the space in that region acquires new properties. This state of space is characterized by the field vectors. According to Maxwell a mechanical tension took place in the ether, as has been shown to be possible from a mathematical standpoint (see 3-§10); but this interpretation is not essential to a development of Maxwell's theory. The state of stress in the ether is replaced by a storage of energy with the well known density (2-33). The elegant hypothesis of the displacement current permitted the prediction that this energy was moving in vacuum with the velocity c. The identity of c with the value of the velocity of light and the circumstance that the electromagnetic field is transverse (perpendicular to the ray) led Maxwell to the conception of the electromagnetic theory of light. This theory raised some doubts and criticism at the time of its publication.

Maxwell died too soon (1879) to see Hertz's experimental proof of the electromagnetic theory (1888). By means of these experiments the theory was confirmed beyond any doubt and through the work of Hertz, Heaviside, Lorentz, Righi, and many others it was going to occupy a most important place in physics.

CHAPTER 4

Electromagnetic Potentials

Vector and Scalar Potentials

§ 1. The integration of the Maxwell equations is complicated by the fact that the two unknown functions are vectors, consequently equivalent to six scalars. For this reason some methods have been imagined to reduce the number of the unknown quantities.

We begin by reducing the unknown functions to a vector and a scalar. Let the medium be a homogeneous dielectric. Since $\operatorname{div} \boldsymbol{B} = 0$, we can put

$$\boldsymbol{B} = \operatorname{curl} \boldsymbol{A}, \tag{4-1}$$

where $\boldsymbol{A}$ represents a vector point function which is called the *vector potential.* Its unit is obviously the *weber/meter.* The second Maxwell equation $\operatorname{curl} \boldsymbol{E} + \partial \boldsymbol{B}/\partial t = 0$ then becomes

$$\operatorname{curl}\left(\boldsymbol{E} + \frac{\partial \boldsymbol{A}}{\partial t}\right) = 0.$$

This equation is satisfied by substituting for the vector within the brackets the gradient of a scalar function. We shall write

$$\boldsymbol{E} = - \operatorname{grad} \varphi - \frac{\partial \boldsymbol{A}}{\partial t}, \tag{4-2}$$

and call φ the *scalar potential.* In a static condition ($\partial \boldsymbol{A}/\partial t = 0$) φ is identical to the potential of elementary physics. It is measured in *volts.*

§ 2. As is well known, φ is determined only apart from an additive constant; but this is not very important. It is more interesting to note that (4-1) determines $\boldsymbol{A}$ apart from an arbitrary gradient. Indeed, since curl grad $\chi = 0$ the vector $\boldsymbol{B}$ of (4-1) remains unchanged if one replaces $\boldsymbol{A}$ by $\boldsymbol{A} - \text{grad}\,\chi$. By (4-2) one must replace φ by $\varphi + \partial\chi/\partial t$ if $\boldsymbol{E}$ is also to remain unchanged (†). We shall take advantage of this fact as follows: Let $\boldsymbol{A}_0$, φ_0 represent a possible determination for $\boldsymbol{A}$ and φ according to (4-1,2), and χ a solution of the differential equation

$$\nabla^2\chi - \frac{1}{v^2}\frac{\partial^2\chi}{\partial t^2} = \text{div}\,\boldsymbol{A}_0 + \frac{1}{v^2}\frac{\partial\varphi_0}{\partial t}, \tag{4-3}$$

where $v^2 = 1/\varepsilon\mu$. We shall choose for the potentials the two functions

$$\begin{cases} \boldsymbol{A} = \boldsymbol{A}_0 - \text{grad}\,\chi, \\ \varphi = \varphi^0 + \dfrac{\partial\chi}{\partial t}. \end{cases} \tag{4-4}$$

Hence it follows that

$$\text{div}\,\boldsymbol{A} = \text{div}\,\boldsymbol{A}_0 - \nabla^2\chi,$$

$$\frac{\partial\varphi}{\partial t} = \frac{\partial\varphi_0}{\partial t} + \frac{\partial^2\chi}{\partial t^2},$$

so that, taking into account (4-3), we have

$$\text{div}\,\boldsymbol{A} + \frac{1}{v^2}\frac{\partial\varphi}{\partial t} = 0. \tag{4-5}$$

The purpose of (4-3) is to give this relation which is very important and is known as the *Lorentz equation.*

Note that χ being an arbitrary solution of (4,3) is only determined apart from a solution of the homogeneous equation $\nabla^2\chi - (1/v^2)\partial^2\chi/\partial t^2 = 0$. However, even if we add such a solution it is evident that (4-5) still holds and $\boldsymbol{E}$ and $\boldsymbol{B}$ still remain unchanged.

§ 3. Let us now substitute $\boldsymbol{H} = \boldsymbol{B}/\mu = (\text{curl}\,\boldsymbol{A})/\mu$ and $\boldsymbol{D} = \varepsilon\boldsymbol{E} = -\varepsilon\,\text{grad}\,\varphi - \varepsilon\partial\boldsymbol{A}/\partial t$ into the first Maxwell equation

(†) This type of invariance is called *gage invariance.*

written in the form curl $\boldsymbol{H} - \partial \boldsymbol{D}/\partial t = \boldsymbol{J}^i$, where $\boldsymbol{J}^i$ designates the impressed current. Assuming the medium to be homogeneous, we obtain

$$\frac{1}{\mu} \text{ curl curl } \boldsymbol{A} + \frac{\partial}{\partial t}\left(\varepsilon \text{ grad } \varphi + \varepsilon \frac{\partial \boldsymbol{A}}{\partial t}\right) = \boldsymbol{J}^i,$$

or by (M1-30) upon multiplication by μ

$$\text{grad div } \boldsymbol{A} - \nabla^2 \boldsymbol{A} + \text{grad}\left(\varepsilon\mu \frac{\partial \varphi}{\partial t}\right) + \varepsilon\mu \frac{\partial^2 \boldsymbol{A}}{\partial t^2} = \mu \boldsymbol{J}^i,$$

and finally by (4-5)

$$\nabla^2 \boldsymbol{A} - \frac{1}{v^2}\frac{\partial^2 \boldsymbol{A}}{\partial t^2} = -\mu \boldsymbol{J}^i. \tag{4-6}$$

By substituting the same expression for $\boldsymbol{D}$ into the equation div $\boldsymbol{D} = \varrho$, we have

$$\text{div}\left(-\varepsilon \text{ grad } \varphi - \varepsilon \frac{\partial \boldsymbol{A}}{\partial t}\right) = \varrho,$$

whence, by virtue of (4-5), we derive

$$\nabla^2 \varphi - \frac{1}{v^2}\frac{\partial^2 \varphi}{\partial t^2} = -\frac{1}{\varepsilon}\varrho. \tag{4-7}$$

Thus we have found two important differential equations which must be satisfied by the vector and scalar potentials.

§ 4. It is of interest to note that in a region of space where no charges nor currents are present the unknown functions may be reduced to the vector potential alone. Inside that region (4-6, 7) reduce to the homogeneous equations

$$\nabla^2 \boldsymbol{A} - \frac{1}{v^2}\frac{\partial^2 \boldsymbol{A}}{\partial t^2} = 0, \qquad \nabla^2 \varphi - \frac{1}{v^2}\frac{\partial^2 \varphi}{\partial t^2} = 0. \tag{4-8}$$

Suppose now we have found a possible solution $\boldsymbol{A}$, φ which also satisfies (4-5). As shown in (4-§2), the field remains unchanged if one adds $-$ grad χ to $\boldsymbol{A}$ and $\partial\chi/\partial t$ to φ where χ is any solution of the homogeneous equation $\nabla^2\chi - (1/v^2)\partial^2\chi/\partial t^2 = 0$. By taking the derivative with respect to t we see that the same equation is satisfied also by $\partial\chi/\partial t$. Again this equation is satisfied by φ so that we are justified in putting $\partial\chi/\partial t = -\varphi$, whence $\varphi + \partial\chi/\partial t = 0$. Thus there remains only the vector potential, which satisfies the first of (4-8) and div $\boldsymbol{A} = 0$, by virtue of (4-5). Having found the expression of $\boldsymbol{A}$, we have from (4-1, 2)

$$(4\text{-}9) \qquad \boldsymbol{B} = \operatorname{curl} \boldsymbol{A}, \qquad \boldsymbol{E} = -\frac{\partial \boldsymbol{A}}{\partial t},$$

so that the field is perfectly determined.

Hertz and Fitzgerald Vectors

§ 5. Consider again a homogeneous dielectric. Let the impressed current be a *polarization current*. That is to say we assume that in the medium there is a certain distribution of *impressed polarization* or an electric moment per unit volume caused by a force other than the field and variable with time. This impressed polarization will be denoted by $\boldsymbol{P}_e^i$ and is to be distinguished from the polarization $\boldsymbol{P}_e$ caused by the field. According to 2-§11 the impressed current will be $\boldsymbol{J}^i = \partial\boldsymbol{P}_e^i/\partial t$ and one must also take into account a charge density $\varrho^i = -\operatorname{div} \boldsymbol{P}_e^i$. Then (4-6, 7) will become

$$(4\text{-}10) \quad \nabla^2\boldsymbol{A} - \frac{1}{v^2}\frac{\partial^2\boldsymbol{A}}{\partial t^2} = -\mu\frac{\partial \boldsymbol{P}_e^i}{\partial t}, \quad \nabla^2\varphi - \frac{1}{v^2}\frac{\partial^2\varphi}{\partial t^2} = \frac{1}{\varepsilon}\operatorname{div} \boldsymbol{P}_e^i.$$

It is obvious that (4-5) will be automatically satisfied by putting

$$(4\text{-}11) \qquad \boldsymbol{A} = \frac{1}{v^2}\frac{\partial \boldsymbol{\Pi}}{\partial t}, \qquad \varphi = -\operatorname{div} \boldsymbol{\Pi},$$

where $\boldsymbol{\Pi}$ represents a new vector function, known as the *Hertz vector*. It will be measured in *volt · meters*.

Upon substitution into (4-10) one arrives at the equation

$$(4\text{-}12) \qquad \nabla^2\boldsymbol{\Pi} - \frac{1}{v^2}\frac{\partial^2\boldsymbol{\Pi}}{\partial t^2} = -\frac{1}{\varepsilon}\boldsymbol{P}_e^i.$$

This is the differential equation that must be satisfied by the Hertz vector. Having found $\mathbf{\Pi}$, (4-11) give the potentials and by substituting into (4-1) we have

$$\boldsymbol{B} = \frac{1}{v^2} \operatorname{curl} \frac{\partial \mathbf{\Pi}}{\partial t}, \tag{4-13}$$

while (4-2) yields

$$\boldsymbol{E} = \operatorname{grad} \operatorname{div} \mathbf{\Pi} - \frac{1}{v^2} \frac{\partial^2 \mathbf{\Pi}}{\partial t^2}. \tag{4-14}$$

Inside a region where the impressed polarization is zero we have by (4-12)

$$\operatorname{grad} \operatorname{div} \mathbf{\Pi} - \frac{1}{v^2} \frac{\partial^2 \mathbf{\Pi}}{\partial t^2} = \operatorname{grad} \operatorname{div} \mathbf{\Pi} - \nabla^2 \mathbf{\Pi} = \operatorname{curl} \operatorname{curl} \mathbf{\Pi},$$

whence (4-14) simply becomes

$$\boldsymbol{E} = \operatorname{curl} \operatorname{curl} \mathbf{\Pi}. \tag{4-15}$$

No limitation to generality is caused by our assumption that the impressed current consists of only a polarization current. Note that for any value of $\boldsymbol{J}^i$ (impressed current) one can determine the vector $\boldsymbol{P}^i_e$ such that $\boldsymbol{J}^i = \partial \boldsymbol{P}^i_e / \partial t$. From the equation of continuity $\operatorname{div} \boldsymbol{J}^i + \partial \varrho^i / \partial t = 0$ it will also follow $\operatorname{div} \boldsymbol{P}^i_e = -\varrho^i$. The arbitrary integration constants, which are of no interest, have been omitted.

We conclude that in all cases one can express the field generated by the impressed current by means of a single vector $\mathbf{\Pi}$.

§ 6. The electric and magnetic vectors appear in the Maxwell equations in a symmetrical way (except that the correspondent of $\boldsymbol{B}$ is $-\boldsymbol{D}$). It is evident without repeating the entire argument that for an impressed magnetic polarization $\boldsymbol{P}^i_m$ one can introduce the vector $\boldsymbol{F}$ satisfying the equation analogous to (4-12)

$$\nabla^2 \boldsymbol{F} - \frac{1}{v^2} \frac{\partial^2 \boldsymbol{F}}{\partial t^2} = -\frac{1}{\mu} \boldsymbol{P}^i_m, \tag{4-16}$$

and characterizing the field through the formulas

$$\text{(4-17)} \qquad \boldsymbol{D} = -\frac{1}{v^2}\,\text{curl}\,\frac{\partial \boldsymbol{F}}{\partial t}, \qquad \boldsymbol{H} = \text{curl curl}\,\boldsymbol{F}.$$

The vector $\boldsymbol{F}$ is known as the *Fitzgerald vector.* Its unit is the *ampere · meter.*

D'Alembert's Equation

§ 7. Equations (4-6, 7) and (4-2, 16) show that the electromagnetic potentials as well as the Hertz and Fitzgerald vectors obey a differential equation of the form

$$\text{(4-18)} \qquad \nabla^2 f - \frac{1}{v^2}\frac{\partial^2 f}{\partial t^2} = h.$$

Here by $f(P, t)$ and $h(P, t)$ we designate two scalar functions. In the case of the above-mentioned vectors (4-18) represents the equation satisfied by each Cartesian component. The unknown function is f, while h is given.

Let us begin by the homogeneous equation corresponding to (4-18)

$$\text{(4-19)} \qquad \nabla^2 f - \frac{1}{v^2}\frac{\partial^2 f}{\partial t^2} = 0,$$

which is called the d'Alembert equation.

It is of interest to investigate whether (4-19) has a solution $g(P, t)$ with spherical symmetry. If one remembers the expression (M1-33) of ∇^2 in spherical coordinates and takes into account the independence of g from φ and θ there follows

$$\frac{1}{r^2}\frac{\partial}{\partial r}\left(r^2\frac{\partial g}{\partial r}\right) - \frac{1}{v^2}\frac{\partial^2 g}{\partial t^2} = 0.$$

By putting $u = rg$ it is easily verified that the left side may be written $r^{-1}\partial^2 u/\partial r^2$ so that upon multiplication of both sides by r one obtains

$$\text{(4-20)} \qquad \frac{\partial^2 u}{\partial r^2} - \frac{1}{v^2}\frac{\partial^2 u}{\partial t^2} = 0.$$

We shall put now $t_1 = r/v$; in other words we shall call t_1 the time necessary to cover the distance r with the velocity v. Equation (4-20) becomes

$$\frac{\partial^2 u}{\partial t_1^2} - \frac{\partial^2 u}{\partial t^2} = \left(\frac{\partial^2}{\partial t_1^2} - \frac{\partial^2}{\partial t^2}\right) u = 0.$$

The differential operator acting upon u is the difference of the squares of two operators and can be written (as may be easily verified) in the form

$$\left(\frac{\partial}{\partial t_1} + \frac{\partial}{\partial t}\right)\left(\frac{\partial}{\partial t_1} - \frac{\partial}{\partial t}\right) u = 0.$$

To satisfy this equation either of the two following conditions is sufficient

$$\left(\frac{\partial}{\partial t_1} \pm \frac{\partial}{\partial t}\right) u = 0.$$

It is then obvious that the two solutions $u = u(t \pm t_1)$ hold, u being an arbitrary function. Consequently (4-19) has the spherically symmetrical solutions $g = u(t \pm t_1)/r$.

Let us represent by t_0 any fixed time. We shall give the name of *retarded time* to the expression $t_r = t_0 - r/v$. We shall then define the *Green function*

$$g(r, t) = \frac{\delta(t - t_r)}{4\pi r}, \tag{4-21}$$

where δ represents the Dirac function (see M3-§3) and $r = | P - Q |$. The function g thus defined satisfies (4-19) everywhere but at the origin Q ($r = 0$) where it presents a singularity. To remove this restriction consider the integral

$$\iiint\limits_V \left(\nabla_P^2 g - \frac{1}{v^2}\frac{\partial^2 g}{\partial t^2}\right) \mathrm{d}V_P.$$

If the integration volume V does not contain the origin, the integral vanishes, because g satisfies (4-19). Let us then suppose that

V does contain the origin Q. We shall divide V into two parts by means of a small sphere of radius r_0 (volume V_0, surface Σ_0) with its center at Q. The region outside V_0 will give no contribution to the integral. As to the inside, we recall that $\nabla^2 g = \operatorname{div} \operatorname{grad} g$ is by definition the outward flux of grad g across Σ_0, divided by V_0. Then by (M2-4) (where we first interchange P and Q) we shall get

$$\iiint\limits_{V_0} \left(\nabla_P^2 g - \frac{1}{v^2}\frac{\partial^2 g}{\partial t^2}\right) \mathrm{d}V_P = \iint\limits_{\Sigma_0} (\operatorname{grad}_P g) \cdot \boldsymbol{s}\, \mathrm{d}\Sigma - \frac{1}{v^2} \iiint\limits_{V_0} \frac{\partial^2 g}{\partial t^2} \mathrm{d}V_P =$$

$$= 4\pi r_0^2 \left(-\frac{\delta(t-t_r)}{4\pi r^2} + \frac{\delta'(t-t_r)}{4\pi v r}\right)_{r=r_0} - \frac{1}{v^2} \iiint\limits_{V_0} \frac{\delta''(t-t_r)}{4\pi r} \mathrm{d}V_P .$$

By writing $4\pi r^2 \mathrm{d}r$ in place of $\mathrm{d}V_P$ and utilizing (M3-22) we find that the last integral vanishes. Furthermore it is easily seen that for $r_0 \to 0$ the preceding term reduces simply to $-\delta(t-t_0)$. These considerations show that g obeys the equation

$$\nabla_P^2 g - \frac{1}{v^2}\frac{\partial^2 g}{\partial t^2} = -\delta(t-t_0)\,\delta(P-Q), \tag{4-22}$$

where $\delta(P-Q)$ is the Dirac function in space (see M3-§6). This is readily verified by integrating both sides of the equation over V.

Kirchhoff's Formula

§ 8. Consider a solution $f(P, t)$ of (4-18), which is regular inside a domain V. By (4-22) we get

$$\int\limits_{-\infty}^{+\infty} \mathrm{d}t \iiint\limits_{V} \left[g\left(\nabla_P^2 f - \frac{1}{v^2}\frac{\partial^2 f}{\partial t^2}\right) - f\left(\nabla_P^2 g - \frac{1}{v^2}\frac{\partial^2 g}{\partial t^2}\right)\right] \mathrm{d}V_P = \tag{4-23}$$

$$= \int\limits_{-\infty}^{+\infty} \mathrm{d}t \iiint\limits_{V} \frac{\delta(t-t_r)}{4\pi r} h(P, t) \mathrm{d}V_P + \int\limits_{-\infty}^{+\infty} \mathrm{d}t \iiint\limits_{V} f(P, t)\delta(t-t_0)\delta(P-Q)\mathrm{d}V_P =$$

$$= \frac{1}{4\pi} \iiint\limits_{V} \frac{h(P, t_r)}{r} \mathrm{d}V_P + f(Q, t_0).$$

On the other hand, by the second Green formula (M1-35) and by (M3-21) the left side of (4-23) becomes successively

$$\text{(4-24)}\quad \int_{-\infty}^{+\infty} dt \iiint_V (g\nabla_P^2 f - f\nabla_P^2 g)\, dV_P - \frac{1}{v^2}\int_{-\infty}^{+\infty} dt \iiint_V \left(g\frac{\partial^2 f}{\partial t^2} - f\frac{\partial^2 g}{\partial t^2}\right) dV_P =$$

$$= \int_{-\infty}^{+\infty} dt \oiint_\Sigma \left(g\frac{\partial f}{\partial n} - f\frac{\partial g}{\partial n}\right) d\Sigma_P - \int_{-\infty}^{+\infty} dt \iiint_V \frac{\partial}{\partial t}\left(g\frac{\partial f}{\partial t} - f\frac{\partial g}{\partial t}\right) dV_P =$$

$$= \frac{1}{4\pi}\int_{-\infty}^{+\infty} dt \oiint_\Sigma \left\{\frac{\delta(t-t_r)}{r}\frac{\partial f}{\partial n} - f\frac{\partial}{\partial r}\left[\frac{\delta(t-t_r)}{r}\right]\frac{\partial r}{\partial n}\right\} d\Sigma_P -$$

$$- \frac{1}{v^2}\iiint_V \left[\frac{\delta(t-t_r)}{r}\frac{\partial f}{\partial t} - f\frac{\delta'(t-t_r)}{r}\right]_{-\infty}^{+\infty} dV_P =$$

$$= \frac{1}{4\pi}\oiint_\Sigma \left[\frac{1}{r}\frac{\partial f}{\partial n} + \left(\frac{1}{r^2}f + \frac{1}{vr}\frac{\partial f}{\partial t}\right)\frac{\partial r}{\partial n}\right]_{t=t_r} d\Sigma_P\,,$$

because both δ and its derivative vanish at infinity.

By comparing (4-23) and (4-24) one finally obtains

$$\text{(4-25)}\quad f(Q, t_0) = -\frac{1}{4\pi}\iiint_V \frac{h(P, t_r)}{r}\, dV_P +$$

$$+ \frac{1}{4\pi}\oiint_\Sigma \left[\frac{1}{r}\frac{\partial f}{\partial n} + \left(\frac{1}{r^2}f + \frac{1}{vr}\frac{\partial f}{\partial t}\right)\frac{\partial r}{\partial n}\right]_{t=t_r} d\Sigma_P\,.$$

This is known as the *Kirchhoff formula.* It is clear that only a formal meaning attaches to the choice of Q as origin. Actually Q may be any point of space within Σ and P is the variable integration point, with $r = \text{mod}\,(P - Q)$.

§ 9. Kirchhoff's formula shows that the value of f at point Q and time t_0 is the sum of the contributions due to the elementary volumes dV and the contributions due to the elementary surfaces

$d\Sigma$. But each contribution depends on the state of the corresponding element at the time $t_r = t_0 - r/v$. The interpretation of this fact is that the action of each element travels with the finite velocity v and consequently arrives at Q with a retardation proportional to the distance apart of the element from Q.

If we now assume that h vanishes everywhere outside a finite region of space and shift Σ toward infinity, to the regions not yet attained by the field, (4-25) becomes

$$f(Q, t_0) = -\frac{1}{4\pi}\iiint_V \frac{h(P, t_r)}{r}\, dV_P, \tag{4-26}$$

dV_P representing the elementary volume around the variable point P. This is obviously a particular solution of the inhomogeneous equation (4-18); it expresses the field due to the distribution of the quantity h. Thus, for such field, h represents the *source density*.

To (4-26) one may add any solution of the homogeneous equation (4-18); it is clear that this solution is expressed by the surface integral in (4-25). The corresponding field is due to the sources located outside of Σ.

Retarded Potentials

§ 10. The above results apply immediately to the case of electromagnetic potentials. Consider a given distribution of current $\boldsymbol{J}(P, t)$ and of charge $\varrho(P, t)$ in a finite region of space. We want to evaluate the field created by this distribution of sources. To this end it is sufficient to recall (4-6, 7) and to apply (4-26) (to each Cartesian component in the case of the vector potential). Thus we get

$$\boldsymbol{A}(Q, t) = \frac{\mu}{4\pi}\iiint_V \frac{\boldsymbol{J}(P, t - r/v)}{r}\, dV_P, \tag{4-27}$$

$$\varphi(Q, t) = \frac{1}{4\pi\varepsilon}\iiint_V \frac{\varrho(P, t - r/v)}{r}\, dV_P, \tag{4-28}$$

dV_P being the elementary volume around the integration point and $r = |P - Q|$. We shall show in the next section that the $\boldsymbol{A}$ and φ thus defined satisfy the Lorentz relation (4-5). For the time being we remark that the current is the source of the vector potential, while the charge is the source of the scalar potential. But the sources act upon each point of space with a retardation equal to the time taken by light to reach it. For this reason (4-27, 28) are called the formulas of the *retarded potentials*.

The time is come to remark that in the Green function (4-21) we could have put $-r/v$ in place of r/v, obtaining as a consequence an *advanced* in place of a retarded time. We could have repeated all the preceding work arriving at the advanced instead of the retarded quantities. Now this is absurd from a physical standpoint because it is impossible for the electromagnetic field to exist before the variations of currents and charges which give rise to it. For this reason between the two possible Green functions it is customary to choose that which leads to retarded quantities. By this procedure one applies the so-called *radiation condition*; this amounts to the same as to require that the electromagnetic field emanate form its sources instead of converging onto them.

§ 11. Let us now consider a vector $\mathbf{v}(P, t)$ which is a function of the point P and of the scalar parameter t. If t does not depend on P there is no ambiguity in the definition of divergence. But if t is a function of P one must introduce a distinction analogous to that between the partial and total derivatives. We shall call *partial divergence* ($\partial\mathrm{iv}\,\mathbf{v}$) that computed ignoring the dependence of t on P and total divergence ($\mathrm{div}\,\mathbf{v}$) that computed taking into account such dependence. Obviously we shall have (convention of the repeated subscripts, see M2-§4)

$$\text{(4-29)} \qquad \mathrm{div}\,\mathbf{v} = \frac{\partial v_k}{\partial x_k} + \frac{\partial v_k}{\partial t}\frac{\partial t}{\partial x_k} = \partial\mathrm{iv}\,\mathbf{v} + \frac{\partial \mathbf{v}}{\partial t}\cdot \mathrm{grad}\, t.$$

Let us now evaluate the divergence with respect to Q of the vector $\boldsymbol{J}(P, t_r)/r$ appearing in (4-27), putting $t_r = t - r/v$ (retarded time). We have ($\partial\mathrm{iv}_Q \boldsymbol{J} = 0$)

$$\mathrm{div}_Q \frac{\boldsymbol{J}}{r} = \frac{1}{r} \mathrm{div}_Q \boldsymbol{J} + \boldsymbol{J} \cdot \mathrm{grad}_Q \frac{1}{r} =$$

$$= \frac{1}{r} \partial \mathrm{iv}_Q \boldsymbol{J} + \frac{1}{r} \frac{\partial \boldsymbol{J}}{\partial t_r} \cdot \mathrm{grad}_Q t_r + \boldsymbol{J} \cdot \mathrm{grad}_Q \frac{1}{r} =$$

$$= -\frac{1}{r} \frac{\partial \boldsymbol{J}}{\partial t_r} \cdot \mathrm{grad}_P t_r - \boldsymbol{J} \cdot \mathrm{grad}_P \frac{1}{r} =$$

$$= \frac{1}{r} \partial \mathrm{iv}_P \boldsymbol{J} - \frac{1}{r} \mathrm{div}_P \boldsymbol{J} - \boldsymbol{J} \cdot \mathrm{grad}_P \frac{1}{r} = \frac{1}{r} \partial \mathrm{iv}_P \boldsymbol{J} - \mathrm{div}_P \frac{\boldsymbol{J}}{r}.$$

The second term of the last expression when integrated according to (4-27) gives the flux of $\boldsymbol{J}/r$ across Σ which vanishes, because Σ by hypothesis surrounds all the charges and currents. Consequently we get

$$\mathrm{div}_Q \boldsymbol{A} + \frac{1}{v^2} \frac{\partial \varphi}{\partial t} = \frac{\mu}{4\pi} \iiint_V \frac{1}{r} \left(\partial \mathrm{iv}_P \boldsymbol{J} + \frac{\partial \varrho}{\partial t} \right)_{t=t_r} \mathrm{d}V_P.$$

But the expression within the brackets vanishes (equation of continuity) everywhere at any time, in particular for $t = t_r$ (and it does not matter that the time considered is different from point to point). As a result the Lorentz relation is satisfied and we are allowed to assume the expressions (4-27, 28) for the electromagnetic potentials.

Retarded Hertz Vector

§ 12. On the basis of the preceding discussion the Hertz vector, which obeys (4-12) will be expressed by

$$\text{(4-30)} \qquad \boldsymbol{\Pi}(Q, t) = \frac{1}{4\pi\varepsilon} \iiint_V \frac{\boldsymbol{P}_e^i(P, t_r)}{r} \mathrm{d}V_P,$$

where $\boldsymbol{P}_e^i$ represents the impressed polarization and is a function of the variable point P. The formula is similar to those of the retarded potentials. The source of $\boldsymbol{\Pi}$ is the impressed polarization.

If the impressed polarization is of the type $\boldsymbol{L}(t)\delta(P - P_0)$ and δ represents the Dirac function, the electric moment vanishes everywhere except at P_0, where it takes the finite value $\boldsymbol{L}(t)$. We shall say then that an electric dipole of moment $\boldsymbol{L}(t)$ is located at P_0.

In this case, recalling (M3-24), (4-30) yields

$$\boldsymbol{\Pi}(Q, t) = \frac{1}{4\pi\varepsilon r}\boldsymbol{L}(t_r), \tag{4-31}$$

with $r = \operatorname{mod}(Q - P_0)$ and $t_r = t - r/v$.

The field is evaluated by means of (4-13, 15), with the result

$$\boldsymbol{E}(Q, t) = \frac{1}{4\pi\varepsilon}\operatorname{curl}_Q \operatorname{curl}_Q \frac{\boldsymbol{L}(t_r)}{r}, \quad \boldsymbol{H}(Q, t) = \frac{1}{4\pi}\operatorname{curl}_Q \frac{\boldsymbol{L}'(t_r)}{r}. \tag{4-32}$$

This is the field generated by an electric dipole whose moment is given as a time function.

In a similar manner by (4-16, 17) a magnetic dipole of moment $\boldsymbol{N}(t)$, located at P_0 will give rise to the field

$$\boldsymbol{E}(Q,t) = -\frac{1}{4\pi}\operatorname{curl}_Q \frac{\boldsymbol{N}'(t_r)}{r}, \quad \boldsymbol{H}(Q, t) = \frac{1}{4\pi\mu}\operatorname{curl}_Q \operatorname{curl}_Q \frac{\boldsymbol{N}(t_r)}{r}. \tag{4-33}$$

The formulas derived in the present section are important in the theory of radiation.

CHAPTER 5

The Field in a Moving System

The Galileo Transformation

§ 1. A physical event is characterized not only by its particular qualitative and quantitative features, but also by the location and the time where and when it takes place. This external framework in which all the phenomena of physics are ordered requires that for every event four scalar parameters x, y, z, t be given; it has *four dimensions.*

The transformations of the coordinates which take place when the spatial axes are rotated or the origin is displaced in space or time are well known.

It is more interesting to investigate the case where two systems are moving with respect to one another. Let x, y, z, t represent the

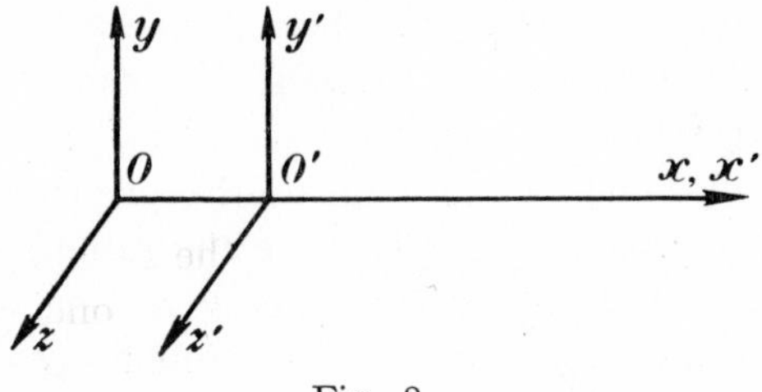

Fig. 8

coordinates of an event in a fixed frame K and x', y', z', t' the coordinates of the same event in a moving frame K'. We shall assume that the motion of K' is a uniform translation in a straight line. To simplify we shall also assume that the axes x and x' are coincident at any time (Fig. 8), that y and z are parallel to y' and z' respectively, and that the origin O' is moving along x with a constant velocity v. Further we suppose that zero time occurs in both reference frames K and K' simultaneously when O and O'

coincide. Under these conditions it is shown in classical mechanics that the following transformation holds

$$(5\text{-}1) \qquad x' = x - vt, \quad y' = y, \quad z' = z, \quad t' = t.$$

This is called *the Galileo transformation.*

The Galileo transformation is linear. Besides, by recalling the fundamental differential equation of dynamics $m\mathrm{d}^2P/\mathrm{d}t^2 = \boldsymbol{F}$ and noticing that obviously $\mathrm{d}^2P'/\mathrm{d}t'^2 = \mathrm{d}^2P/\mathrm{d}t^2$, we see that any force gives rise to the same acceleration in both systems K and K'. An observer, making purely mechanical experiments in one of the two systems cannot reveal whether the system is fixed or moving. All the systems in straight and uniform movement with respect to one another are equivalent from the mechanical standpoint (*the principle of Galileian relativity*).

The Lorentz Transformation

§ 2. Maxwell's equations are not invariant to a Galileo transformation. As a consequence the electrodynamics of a moving body should be different from that of a fixed body; in particular it should be possible by means of experiments executed wholly within a system to decide whether the system is at rest or is moving uniformly in a straight line. Several experimental facts have suggested that this is not the case.

More generally Einstein formulated the principle that all the laws of physics must necessarely have the same form in all the systems moving uniformly with respect to one another. Consequently the Galileo transformation cannot present a general validity; it must instead be in some way a particular case of the correct transformation.

In order to find the new transformation replacing that of Galileo, one must have recourse to a second principle, which was also formulated by Einstein, stating that the velocity of light is a universal constant, independent of the motions of the source and of the observer.

§ 3. As a natural generalization of the Galileian transformation we shall suppose that the new transformation is linear.

Let a light signal be sent out from O (Fig. 8) at the time $t = 0$ when O is coincident with O'. An observer at rest in K will see the signal traveling on a spherical wave front of equation

$$x^2 + y^2 + z^2 - c^2t^2 = 0. \tag{5-2}$$

On the other hand also in K' the velocity of light will be c in all directions, so that an observer at rest in that system will see the signal traveling on a spherical wave front of equation

$$x'^2 + y'^2 + z'^2 - c^2t'^2 = 0. \tag{5-3}$$

The left sides of (5-2, 3) recall the square of a vector, excepting that the last term has the minus sign. For this reason it is customary to assume in space-time the following coordinates

$$x_1 = x, \qquad x_2 = y, \qquad x_3 = z, \qquad x_4 = ict. \tag{5-4}$$

After this substitution the left hand sides of (5-2, 3) represent exactly x_ix_i and $x'_ix'_i$ respectively, or the square of the distance from the origin (see M2-§4). Since this square is invariant to an orthogonal transformation, we are led to suppose that the desired transformation is orthogonal. In that case (5-3) would be a consequence of (5-2). Thus we shall write

$$x'_j = \alpha_{jk}x_k. \tag{5-5}$$

Now it seems reasonable that the second and third equations (5-1) should be preserved. The symmetry requires that from $y = 0$ there follows $y' = 0$ and from $z = 0$ there follows $z' = 0$. On the other hand the scale of y and z cannot change in the transformation because this would attribute an absurd distinction to K or K'. Besides y and z should not appear in the first and fourth equations (5-1), because from $x = t = 0$ one must obtain $x' = t' = 0$. Consequently of the sixteen α_{jk} only α_{11}, α_{14}, α_{41}, α_{44} as well as $\alpha_{22} = \alpha_{33} = 1$ can have non-vanishing values.

The orthogonality conditions (M2-6) reduce then to

$$\alpha_{11}^2 + \alpha_{14}^2 = 1, \qquad \alpha_{41}^2 + \alpha_{44}^2 = 1, \qquad \alpha_{11}\alpha_{41} + \alpha_{14}\alpha_{44} = 0.$$

To these we add (M2-7), which becomes

$$\alpha_{11}\alpha_{44} - \alpha_{14}\alpha_{41} = 1.$$

We thus have four equations with four unknowns; but the last equation is a consequence of the first three and we are left with an arbitrary parameter at our disposal. Multiplying the third equation by α_{11} we get $\alpha_{11}^2\alpha_{41} + \alpha_{14}\alpha_{11}\alpha_{44} = 0$. By substituting in the last term the value of $\alpha_{11}\alpha_{44}$ derived from the fourth equation we have $\alpha_{11}^2\alpha_{41} + \alpha_{14}^2\alpha_{41} + \alpha_{14} = 0$ and by the first equation $\alpha_{41} = -\alpha_{14}$. In a similar way by multiplying the fourth equation by α_{11} we have $\alpha_{11}^2\alpha_{44} - \alpha_{14}\alpha_{11}\alpha_{41} = \alpha_{11}$; by substituting the value of $\alpha_{11}\alpha_{41}$ derived from the third equation we get $\alpha_{11}^2\alpha_{44} + \alpha_{14}^2\alpha_{44} = \alpha_{11}$ whence by the first equation $\alpha_{44} = \alpha_{11}$. Then, if we fix the arbitrary parameter by putting $\alpha_{11} = 1/\sqrt{1-\beta^2}$, we get $\alpha_{44} = 1/\sqrt{1-\beta^2}$, $\alpha_{14} = \pm\, i\beta/\sqrt{1-\beta^2}$, $\alpha_{41} = \mp\, i\beta/\sqrt{1-\beta^2}$ and the four equations are satisfied.

§ **4.** Let us now write explicitly the transformation (5-5) with the values we have found for the coefficients and without the useless plus or minus sign (β may be both positive or negative)

$$x_1' = \frac{x_1 + i\beta x_4}{\sqrt{1-\beta^2}}, \quad x_2' = x_2, \quad x_3' = x_3, \quad x_4' = \frac{x_4 - i\beta x_1}{\sqrt{1-\beta^2}}. \tag{5-6}$$

Coming back to the coordinates x, y, z, t, these equations become

$$x' = \frac{x - c\beta t}{\sqrt{1-\beta^2}}, \quad y' = y, \quad z' = z, \quad t' = \frac{t - \beta x/c}{\sqrt{1-\beta^2}}.$$

Note that for the origin O' we must have $x' = 0$ and $x = vt$. Therefore by the first equation we get $\beta = v/c$. In conclusion the required transformation is the following:

$$x' = \frac{x - vt}{\sqrt{1 - v^2/c^2}}, \quad y' = y, \quad z' = z, \quad t' = \frac{t - vx/c^2}{\sqrt{1 - v^2/c^2}}. \tag{5-7}$$

This is the famous *Lorentz transformation* which guarantees the constancy of the velocity of light, the invariance of the equations of dynamics and, as we shall see shortly, the invariance of the equations of the electromagnetic field.

The Galileo transformation is a particular case holding when v is negligible as compared with c, that is in almost all practical cases.

Space-Time

§ 5. We have found that the passage from a system K to another system in uniform translation relative to the first one is equivalent to an orthogonal transformation of the four coordinates x_1, x_2, x_3, x_4. As a consequence we conclude that space and time must be conceived as constituting a four-dimensional whole (*space-time*). Time is not an absolute entity but depends in some way on the spatial relations.

This fact appears more evident if one puts $\cos\varphi = 1/\sqrt{1-\beta^2}$, whence $\sin\varphi = i\beta\sqrt{1-\beta^2}$. The transformation (5-6) between x_1 and x_4 becomes

$$x_1' = x_1 \cos\varphi + x_4 \sin\varphi,$$
$$x_4' = -\, x_1 \sin\varphi + x_4 \cos\varphi,$$

or a rotation. There follows that a uniform translation is equivalent to a rotation in the plane containing the direction of the motion and the time axis. Of course it will be noted that the angle φ is imaginary, since $\tan\varphi = i\beta$. If we put $\varphi = i\theta$, the foregoing equations may be written

$$\begin{cases} x' = x\cosh\theta - ct\sinh\theta, \\ ct' = -\, x\sinh\theta + ct\cosh\theta. \end{cases} \tag{5-8}$$

This is *hyperbolic rotation* with a real angle. Precisely we have $\tanh\theta = \beta = v/c$.

Four-Current

§ 6. Since we have found that a uniform translation is equivalent to an orthogonal transformation in space-time, the laws of electromagnetism will show the same form in K and K' if it is possible to show that the field equations are relations between vectors and tensors of this four-dimensional space. This follows from the fact that vectors and tensors are intrinsic entities and do not change for a transformation of the reference frame.

Let us start from the well established experimental fact that the electric charge is invariant, i.e., maintains the same value in all systems. Then we have

$$\text{(5-9)} \qquad dQ = \varrho\, dx_1 dx_2 dx_3 = \varrho'\, dx_1' dx_2' dx_3'.$$

On the other hand the elementary volume $dx_1 dx_2 dx_3 dx_4$ of space-time is invariant to an orthogonal transformation, because for any transformation of the coordinates its value is to be multiplied by the Jacobian determinant of the transformation which in the present case is the determinant of the α_{jk} and equals 1 (see M2-7). Thus we shall write

$$dx_1 dx_2 dx_3 dx_4 = dx_1' dx_2' dx_3' dx_4'.$$

From this equation and from (5-9) we derive $\varrho'/dx_4' = \varrho/dx_4$ and by the general law of transformation $dx_4' = \alpha_{4k} dx_k$ we can write

$$\varrho' = \varrho \alpha_{4k} \frac{dx_k}{dx_4},$$

or else

$$ic\varrho' = ic\varrho' \frac{dx_4'}{dx_4'} = \alpha_{4k}\, ic\varrho \frac{dx_k}{dx_4}.$$

Hence we see that $ic\varrho$ transforms like the fourth component of a *four-vector* (a vector in four-dimensional space) whose kth component is $ic\varrho dx_k/dx_4$. For the other components ($k = 1, 2, 3$) we get $ic\varrho dx_k/dx_4 = \varrho dx_k/dt = \varrho v_k = J_k$ or the components of the current density. This suggests that $J_1 = J_x$, $J_2 = J_y$, $J_3 = J_z$, $J_4 = ic\varrho$ are the components of a four-vector in space-time which will be called the four-current. For the fourth component the law of variance has already been verified. For another component, say the first, we have

$$J_1' = ic\varrho' \frac{dx_1'}{dx_4'} = \alpha_{4k}\, ic\varrho \frac{dx_k}{dx_4} \frac{\alpha_{1l}\, dx_l}{\alpha_{4j}\, dx_j} = \alpha_{1l}\, ic\varrho \frac{dx_l}{dx_4} = \alpha_{1l} J_l,$$

so that the law is again verified.

It is evident that the equation of continuity (2-8), if we maintain the symbol $\boldsymbol{J}$ for the four-current, takes the form

$$\operatorname{div} \boldsymbol{J} = 0, \tag{5-10}$$

in both K and K' since div is an invariant operator (see M2-§4).

Four-Potential

§ **7.** It is customary to indicate the symbolic vector $\boldsymbol{i}_k \partial/\partial x_k$ of space-time by $\square$ and to call its square $\square^2 = \partial^2/\partial x^i \partial x^i$ the *d'Alembertian* operator. The latter is an invariant operator (see M2-§4). Now the differential equations (4-6, 7) of the electromagnetic potentials may be written

$$\begin{aligned} \square^2 A_x &= -\mu_0 J_x, & \square^2 A_y &= -\mu_0 J_y, \\ \square^2 A_z &= -\mu_0 J_z, & \square^2 \varphi &= -\frac{1}{\varepsilon_0}\varrho. \end{aligned} \tag{5-11}$$

There follows that A_x, A_y, A_z, $i\varphi/c$ present the variance of the components of a four-vector (because the right hand sides are the components of the four-vector $\boldsymbol{J}$, multiplied by μ_0). This vector will be called the *four-potential* and will be designated by $\boldsymbol{A}$. Thus equations (5-11) can be summarized by

$$\square^2 \boldsymbol{A} = -\mu_0 \boldsymbol{J}, \tag{5-12}$$

where the four-current appears on the right side.

The Lorentz relation $\operatorname{div} A + (1/c^2)\partial\varphi/\partial t = 0$ can be written simply as follows:

$$\operatorname{div} \boldsymbol{A} = 0. \tag{5-13}$$

Equations (5-12, 13) are invariant to a Lorentz transformation.

Electromagnetic Tensors

§ **8.** Consider now the tensor $\boldsymbol{f} = \square \boldsymbol{A} - \boldsymbol{A}\overleftarrow{\square}$ where the arrow indicates that $\square$ operates on the left. The components of $\boldsymbol{f}$ will be

(5-14) $$f_{jk} = \frac{\partial A_k}{\partial x_j} - \frac{\partial A_j}{\partial x_k}.$$

This obviously represents an antisymmetrical tensor.

By means of the tensor $\boldsymbol{f}$ the ordinary equations for the evaluation of the field vectors $\boldsymbol{B} = \text{curl}\, \boldsymbol{A}$ and $\boldsymbol{E}/ic = \text{grad}\,(i\varphi/c) - \partial \boldsymbol{A}/\partial ict$ become simply

(5-15) $$B_x = f_{23}, \quad B_y = f_{31}, \quad B_z = f_{12},$$
$$\frac{E_x}{ic} = f_{14}, \quad \frac{E_y}{ic} = f_{24}, \quad \frac{E_z}{ic} = f_{34}.$$

Thus the components of $\boldsymbol{B}$ and of $\boldsymbol{E}/ic$ together form the non-vanishing components of an antisymmetrical tensor in space-time.

By means of (5-15) the second Maxwell equation $\text{curl}\, \boldsymbol{E} + \partial \boldsymbol{B}/\partial t = 0$ and the equation $\text{div}\, \boldsymbol{B} = 0$ may be written

(5-16) $$\begin{cases} \dfrac{\partial f_{34}}{\partial x_2} - \dfrac{\partial f_{24}}{\partial x_3} + \dfrac{\partial f_{23}}{\partial x_4} = 0, \\[2ex] \dfrac{\partial f_{14}}{\partial x_3} - \dfrac{\partial f_{34}}{\partial x_1} + \dfrac{\partial f_{31}}{\partial x_4} = 0, \\[2ex] \dfrac{\partial f_{24}}{\partial x_1} - \dfrac{\partial f_{14}}{\partial x_2} + \dfrac{\partial f_{12}}{\partial x_4} = 0, \\[2ex] \dfrac{\partial f_{23}}{\partial x_1} + \dfrac{\partial f_{31}}{\partial x_2} + \dfrac{\partial f_{12}}{\partial x_3} = 0. \end{cases}$$

Since $\boldsymbol{f}$ is antisymmetrical it is easy to verify by (M2-45) that (5-16) can be represented by the single equation

(5-17) $$\text{curl}\, \boldsymbol{f} = 0,$$

which is invariant to an orthogonal transformation. We find that the tensor $\boldsymbol{f}$ is irrotational.

§ 9. Equations (5-15) suggest to investigate whether an antisymmetrical tensor of space-time can also be constructed with the components of $\boldsymbol{H}$ and $\boldsymbol{D}$. The first Maxwell equation curl

$\boldsymbol{H} - \partial \boldsymbol{D}/\partial t = \boldsymbol{J}$ and the equation div $\boldsymbol{D} = \varrho$ may be written in the four-dimensional notation giving

$$
(5\text{-}18) \qquad \begin{cases} \dfrac{\partial H_z}{\partial x_2} - \dfrac{\partial H_y}{\partial x_3} - \dfrac{\partial icD_x}{\partial x_4} = J_x, \\ \dfrac{\partial H_x}{\partial x_3} - \dfrac{\partial H_z}{\partial x_1} - \dfrac{\partial icD_y}{\partial x_4} = J_y, \\ \dfrac{\partial H_y}{\partial x_1} - \dfrac{\partial H_x}{\partial x_2} - \dfrac{\partial icD_z}{\partial x_4} = J_z, \\ \dfrac{\partial icD_x}{\partial x_1} + \dfrac{\partial icD_y}{\partial x_2} + \dfrac{\partial icD_z}{\partial x_3} = ic\varrho. \end{cases}
$$

The right sides represent the components of the four-current $\boldsymbol{J}$. Therefore, by putting

$$
(5\text{-}19) \qquad \begin{cases} H_x = h_{23}, & H_y = h_{31}, & H_z = h_{12}, \\ -icD_x = h_{14}, & -icD_y = h_{24}, & -icD_z = h_{34}, \end{cases}
$$

and assuming that the h_{jk} thus defined represent the components of an antisymmetrical tensor $\boldsymbol{h}$ of space-time, (5-18) transform simply into

$$
(5\text{-}20) \qquad \operatorname{div} \boldsymbol{h} = \boldsymbol{J}.
$$

Since $\boldsymbol{J}$ is a vector and the operator div is invariant, we may conclude that $\boldsymbol{h}$ is really a tensor.

Transformations of the Field Vectors

§ 10. Let us now apply to the vectors and tensors introduced in the foregoing section the laws of variance (M2-4, 10) taking into account that for a Lorentz transformation $\alpha_{11} = \alpha_{44} = 1/\sqrt{1-\beta^2}$, $\alpha_{14} = -\alpha_{41} = i\beta/\sqrt{1-\beta^2}$, $\alpha_{22} = \alpha_{33} = 1$, while all the other α_{jk} vanish. We shall find some interesting relation which can immediately be transposed into visual three-dimensional space.

For the components of the four-current we obtain

$$
J_1' = \frac{J_1 + i\beta J_4}{\sqrt{1-\beta^2}}, \quad J_2' = J_2, \quad J_3' = J_3, \quad J_4' = \frac{-i\beta J_1 + J_4}{\sqrt{1-\beta^2}}.
$$

If we now designate by $\boldsymbol{J}$ the three-dimensional current, these equations become

$$(5\text{-}21) \qquad \boldsymbol{J}'_{\parallel} = \frac{\boldsymbol{J}_{\parallel} - \varrho \boldsymbol{v}}{\sqrt{1-\beta^2}}, \quad \boldsymbol{J}'_{\perp} = \boldsymbol{J}_{\perp}, \quad \varrho' = \frac{\varrho - \boldsymbol{v}\cdot\boldsymbol{J}/c^2}{\sqrt{1-\beta^2}},$$

where $\parallel$ indicates the parallel component and $\perp$ the component perpendicular to $\boldsymbol{v}$. The first equation shows that if $\boldsymbol{J} = 0$, that is if the charges are at rest in K', an observer in K will notice a current $\boldsymbol{J} = \varrho\boldsymbol{v}$, as is obvious. On the contrary the third equation which states the relativistic variance of the charge density is not so trivial. The quantity $\boldsymbol{v}\cdot\boldsymbol{J}/c^2$ which is added to ϱ, is termed the *compensation charge.*

Let us now pass to the tensor quantites. We have

$$B'_x = f'_{23} = \alpha_{2j}\alpha_{3k}f_{jk} = \alpha_{22}\alpha_{33}f_{23} = B_x,$$

$$B'_y = f'_{31} = \alpha_{3j}\alpha_{1k}f_{jk} = \alpha_{33}\alpha_{11}f_{31} + \alpha_{33}\alpha_{14}f_{34} = \frac{B_y + vE_z/c^2}{\sqrt{1-\beta^2}},$$

$$B'_z = f'_{12} = \alpha_{1j}\alpha_{2k}f_{jk} = \alpha_{11}\alpha_{22}f_{12} + \alpha_{14}\alpha_{22}f_{42} = \frac{B_z - vE_y/c^2}{\sqrt{1-\beta^2}},$$

$$E'_x = icf'_{14} = ic\alpha_{1j}\alpha_{4k}f_{jk} = ic(\alpha_{11}\alpha_{41}f_{11} + \alpha_{11}\alpha_{44}f_{14} + \\ + \alpha_{14}\alpha_{41}f_{41} + \alpha_{14}\alpha_{44}f_{44}) = E_x,$$

$$E'_y = icf'_{24} = ic\alpha_{2j}\alpha_{4k}f_{jk} = ic(\alpha_{22}\alpha_{41}f_{21} + \alpha_{22}\alpha_{44}f_{24}) = \frac{E_y - vB_z}{\sqrt{1-\beta^2}},$$

$$E'_z = icf'_{34} = ic\alpha_{3j}\alpha_{4k}f_{jk} = ic(\alpha_{33}\alpha_{41}f_{31} + \alpha_{33}\alpha_{44}f_{34}) = \frac{E_x + vB_y}{\sqrt{1-\beta^2}}.$$

If we label by $\parallel$ and $\perp$ respectively the components parallel and perpendicular to $\boldsymbol{v}$, these equations may simply be written

$$(5\text{-}22) \qquad \begin{cases} \boldsymbol{B}'_{\parallel} = \boldsymbol{B}_{\parallel}, & \boldsymbol{B}'_{\perp} = \dfrac{\boldsymbol{B}_{\perp} - \boldsymbol{v}\wedge\boldsymbol{E}/c^2}{\sqrt{1-\beta^2}}, \\ \boldsymbol{E}'_{\parallel} = \boldsymbol{E}_{\parallel}, & \boldsymbol{E}'_{\perp} = \dfrac{\boldsymbol{E}_{\perp} + \boldsymbol{v}\wedge\boldsymbol{B}}{\sqrt{1-\beta^2}}. \end{cases}$$

A similar argument for the tensor $\boldsymbol{h}$ leads to the equations (it is sufficient to substitute in the foregoing equation $\boldsymbol{H}$ for $\boldsymbol{B}$ and $-ic\boldsymbol{D}$ for $\boldsymbol{E}/ic$, or $c^2\boldsymbol{D}$ for $\boldsymbol{E}$)

$$(5\text{-}23)\qquad \begin{cases} \boldsymbol{H}'_{\parallel} = \boldsymbol{H}_{\parallel}, & \boldsymbol{H}'_{\perp} = \dfrac{\boldsymbol{H}_{\perp} - \mathbf{v} \wedge \boldsymbol{D}}{\sqrt{1-\beta^2}}, \\ \boldsymbol{D}'_{\parallel} = \boldsymbol{D}_{\parallel}, & \boldsymbol{D}'_{\perp} = \dfrac{\boldsymbol{D}_{\perp} + \mathbf{v} \wedge \boldsymbol{H}/c^2}{\sqrt{1-\beta^2}}. \end{cases}$$

These interesting equations give the field $\boldsymbol{H}'$, $\boldsymbol{B}'$, $\boldsymbol{E}'$, $\boldsymbol{D}'$ as it appears to an observer at rest in K' when the same field appears to be $\boldsymbol{H}$, $\boldsymbol{B}$, $\boldsymbol{E}$, $\boldsymbol{D}$ to an observer at rest in K.

Note that (5-23) are simple consequences of (5-22); this can be verified by dividing the first two by μ_0 and multiplying the last two by ε_0, provided we assume that μ_0 and ε_0 are invariant.

Motional Terms

§ 11. We shall remark now that in most practical cases $\beta = v/c$ is extremely small and may be neglected with respect to unity. As a consequence the transformation equations for $\boldsymbol{E}$ and $\boldsymbol{H}$ will simply read

$$(5\text{-}24)\qquad \boldsymbol{E}' = \boldsymbol{E} + \mathbf{v} \wedge \boldsymbol{B}, \qquad \boldsymbol{H}' = \boldsymbol{H} - \mathbf{v} \wedge \boldsymbol{D}.$$

The vector products of the right hand sides represent the so-called *motional terms* which are added to the field forces because of the motion of the observer.

In the approximation where $\beta = 0$ we see by inspection of (5-21) that $\varrho = \varrho'$ which means that the charge density is invariant. Then if we multiply by ϱ the first of (5-24), we shall obtain the force acting on the charges contained in a unit volume when these charges move with the velocity $\mathbf{v}$. Remembering that $\varrho\mathbf{v} = \boldsymbol{J}$ we get

$$\boldsymbol{F} = \varrho\boldsymbol{E} + \boldsymbol{J} \wedge \boldsymbol{B},$$

or (3-14) and hence (1-11). Thus we discover the profound relativistic meaning of these formulas.

Consider now an element $d\boldsymbol{l}$ of a wire moving with velocity $\mathbf{v}$

in a region of space where a magnetic field is present. The area covered by $\mathrm{d}\boldsymbol{l}$ in a unit time will be $\boldsymbol{v} \wedge \mathrm{d}\boldsymbol{l}$ and the flux $\mathrm{d}\Phi$ of $\boldsymbol{B}$ across this area will be $\mathrm{d}\Phi = \boldsymbol{B} \cdot \boldsymbol{v} \wedge \mathrm{d}\boldsymbol{l}$. On the other hand the electrons of $\mathrm{d}\boldsymbol{l}$ will be acted upon by an electric field equal to the motional term $\boldsymbol{v} \wedge \boldsymbol{B}$ or by an electromotive force $\mathrm{d}V = \boldsymbol{v} \wedge \boldsymbol{B} \cdot \mathrm{d}\boldsymbol{l}$. As a result the electromotive force equals the flux across the surface swept by $\mathrm{d}\boldsymbol{l}$ in a unit time but with the opposite sign. If $\mathrm{d}\boldsymbol{l}$ is an element of a closed loop of varying shape, by adding the contributions of all the elements and applying the rule of the corkscrew, we arrive at the result that the motional electromotive force is equal and opposite to the increase of the magnetic flux across the loop. This result enables us to rewrite the law of electromagnetic induction (1-13) in the form

$$V = -\frac{\mathrm{d}\Phi}{\mathrm{d}t}, \tag{5-25}$$

where the replacement of the partial by the total derivative means that one must take into account both the variation of Φ due to the increase of $\boldsymbol{B}$ and the variation due to the deformation of the coil.

All these conclusions are in perfect agreement with the experience and show the wonderful power of synthesis of the relativistic concepts.

Energy Tensor

§ 12. Let us consider the scalar product

$$\boldsymbol{F} = \boldsymbol{f} \cdot \boldsymbol{J} \tag{5-26}$$

of the tensor $\boldsymbol{f}$ defined by (5-14) and the four-current $\boldsymbol{J}$; this product is a vector and for a reason which will be seen presently is denoted by $\boldsymbol{F}$. By expanding the scalar product in components and making use of (5-15) we get

$$\begin{aligned}
F_1 &= f_{11}J_1 + f_{12}J_2 + f_{13}J_3 + f_{14}J_4 = B_zJ_y - B_yJ_z + E_x\varrho, \\
F_2 &= f_{21}J_1 + f_{22}J_2 + f_{23}J_3 + f_{24}J_4 = -B_zJ_x + B_xJ_z + E_y\varrho, \\
F_3 &= f_{31}J_1 + f_{32}J_2 + f_{33}J_3 + f_{34}J_4 = -B_yJ_x - B_xJ_y + E_z\varrho, \\
F_4 &= f_{41}J_1 + f_{42}J_2 + f_{43}J_3 + f_{44}J_4 = -\frac{E_x}{ic}J_x - \frac{E_y}{ic}J_y - \frac{E_z}{ic}J_z.
\end{aligned}$$

We see at once that F_1, F_2, F_3 are equal respectively to the components F_x, F_y, F_z of the vector of ordinary space $\boldsymbol{F} = \boldsymbol{J} \wedge \boldsymbol{B} + \varrho \boldsymbol{E}$ representing by (3-14) the force acting on the unit volume. The foregoing equations show that such vector becomes a four-vector of space-time when completed by the fourth component $F_4 = -\boldsymbol{E} \cdot \boldsymbol{J}/ic$. This is the four-vector appearing on the left side of (5-26). If this is taken into account and (3-15) is substituted into (3-19) we can write in components (†)

$$(5\text{-}27) \qquad \begin{cases} \dfrac{\partial T_{11}}{\partial x_1} + \dfrac{\partial T_{12}}{\partial x_2} + \dfrac{\partial T_{13}}{\partial x_3} + \dfrac{\partial S_x/ic}{\partial x_4} = F_1, \\[2ex] \dfrac{\partial T_{21}}{\partial x_1} + \dfrac{\partial T_{22}}{\partial x_2} + \dfrac{\partial T_{23}}{\partial x_3} + \dfrac{\partial S_y/ic}{\partial x_4} = F_2, \\[2ex] \dfrac{\partial T_{31}}{\partial x_1} + \dfrac{\partial T_{32}}{\partial x_2} + \dfrac{\partial T_{33}}{\partial x_3} + \dfrac{\partial S_z/ic}{\partial x_4} = F_3. \end{cases}$$

To these equations we add (3-13) which can be written as

$$(5\text{-}28) \qquad \frac{\partial S_x/ic}{\partial x_1} + \frac{\partial S_y/ic}{\partial x_2} + \frac{\partial S_z/ic}{\partial x_3} + \frac{\partial U}{\partial x_4} = F_4,$$

U being the density of the electromagnetic energy. The right sides of the last four equations represent the components of the four-vector $\boldsymbol{F}$; hence the left sides must be the components of a four-vector also. We are induced to complete the tensor $\boldsymbol{T}$ of ordinary space with the components

$$(5\text{-}29) \quad T_{14} = T_{41} = \frac{S_x}{ic}, \quad T_{24} = T_{42} = \frac{S_y}{ic}, \quad T_{34} = T_{43} = \frac{S_z}{ic}, \quad T_{44} = U,$$

so as to transform it into a tensor of space-time. Hence (5-27, 28) can be written in the compact form

$$(5\text{-}30) \qquad \operatorname{div} \boldsymbol{T} = \boldsymbol{F}.$$

The tensor $\boldsymbol{T}$ thus defined is very important in theoretical physics. It is called the *energy tensor*. A compact definition of it can be

(†) It must be remembered that in the present chapter we always refer to empty space.

given by means of the electromagnetic tensors $\boldsymbol{f}$ and $\boldsymbol{h}$ and the fundamental tensor $\boldsymbol{U}$. The definition is

$$\boldsymbol{T} = \boldsymbol{f} \cdot \boldsymbol{h} - \frac{1}{4}(\boldsymbol{f} : \boldsymbol{h})\boldsymbol{U}, \tag{5-31}$$

as it may be easily verified by expanding in components and remembering (M2-19).

Historical Outline of the Development of Special Relativity

§ 13. Soon after the advent of the wave theory of light, which was mainly due to the work of Young and Fresnel (see 10-§16), physicists began to speculate about the nature of the medium where the vibrations take place. This medium was called the *ether*.

At first it was surmized that the ether was an elastic medium, qualitatively similar to solid bodies and consequently capable of transmitting transverse vibrations, as it was required by the phenomenon of polarization. Maxwell instead conceived the ether as the seat of the electromagnetic disturbances, though he still clung somewhat to the mechanical conception.

Anyhow, once the ether is assumed as something homogeneous filling the whole universe, the motion of a material body with respect to the ether should have a physical meaning and be subject to study. In particular the Maxwell equations, even taking into account the motional terms, do not prove invariant to a Galileian transformation. Hence the electrodynamics of moving systems should be different from that of the systems at rest with respect to the ether. It should be possible by means of electromagnetic experiments (in particular by means of optical experiments) performed in a given system to detect the motion of the system relative to ether.

However all the experiments imagined to this end gave a negative result. The motions of material bodies, and in particular of the Earth, relative to ether could not be revealed.

Several attempts were made to give a theoretical justification of this curious result. Physicists had recourse to some hypothesis, like that of the partial or total drag of the ether by moving objects. By these ingenious hypotheses they often succeeded in explaining the negative results of the experiments, but only up to terms of the first order in $\beta = v/c$. However the second order terms could not give an appreciable contribution, due to their smallness.

The last and very remarkable contribution in this direction was Lorentz's discovery (1895) that if in the moving system the absolute time was replaced by a time varying linearly with position, one could account for the first order effects. The introduction of this *local time* was only a mathematical trick of very obscure significance.

However, since 1881 Michelson had made a famous interferometric experiment, which he repeated with Morley in 1887. This experiment ruled out the existence of second order effects of the terrestrial motion on the propagation of light. Several scientists, among them Poincaré (1900), began to suspect that the invariance of the electromagnetic equations should hold up to terms of any order. Meanwhile Lorentz arrived in 1904 at the transformation which bears his name and guarantees the invariance of Maxwell's equations, provided the field vectors are suitably determined in the moving frame. But the meaning of the transformation remained still very formal and obscure from the physical standpoint.

A very bright light was thrown on the problem by Einstein with his classical paper of 1905. He was not aware of Lorentz's last results and took as his starting point a profound criticism of the measurements of time and of simultaneity. The statement that two events at different points of space are simultaneous acquires a meaning only after we have specified the procedure by which we want to establish such simultaneity. It is necessary to send a signal from one point to the other, for example a light signal.

Starting from this remark, if one accepts the two fundamental principles formulated by Einstein: (1) the principle of relativity for all physical laws (their invariance to a uniform translation), and (2) the independence of the velocity of light from the motions of both the observer and the source, one arrives to the Lorentz transformation. After Einstein this transformation no longer represents a strange mathematical trick; it reflects instead the physical nature of space-time.

These concepts reached an exceptional clarity through the investigations of Minkowski, who worked on the subject from 1907 to 1909, considering space-time as a four-dimensional whole and making use of the four coordinates x_1, x_2, x_3, x_4.

Minkowski's ideas certainly played an important role in the introduction of general relativity, developed later by Einstein. We will not enter into this field and will limit ourselves to the foregoing historical outline of *special relativity*.

CHAPTER 6

Electric Circuits and Transmission Lines

Oscillating Quantities and Complex Exponentials

§ 1. In many fields of physics it is of interest to consider oscillating quantities of the type

$$(6\text{-}1) \qquad A_0(P)\cos(\omega t+\varphi), \qquad A_0(P)\sin(\omega t+\varphi),$$

where $A_0(P)$ is a position function (scalar or vector) which is called the *amplitude*. The expression $\omega t+\varphi$ is called the *phase* and is a linear function of time. The *circular frequency* ω is clearly equal to $2\pi/T = 2\pi\nu$ where T designates the *period* (expressed in *seconds*) and ν the *frequency* (†) (expressed in $seconds^{-1}$ = *hertz* or *cycles per second* (††)) of the oscillation. At $t=0$ the phase is φ and is called the *initial phase*; however in most cases φ is simply called the *phase* without possible confusion. In general also φ will be a function of position.

Instead of representing an oscillating quantity by one of the expressions (6-1) it is often convenient to set up the following linear combination of them

$$(6\text{-}2) \qquad A_0[\cos(\omega t+\varphi)+i\sin(\omega t+\varphi)] = A_0\exp[i(\omega t+\varphi)].$$

Further putting

$$(6\text{-}3) \qquad A = A_0\exp(i\varphi),$$

the expression (6-2) becomes simply $A\exp(i\omega t)$. The complex quantity A is called the *complex amplitude*; its modulus represents the true amplitude and its argument φ the initial phase.

Two oscillating quantities with the same frequency are said to

(†) For convenience the name of frequency is often given to ω.

(††) In the applications it is customary to suppress the words *per second*, and to speak of *cycles, kilocycles, megacycles*.

have the same or opposite phase depending upon whether their phases differ by a multiple of 2π or by an odd multiple of π. In the first case they are also said to be *in phase*. If the phase difference is $\pi/2$ (apart from a multiple of 2π) the two oscillations are in *quadrature*.

§ 2. The method of the complex exponentials presented in the foregoing section may be justified by the following argument.

All the physical quantities to which that procedure will be applied are subject to an equation of the type

$$\mathscr{L}(x) = C_0 \cos(\omega t + \theta), \tag{6-4}$$

where $\mathscr{L}$ is a real and linear operator independent of time and C_0, θ two given real constants. We recall that by definition of a linear operator $\mathscr{L}(a + b) = \mathscr{L}(a) + \mathscr{L}(b)$ and $\mathscr{L}(ma) = m\mathscr{L}(a)$.

Let now $z = x + iy$ be a complex quantity and write the equation

$$\mathscr{L}(z) = C \exp(i\omega t), \tag{6-5}$$

where $C = C_0 \exp(i\theta)$. This is equivalent to

$$\mathscr{L}(x) + i\mathscr{L}(y) = C_0 \cos(\omega t + \theta) + iC_0 \sin(\omega t + \theta),$$

and since $\mathscr{L}$ is a real operator can be split into the two equations

$$\begin{cases} \mathscr{L}(x) = C_0 \cos(\omega t + \theta), \\ \mathscr{L}(y) = C_0 \sin(\omega t + \theta). \end{cases} \tag{6-6}$$

Thus if we know a complex solution z of (6-5) its real part x is a solution of the first equation of (6-6) which is identical to the original equation (6-4). Consequently x represents the required physical quantity.

Let us now put $z = A \exp(i\omega t)$ and substitute into (6-5). Upon division by $\exp(i\omega t)$ we easily obtain

$$\mathscr{L}(A) = C. \tag{6-7}$$

By solving this equation one finds A and forms the complex quantity $z = A \exp(i\omega t) = A_0 \exp[i(\omega t + \varphi)]$. The real part $x =$

$= A_0 \cos(\omega t + \varphi)$ represents as stated above, the true physical quantity and has the same cosine form as the first of (6-1).

It is evident that in practice all this reasoning can be dispensed with. All one has to do is to solve equation (6-7) and to find the complex amplitude. Its modulus A_0 is the real amplitude and its argument φ the phase. The factor $\exp(i\omega t)$ can be suppressed by convention and does not appear in the actual computations.

§ 3. Two very important types of linear operations are represented by the derivations and integrations. It is easily seen, and it is well to remember, that taking the derivative of z with respect to t is equivalent to multiplying the complex amplitude by $i\omega$; and an indefinite integration with respect to t amounts to the same as dividing the complex amplitude by $i\omega$. This fact makes it possible to pass from (6-5) to (6-7) with a simple division by $\exp(i\omega t)$, even when $\mathscr{L}$ implies differential or integral operations with respect to t.

Note that the above argument is not in contradiction with the admission that $\mathscr{L}$ is a real operator or such that operating on a real quantity yields a real result. Indeed the derivations and integrations with respect to t are operations of this kind.

Electric Impedance

§ 4. We shall give the name *impedor* to any passive (not containing generators) network with two accessible terminals T_1, T_2

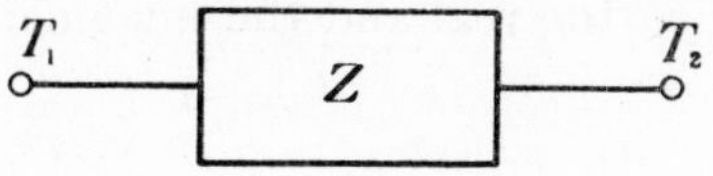

Fig. 9

(Fig. 9) such that when an alternating harmonic voltage is applied to T_1, T_2 an alternating current arises which is harmonic with the same frequency and with an amplitude proportional to that of the voltage (†).

(†) We shall assume that no accumulation of charges takes place inside the impedor so that the current entering through T_1 is always equal to that going out from T_2 and vice versa. Thus no ambiguity arises in the definition of the current.

Let $V = V_0 \exp(i\varphi_V)$ and $I = I_0 \exp(i\varphi_I)$ be respectively the complex amplitudes of the voltage applied to T_1T_2 and of the current. The amplitudes being proportional to one another, we shall write

$$V_0 = Z_0 I_0,$$

where Z is a real constant. Let us put then $\varphi_V = \varphi_Z + \varphi_I$, by which a new constant φ_Z is determined; it follows

$$\exp(i\varphi_V) = \exp(i\varphi_Z)\exp(i\varphi_I).$$

By multiplying the last two equations by one another we obtain

$$V = ZI, \tag{6-8}$$

where $Z = Z_0 \exp(i\varphi_Z)$. Equation (6-8) represents a generalization of the Ohm law, holding for alternating currents.

The complex quantity Z is called the *impedance* and is measured in *ohms* (it is a complex number of *ohms*) and generally speaking is a function of the frequency.

From the definition there follows that the modulus of the impedance is the quotient of the amplitude of the voltage by the amplitude of the current while the argument of the impedance is the phase difference between the voltage and the current. The voltage leads the current if φ_Z is positive and vice versa. When $\varphi_Z = 0$ the voltage and the current are in phase and when $\varphi = \pm \pi/2$ they are in quadrature.

§ 5. By separating the real and the imaginary parts of Z one can write

$$Z = R + iX. \tag{6-9}$$

Here R is called the *resistance* and X the *reactance*.

The reciprocal of Z is called the *admittance* and is denoted by Y; it is measured in *mhos*.

It is customary to put

$$Y = G + iB, \tag{6-10}$$

and to call G the *conductance* and B the *susceptance*.

Generators and Impressed Voltages

§ 6. So far we have spoken of voltages applied to impedors, making use of a well-known concept of elementary physics. Now we want to make this concept more explicit. To begin with, the impedance will be supposed to show a pure resistance only ($X = 0$) and a direct current I will flow through it in the positive direction $T_1 \to T_2$ (Fig. 10). Experience shows that in this case an electric field exists between T_1 and T_2 and is directed from T_1 to T_2; hence an electromotive force will arise also, directed from

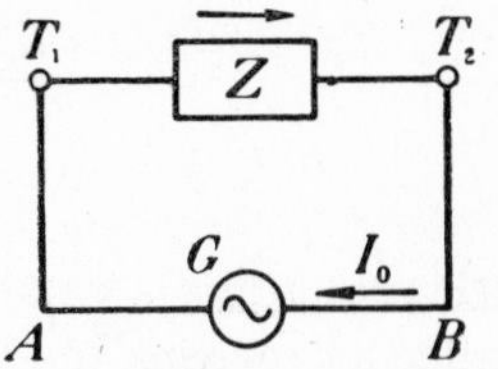

Fig. 10

T_1 to T_2 and having the magnitude $V_0 = RI_0$. In a situation where no magnetic current is present the same electromotive force will exist along the path T_1ABT_2 (because the total electromotive force acting on the circuit $T_1T_2BAT_1$ vanishes). Hence in order to maintain the current I_0 it is necessary to counteract the electromotive force of the field, along the path T_2BAT_1. Every second a positive charge I_0 is carried in the direction opposite to the electromotive force and a work V_0I_0 is done (by definition of electromotive force). This work is supplied by the *generator* G, to which an electromotive force V_0 is attributed, having along the path T_2BAT_1 a direction opposite to that of the field. This impressed electromotive force is called the *applied* or *impressed voltage.*

The above analysis is easily extended to the case of an alternating current I and of an impedance Z of any kind. The applied voltage is $V = ZI$.

Sometimes in speaking the roles, as it were, are interchanged and the generator is said to apply the electromotive force V, which is counteracted by the *counter-electromotive* force $- ZI$ developed by the impedor.

Resistors, Capacitors, Inductors

§ 7. Let us present some simple and important examples of impedors.

The name *resistor* is given to an impedor presenting a pure resistance only, or having a real impedance; graphically it is indicated as in Fig. 11. In this case the simple form of Ohm's law holds. Wires, adjustable resistances (†), rheostats, and so on are very approximately resistors. Within a resistor the current is in phase with the voltage.

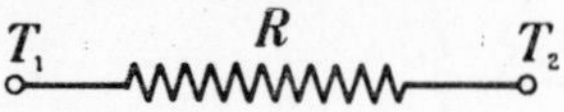

Fig. 11

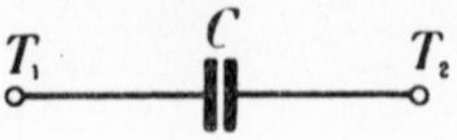

Fig. 12

Any part of a network presenting a capacitance in the sense of elementary physics is called a *capacitor* and is indicated graphically as in Fig. 12. The following relation is well known

$$V = \frac{Q}{C}, \tag{6-11}$$

where V stands for the impressed voltage, $|Q|$ for the charge stored by either plate of the capacitor and C for the capacitance. This relation is valid also when V and Q are variable, in particular when they are alternating. Hence (6-11) still holds when V and Q stand for the complex amplitudes of voltage and charge.

If by I we designate the current flowing between T_1 and T_2 we have

$$Q = \int^t I \, \mathrm{d}t = I/i\omega.$$

Hence (6-11) becomes

$$V = \frac{1}{i\omega C} I = -i \frac{1}{\omega C} I. \tag{6-12}$$

We can draw the conclusion that a capacitor presents an im-

(†) It is customary though incorrect to say *resistance, capacitance, inductance* and *impedance* respectively instead of *resistor, capacitor, inductor, impedor.*

pedance equal to $1/i\omega C$. The resistance vanishes and the reactance equals $-1/\omega C$. The argument of the impedance is $-\pi/2$; the voltage is therefore in quadrature and lags with respect to the current.

An impedance presenting inductance and negligible resistance, such as a coil of high-conductivity wire, is called an *inductor* and is usually indicated as in Fig. 13. The magnetic flux Φ linked with

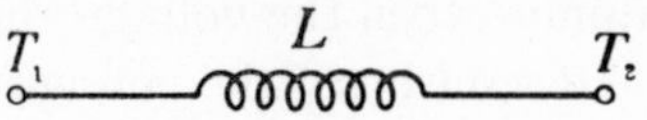

Fig. 13

the coil (namely the sum of the fluxes linked with each turn) is proportional to the current I. The corresponding relation $\Phi = LI$ where L stands for the inductance, holds no matter whether the current is steady or variable. The law of electromagnetic induction $V = -\,\mathrm{d}\Phi/\mathrm{d}t$ becomes now $V = -\,L\mathrm{d}I/\mathrm{d}t$ and for an alternating current $V = -\,i\omega LI$. Of course it will be noted that in these equations V represents the counter-electromotive force arising in the inductor owing to the variations of the current. The impressed voltage is equal and opposite to it. Accordingly, we shall write

$$V = i\omega LI. \tag{6-13}$$

This equation shows that an inductor presents the impedance $i\omega L$. The resistance vanishes and the reactance is ωL. The argument of the impedance is $\pi/2$ so that the voltage is in quadrature and leads the current.

Electric Power

§ **8.** Let $V_0 \cos(\omega t + \varphi_V)$ be the voltage applied to the impedor and $I_0 \cos(\omega t + \varphi_I)$ the resultant current. The power W_0 expended by the generator at any given time t will be the product

$$W_0(t) = V_0 I_0 \cos(\omega t + \varphi_V) \cos(\omega t + \varphi_I).$$

By a well-known trigonometric transformation we may also write

$$W_0(t) = \frac{1}{2} V_0 I_0 [\cos(\varphi_V - \varphi_I) + \cos(2\omega t + \varphi_V + \varphi_I)].$$

The term containing ωt is oscillating and in the average vanishes. Hence the average power expended by the generator is

$$\overline{W} = \frac{1}{2} V_0 I_0 \cos(\varphi_V - \varphi_I) = \frac{1}{2} V_0 I_0 \cos\varphi_Z. \tag{6-14}$$

This power is a maximum when the voltage and the current are in phase ($\varphi_Z = 0$) while it vanishes if the voltage and the current are in quadrature ($\varphi_Z = \pm\pi/2$). For an obvious reason $\cos\varphi_Z$ is called the *power factor*.

By introducing the complex amplitudes V, I and defining the *complex power* (†)

$$W = \frac{1}{2} V I^*, \tag{6-15}$$

one can verify that

$$\overline{W} = \mathscr{Re}\, W, \tag{6-16}$$

where $\mathscr{Re} W$ stands for the real part of W. In conclusion the average power expended by the generator is obtained by forming the complex power (6-15) and taking its real part.

Kirchhoff's Principles

§ 9. When dealing with a network presenting several impedances and generators it is customary to apply the two Kirchhoff principles. Their form in the case of an alternating current is perfectly similar to that holding for the direct current. All we have to do is to replace the alternating quantities by their complex amplitudes, as one can easily verify.

For instance if we consider the junction N (Fig. 14) and denote by I_{01}, I_{02}, ... the amplitudes of the currents flowing into it, since an accumulation of charges at N is impossible, we write

$$I_{01}\cos(\omega t + \varphi_1) + I_{02}\cos(\omega t + \varphi_2) + \ldots = 0,$$

(†) An asterisk denotes the complex conjugate.

or else, by changing the origin of time

$$I_{01} \sin (\omega t + \varphi_1) + I_{02} \sin (\omega t + \varphi_2) + \ldots = 0.$$

If we multiply the second equation by i, add it to the first and divide by exp $(i\omega t)$, we readily obtain the relation between the complex amplitudes $I_1, I_2, \ldots$

(6-17) $$\textstyle\sum_k I_k = 0.$$

This equation represents the first Kirchhoff principle for alternating currents.

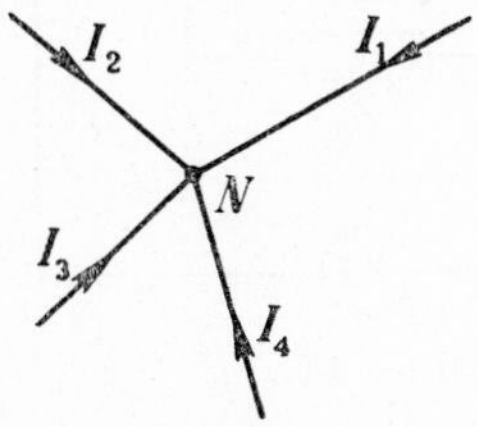

Fig. 14

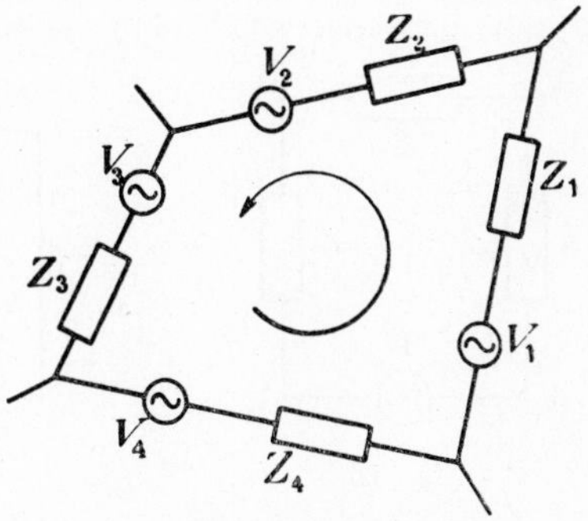

Fig. 15

In a similar manner, if we consider a closed circuit (Fig. 15) of the network and choose a positive direction of current flow, the second principle may be generalized to comprise the alternating currents as follows

(6-18) $$\textstyle\sum_k V_k - \sum_k Z_k I_k = 0.$$

This may be expressed by saying that the sum of all the impressed electromotive forces and all the counter-electromotive forces of the circuit vanishes.

Of course, among the electromotive forces one must include those generated by the magnetic currents and among the counter-electromotive forces those due to the internal impedance of the generators.

§ 10. An application of Kirchhoff's principles to the simple network of Fig. 16, consisting of a single circuit with a single generator leads to the conclusion that the current I is the same in all the branches and that

$$V = I \sum Z_k.$$

The circuit therefore is equivalent to a single impedance, having the impedance Z given by

$$Z = \sum Z_k. \tag{6-19}$$

This is the rule of composition for the impedances *in series.*

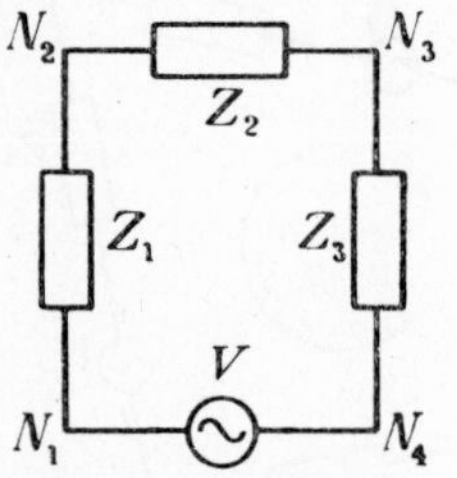

Fig. 16

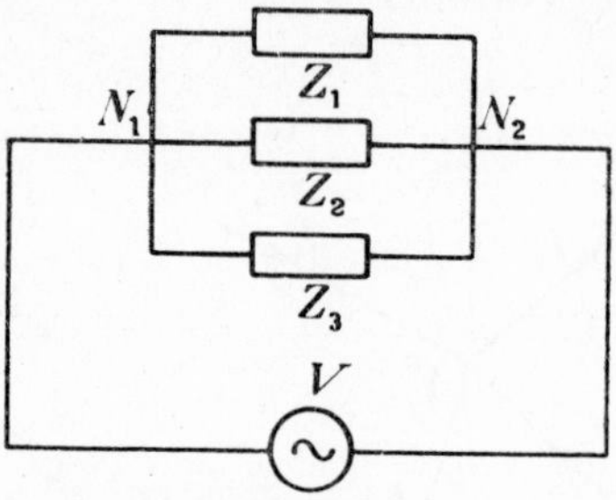

Fig. 17

By an application of the same principles to the network of Fig. 17 one may find most readily the rule for the composition of impedances *in parallel.*

$$\frac{1}{Z} = \sum_k \frac{1}{Z_k} \tag{6-20}$$

or simply

$$Y = \sum_k Y_k. \tag{6-21}$$

In conclusion the impedances add when in series and the admittances add when in parallel.

Resistance, Capacitance, and Inductance in Series

§ **11.** Let us consider the circuit of Fig. 18, presenting an alternating-current generator in series with a resistor, an inductor and a capacitor. The internal impedance of the generator will be disregarded. We have then the overall impedance

$$Z = \left(R + i\omega L - i\frac{1}{\omega C}\right),$$

or the admittance

$$Y = \frac{1}{R + i\left(\omega L - \frac{1}{\omega C}\right)}. \tag{6-22}$$

The amplitude of the current (i.e., the modulus of I) is found to be a function of the frequency of the impressed voltage. It vanishes

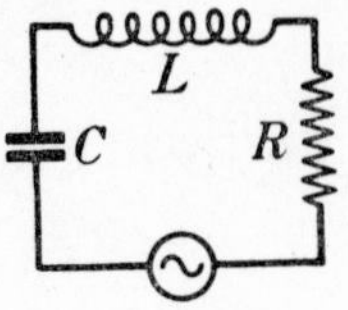

Fig. 18

both for $\omega = 0$ and for $\omega = \infty$, while it presents a maximum when the reactance vanishes, namely for a value ω_0 of ω given by

$$\omega_0 = \frac{1}{\sqrt{LC}}. \tag{6-23}$$

The corresponding frequency is called the *resonance frequency*. At resonance the voltage and the current are in phase. For a fixed value of V, the smaller the resistance the greater the value of the resonance current. Conversely for a fixed value of the current, the smaller the resistance the smaller also the voltage necessary to maintain it. In the ideal case of a vanishing resistance one might have oscillations of finite amplitude without any impressed electromotive force. In this case ω_0 is called *natural frequency* of the circuit.

It is of interest to evaluate the energy stored in the capacitor and in the inductor. In order to apply (1-17) which contain non-linear operations we must go back for a moment to the real quantities. If the current is represented by $I_0 \cos(\omega t + \varphi)$ the charge of the capacitor will be $I_0 \sin(\omega t + \varphi)/\omega$. Hence the energy stored in the capacitor is found by the first equation (1-17) to be

$$U_C = \frac{1}{2}\frac{I_0^2}{\omega^2 C}\sin^2(\omega t + \varphi). \tag{6-24}$$

Since the mean value of $\sin^2(\omega t + \varphi)$ is 1/2, the average energy stored in the capacitor will be

$$\overline{U}_C = \frac{1}{4}\frac{II^*}{\omega^2 C}. \tag{6-25}$$

The energy stored in the inductor is by the second equation (1-17)

$$U_L = \frac{1}{2}LI_0^2\cos^2(\omega t + \varphi), \tag{6-26}$$

and in the average

$$\overline{U}_L = \frac{1}{4}LII^*. \tag{6-27}$$

Let us now evaluate the complex power expended by the generator

$$W = \frac{1}{2}VI^* = \frac{1}{2}ZII^* = \frac{1}{2}RII^* + \frac{1}{2}\left(i\omega L + \frac{1}{i\omega C}\right)II^*.$$

By taking into account (6-25, 27) the last equation may be written

$$W = \overline{W} + 2i\omega(\overline{U}_L - \overline{U}_C), \tag{6-28}$$

where $\overline{W}$ represents the real power expended by the generator. We thus find that the imaginary part of the complex power is proportional to the difference of the energies stored respectively in the inductor and in the capacitor.

The total energy stored in the reactance is found by (6-24, 26) to be

$$U = \frac{1}{2}\frac{I_0^2}{\omega^2 C}\sin^2(\omega t + \varphi) + \frac{1}{2}LI_0^2\cos^2(\omega t + \varphi).$$

This is in general a periodic quantity. As a consequence a certain amount of energy passes alternatively from the generator to the circuit and vice versa. However when ω coincides with the resonance frequency ω_0 we readily obtain by (6-23)

$$U = \frac{1}{2} L I_0^2 = \frac{1}{2} L I I^*, \tag{6-29}$$

that is a constant quantity. This energy is passing indefinitely from the capacitor to the inductor and vice versa, without increasing nor diminishing. The role of the generator is limited solely to supplying the energy

$$\overline{W} = \frac{1}{2} R I I^*, \tag{6-30}$$

per unit time. This energy is dissipated in the resistor.

It is customary to define a quantity Q such that ω_0/Q be equal to the energy lost per unit time divided by the total energy stored at resonance

$$\frac{\omega_0}{Q} = \frac{\overline{W}}{U}. \tag{6-31}$$

As it is obvious Q is a pure number (†). For the circuit under investigation one obtains from (6-29, 30, 31)

$$Q = \frac{\omega_0 L}{R}. \tag{6-32}$$

The physical significance of Q may be seen in two ways. First of all let us assume that the circuit, once excited on the resonance frequency, is disconnected from the generator, short-circuited and left to itself. The oscillations will go on, but will be attenuated, due to the dissipation of energy, which is no longer compensated by the generator. For every small interval of time $\mathrm{d}t$ the loss of energy will be $-\mathrm{d}U = \overline{W}\mathrm{d}t$. Hence, multiplying both sides of (6-31) by $\mathrm{d}t$, we get

$$\frac{\omega_0}{Q}\mathrm{d}t = -\frac{\mathrm{d}U}{U},$$

(†) The symbol is identical with that representing the electric charge. However, no confusion will arise in what follows.

whence by an integration it follows

$$U = U_0 \exp\left[-\frac{\omega_0}{Q}t\right]. \tag{6-33}$$

This is the law of attenuation of the energy and ω_0/Q represents the *attenuation constant.* The greater the value of Q, the longer will the oscillations last.

In most cases one does not work exactly at resonance but in its vicinity. It is then convenient to introduce the relative shift from the resonance frequency by the relation

$$\omega = \omega_0(1 + \delta), \tag{6-34}$$

δ being a pure number, very small compared with unity. By sub-

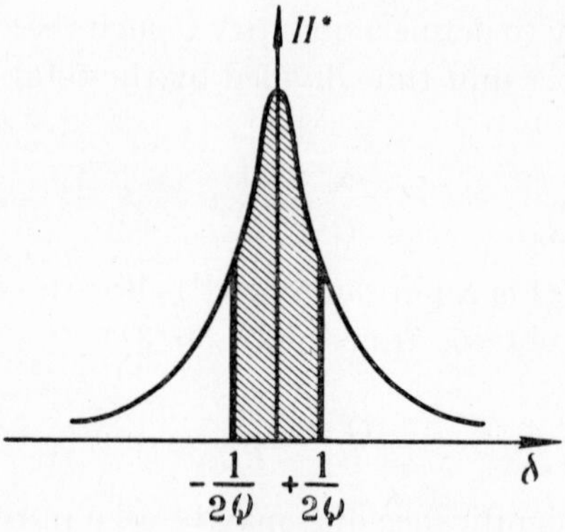

Fig. 19

stituting into (6-22), neglecting δ^2 in comparison to unity and recalling (6-32), we obtain

$$Y = \frac{1}{R}\frac{1}{1 + 2iQ\delta}. \tag{6-35}$$

The square modulus of $I = YV$, which is proportional to all the different energies involved, will be

$$II^* = \frac{VV^*}{R^2}\frac{1}{1 + 4Q^2\delta^2}.$$

This is a maximum for $\delta = 0$ (resonance). For $\delta = \pm 1/2Q$ its value is half of the maximum. For this reason it is customary to call $1/Q$ the *width* of the resonance band. The higher is the value of Q, the more critical is the resonance and the more *selective* is the circuit.

Figure 19 represents qualitatively the resonance curve, constructed by plotting II^* against δ. The resonance band is indicated by the shaded area. The maximum becomes sharper and sharper as Q increases.

Whatever its actual constitution, every circuit behaving like the one just investigated is called a *resonant circuit.*

Resistance, Inductance, and Capacitance in Parallel

§ 12. Suppose now that the resistor, the inductor and the capacitor of Fig. 18 are connected in parallel, instead of being in series. By (6-21) we shall have an overall admittance which is the sum of the admittances involved, namely,

$$Y = G + i\left(\omega C - \frac{1}{\omega L}\right),$$

where we have put $G = 1/R$. Hence we can write

$$Z = \frac{1}{G + i\left(\omega C - \dfrac{1}{\omega L}\right)}.$$

This equation may be obtained formally from (6-22) by interchanging Y with Z, R with G, L with C. As a consequence, it is very easy to discuss the case of a parallel circuit by a simple transposition of the results obtained for a series circuit.

If the current is maintained constant and ω is made to vary, the voltage presents a peak of resonance for a frequency ω_0 still given by (6-23); in the case when $G = 0$ the peak is infinite because the admittance vanishes at resonance.

In the condition of resonance the energy stored in the inductor equals that stored in the capacitor.

The Q of the circuit, which characterises the selectivity of the resonance, is found from (6-32) through the above-mentioned interchanges to be

$$Q = \frac{\omega_0 C}{G}. \tag{6-36}$$

It would be easy to prove that in this case also ω_0/Q represents the quotient of the energy dissipated per unit time by the total energy stored at resonance.

Note that if the applied voltage is maintained constant, the current presents a minimum at resonance. For this reason it is customary to speak of *anti-resonance*; and every circuit showing this behavior is said to be *anti-resonant.*

The circuits considered so far are particularly simple. A more general circuit will present several branches in series and several branches in parallel, each having its own impedance. If this impedance is concentrated, so to speak, in some well-determined circuit elements the circuit is said to have *lumped constants.*

The modulus of the overall admittance of the circuit, considered as a function of ω will have in general a number of maxima, hence the circuit will show a number of resonance frequencies. But it can be shown that in the vicinity of a resonance frequency the admittance always presents a behavior of the type (6-22) or (6-35).

If the circuit presents no dissipation, or a vanishing resistance, the minima of the impedance will be zeros. Thus one will find a number of natural frequencies; at these frequencies the current can go on indefinetly without any impressed voltage. Each oscillation corresponding to a natural frequency is termed a *mode* of the current.

What has been said for the admittance holds, with the necessary changes, for the impedance and for its resonance frequencies; the corresponding phenomena will be those of the anti-resonant circuits instead of those of the resonant circuits.

Differential Equations of Transmission Lines

§ **13.** The transfer of power from the generator to the load is ordinarily carried out by means of a *transmission line.*

Consider the very simple transmission line represented in Fig. 20.

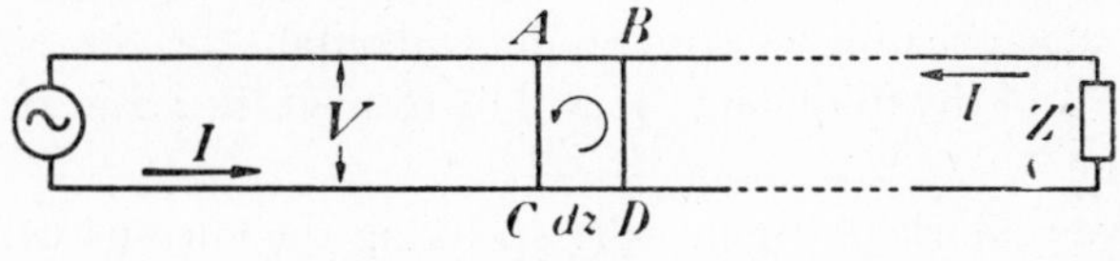

Fig. 20

It consists of two straight and parallel wires connecting the generator to the load represented by the impedance Z'. For simplicity we shall also assume that the system is placed at an infinite distance from every other conductor. Let the positive direction of current flow I be counter-clockwise as represented in the figure.

To specify the points of the line we shall introduce their distance z apart from the generator. At any distance z the electromotive force V will be defined going from one wire to the other along a plane path perpendicular to the wires. This qualification is necessary because, generally speaking, the plane of the wires is crossed by a magnetic current and consequently the transverse electromotive force depends on the path. In the figure V is positive when directed upwards. For $z = 0$, that is at the generator, V is equal and opposite to the electromotive force impressed by the generator. Note that, owing to the symmetry of the system, the currents in both wires for any given value of z must be equal and with the same sign (with respect to the positive direction of current flow).

Consider now the infinitesimal rectangle $ABCD$ and let $AB = \mathrm{d}z$. Apply to this rectangle the second circuit law (2-22). If the resistance of the section AB of the wire is designated by $\mathcal{R}\mathrm{d}z/2$ we have

$$V(z + \mathrm{d}z) - V(z) + \mathcal{R}I\mathrm{d}z = -i\omega\,\mathrm{d}\Phi$$

$\mathrm{d}\Phi$ being the magnetic flux across the rectangle. As this flux is proportional to I and to the surface of the rectangle one may set

$d\Phi = \mathscr{L}I\,dz$ and write

$$\frac{dV}{dz} = -\mathscr{Z}I, \tag{6-37}$$

where $\mathscr{Z} = \mathscr{R} + i\omega\mathscr{L}$ represents a quantity having the dimensions of impedance per unit length and depends upon the characteristics of the line and the frequency. It will be termed the *series impedance* of the line.

Next we remark that generally speaking the current will not be constant on the whole line. This is because the dielectric between the two wires presents a non-vanishing admittance both on account of its own conductivity and because the two wires form a capacitor. The admittance will obviously be of the type $\mathscr{Y}dz$, proportional to the length of the line element considered. Since as has been noted $\mathscr{Y}$ depends on a conductance and a capacitance, one may set $\mathscr{Y} = \mathscr{G} + i\omega\mathscr{C}$. It is customary to call $\mathscr{Y}$ the *shunt admittance* of the line. It depends on the frequency and on the characteristics of the line.

It is evident that for every line element dz the shunt admittance permits a current $\mathscr{Y}V\,dz$ to leak through; this current will be lost to the following section of the line. So we shall write

$$\frac{dI}{dz} = -\mathscr{Y}V. \tag{6-38}$$

Equations (6-37, 38) represent the fundamental differential equations of the theory of transmission lines. Their validity is much more general than might appear from the particular case considered in their derivation.

It is clear that $\mathscr{Z}$ and $\mathscr{Y}$ are measured respectively in *ohms/meter* and *mhos/meter*; the same holds for $\mathscr{R}$ and $\mathscr{G}$. As to $\mathscr{L}$ and $\mathscr{C}$, they will be measured respectively in *henrys/meter* and in *farads/meter*. If the resistance $\mathscr{R}$ and the conductance $\mathscr{G}$ vanish, $\mathscr{Z}$ and $\mathscr{Y}$ are imaginary (or pure reactance and pure susceptance). In this case there is no dissipation of energy by Joule effect and the line is said to be lossless.

Waves in Transmission Lines

§ **14.** Equations (6-37, 38) represent a linear differential system of the first order with constant coefficients. As is customary in dealing with such systems, we shall look for solutions of exponential type, writing in place of V and I respectively $V \exp (h_1 z)$ and $I \exp (h_2 z)$, V and I being two complex constants. Upon substitution into (6-37, 38) we readily derive $h_1 = h_2$ and

$$\left\{\begin{array}{l} h_1 V = - \mathscr{Z} I, \\ h_1 I = - \mathscr{Y} V. \end{array}\right. \tag{6-39}$$

Multiplying and dividing these two equations by one another,

$$h_1^2 = \mathscr{Y}\mathscr{Z}, \qquad \left(\frac{V}{I}\right)^2 = \frac{\mathscr{Z}}{\mathscr{Y}}. \tag{6-40}$$

Let us now set

$$h = \sqrt{\mathscr{Y}\mathscr{Z}}, \qquad Z = \sqrt{\frac{\mathscr{Z}}{\mathscr{Y}}}, \tag{6-41}$$

selecting for h the value which lies in the first quadrant of the complex plane ($\mathscr{R}e\, h \geqq 0$, $\mathscr{T}m\, h \geqq 0$) and for Z the value which lies either in the first or in the fourth quadrant ($\mathscr{R}e Z > 0$); this is possible since $\mathscr{R}$, $\mathscr{L}$, $\mathscr{G}$, $\mathscr{C}$ are positive and consequently $\mathscr{Y}$ and $\mathscr{Z}$ lie in the first quadrant. Hence by the second equation (6-40) two types of solutions will be possible, namely

$$V_p = Z I_p, \qquad V_r = - Z I_r. \tag{6-42}$$

The first equation (6-40) requires that $h_1 = \pm h$. Introducing into (6-39) a solution of the type V_p, I_p it is readily found that h_1 cannot be in the first quadrant; hence for such solution $h_1 = - h$. Introducing instead a solution of the type V_r, I_r, it is found that h_1 cannot be in the third quadrant so that $h_2 = h$. In conclusion we get the two solutions

$$V(z) = V_p \exp (- hz), \qquad I(z) = I_p \exp (- hz), \tag{6-43}$$

with $V_p/I_p = Z$, and

$$V(z) = V_r \exp(hz), \qquad I(z) = I_r \exp(hz), \tag{6-44}$$

with $V_r/I_r = -Z$.

Let us examine these solutions. Since h belongs to the first quadrant, we can put

$$h = \alpha + ik, \tag{6-45}$$

α and k being real and positive. Adding the factor $\exp(i\omega t)$ the solution (6-43) yields

$$V(z, t) = V_p \exp(-\alpha z) \exp[i(\omega t - kz)], \tag{6-46}$$

and a similar expression for I. We see that the amplitude decreases exponentially with increasing z; the coefficient α is called the *attenuation constant*. The second exponential shows that the phase depends both on time t and distance z and is constant for

$$\omega t - kz = \text{constant}.$$

By differentiation one obtains $dz/dt = \omega/k$; hence the points of constant phase travel along the z-axis with a velocity

$$v = \frac{\omega}{k}. \tag{6-47}$$

This velocity is termed the *phase velocity* or velocity of propagation of the waves. Thus we have a wave propagation which is progressive in the positive direction of the z axis. The minimum distance between two points having the same phase is known as *wavelength* and is denoted by λ. From (6-46) one may derive

$$k = \frac{2\pi}{\lambda} \tag{6-48}$$

Thus we find the physical significance of k; this quantity represents the number of wavelengths comprised in 2π meters and consequently is called the *wave number*. (†) The constant h of (6-45)

(†) More often this name is given to $1/\lambda$, i.e., to the number of wavelengths comprised in a *meter*. Our k is a rationalized wave number.

which specifies the main characteristics of propagation (attenuation and wavelength) is called the *propagation constant.*

It is evident now that the second solution found will be written in the form

$$V(z, t) = V_r \exp(\alpha z) \exp[i(\omega t + kz)], \tag{6-49}$$

and will represent regressive waves, attenuated in the negative direction of the z-axis.

Since (6-37, 38) are linear and homogeneous equations, the general solution will be represented by a superposition of the two solutions, i.e., by a train of progressive waves plus a train of regressive waves.

The constants V_p, I_p and V_r, I_r appearing in the two solutions represent the complex amplitudes at the origin (sometimes called simply complex amplitudes).

If the line is lossless ($\mathscr{R} = 0$, $\mathscr{G} = 0$) it is readily verified that the attenuation constant vanishes. Further in this case it is found from the first equation (6-41) and from (6-45): $k = \omega\sqrt{\mathscr{L}\mathscr{C}}$, so that by (6-47) it follows

$$v = \frac{1}{\sqrt{\mathscr{L}\mathscr{C}}}. \tag{6-50}$$

Finally from the second equation (6-41) we have

$$Z = \sqrt{\frac{\mathscr{L}}{\mathscr{C}}} \tag{6-51}$$

so that in this case Z is a real constant.

Characteristic Impedance and Power Flow

§ 15. The constant Z is termed the *characteristic impedance* of the line and its reciprocal $Y = 1/Z$ the *characteristic admittance.* Let us give a justification of these names.

To begin with we remark that by the definition (6-41) Z has the dimensions of an impedance and is measured in *ohms*. Next let us assume that the line is carrying progressive waves and suppose that we cut the line at a point of abscissa z, replacing then the whole left section by a generator of electromotive force $V(z)$ given by (6-43) and of negligible internal impedance. It is evident that the current $I(z)$ in the right section of the line will retain its value as if nothing had changed. Hence we conclude that before the interruption the left side of the line behaved like a generator of electromotive force $V(z)$ applied to the right section. The right section in turn behaved like an impedance $V(z)/I(z) = Z$.

The above considerations show also that the left section transfers to the right section a complex power

$$W = \frac{1}{2} V(z) I^*(z) = \frac{1}{2} V_p I_p^* \exp[-2\alpha z] = \frac{1}{2} Z I_p I_p^* \exp[-2\alpha z], \tag{6-52}$$

which decreases exponentially along the line with the attenuation constant 2α. The real power flow is positive because $\mathscr{R}e Z > 0$. For these reasons the progressive waves are said to carry the power (6-52) towards the right. If the attenuation constant does not vanish, a fraction of the power is dissipated in each small section of the line (lossy line).

Perfectly similar reasoning shows that when the line carries regressive waves the left side of the line yields to the right side the complex power

$$W = \frac{1}{2} V(z) I^*(z) = \frac{1}{2} V_r I_p^* \exp[2\alpha z] = -\frac{1}{2} Z I_r I_r^* \exp[2\alpha z]. \tag{6-53}$$

As the real power flow turns out negative, we conclude that actually the energy flows from the right side to the left.

It is of interest to study the case when both progressive and regressive waves are superimposed on the line. We have

$$V(z) = V_p \exp[-\alpha z - ikz] + V_r \exp[\alpha z + ikz] = ZI_p \exp[-\alpha z - ikz] - ZI_r \exp[\alpha z + ikz],$$

$$I^*(z) = I_p^* \exp[-\alpha z + ikz) + I_r^* \exp[\alpha z - ikz],$$

whence

$$W(z) = \frac{1}{2} V(z)I^*(z) = \frac{1}{2} ZI_pI_p^* \exp[-2\alpha z] - \tag{6-54}$$

$$-\frac{1}{2} ZI_rI_r^* \exp[2\alpha z] + \frac{1}{2} Z[I_pI_r^* \exp(-2ikz) - I_p^*I_r \exp(2ikz)].$$

The expression in the last square brackets is the difference of two complex conjugate quantities, hence is purely imaginary. If Z is real (as in particular in a lossless line) the real power will be given by the two first terms of the right side of (6-54). By comparing with (6-52, 53) it follows that the progressive and regressive waves carry each their power without interfering with one another. On the contrary, if Z has a non-vanishing imaginary part, the third term will also be present. But one may note that, owing to the oscillating properties of the exponential, such term will give rise to a real power which is alternatively positive and negative and vanishes in the average along the line. This corresponds merely to the fact that energy is lost more in some places and less in other places.

Reflection in Transmission Lines

§ 16. So far we have not dealt with the impedance Z' which closes the line (*load*). To simplify let us change the origin of abscissas so that Z' is placed at $z = 0$ (without impairing the generality). Then the presence of Z' sets the conditions $V(0)=Z'I(0)$ which, representing V and I as a sum of progressive as well as regressive waves, transforms into

$$V_p + V_r = ZI_p - ZI_r = Z'(I_p + I_r).$$

Putting $I_r/I_p = r_I$ it follows that

$$r_I = \frac{Z - Z'}{Z + Z'}. \tag{6-55}$$

The pure number r_I thus defined is termed the *reflection coefficient* of the current. The reason for this name is that, if a progressive wave from the generator (which is supposed to be very far away) arrives at Z', there necessarily arises also a regressive wave (reflected wave) having the complex amplitude equal to r_I times that of the incident wave. For the voltage we get

$$r_V = \frac{V_r}{V_p} = \frac{-ZI_r}{ZI_p} = -r_I = \frac{Z' - Z}{Z' + Z}, \tag{6-56}$$

or a reflection coefficient which is equal and opposite to that of the current.

We shall give the name of *reflection factor* to the ratio ϱ of the power carried by the reflected wave and the incident power. It follows from (6-52, 53)

$$\varrho = \frac{\frac{1}{2} ZI_r I_r^*}{\frac{1}{2} ZI_p I_p^*} = rr^* = |r|^2, \tag{6-57}$$

where r can be either r_I or r_V.

The reflection factor is always real and non-negative.

From (6-55) it is seen that the reflection vanishes for $Z = Z'$ and increases with the difference between the characteristic impedance of the line and the load. If $Z' = 0$ the line is short-circuited and we get $r_I = -r_V = 1$; the incident wave is totally reflected with the same phase for the current and opposite phase for the voltage. If $Z' = \infty$ the line is open at its end and we get $r_V = -r_I = 1$; the wave again undergoes total reflection but with opposite phase for the current and the same phase for the voltage.

Impedance Matching

§ 17. The considerations of the preceding section are of interest in a number of practical cases. For instance it may happen that two lines having different characteristic impedances are connected in series. Let Z_1 be the characteristic impedance of the first (left) line and Z_2 that of the second (right) line. If a progressing wave arrives from the first line, a reflected wave will take rise at the connection, the factor of reflection being

$$\varrho = \left| \frac{Z_1 - Z_2}{Z_1 + Z_2} \right|^2.$$

Hence, every time that a transmission line presents a sudden jump of the characteristic impedance, a fraction of the power supplied by the generator is reflected back towards the generator. In many cases this fact is undesiderable and must be avoided by properly *matching* the impedances of two sections of the line.

A simple and intuitive method of matching impedances is represented by the insertion between the two lines of a section of a third line having a characteristic impedance which varies smoothly from Z_1 to Z_2. Actually in this manner the reflection may be substantially attenuated. An other interesting method will be described in next section.

§ 18. Let us consider a lossless line 2 of characteristic impedance Z_2 terminated by an impedance Z_3. This impedance might also consist of a semi-infinite line 3 of characteristic impedance Z_3. We know that, if a progressive wave I_p, V_p arrives from line 2, a reflected wave I_r, V_r will arise at the junction ($z = 0$) of 2 and 3, the reflection coefficients being given by (6-55, 56). Hence in line 2 we have

$$V(z) = V_p \exp[-ik_2z] - \frac{Z_2 - Z_3}{Z_2 + Z_3} V_p \exp[ik_2z],$$

$$I(z) = I_p \exp[-ik_2z] + \frac{Z_2 - Z_3}{Z_2 + Z_3} I_p \exp[ik_2z],$$

k_2 being the propagation constant of line 2 ($\alpha_2 = 0$). By dividing the two equations by one another ($V_p/I_p = Z_2$), we obtain

$$\frac{V(z)}{I(z)} = Z_2 \frac{-iZ_2 \sin k_2z + Z_3 \cos k_2z}{Z_2 \cos k_2z - iZ_3 \sin k_2z}. \tag{6-58}$$

It is evident that this expression represents the overall impedance of a length $-z$ of line 2 (of course z is negative) plus line 3. If we join to the left of this compound line a line 1 of characteristic impedance Z_1 (Fig. 21) a progressive wave arriving from 1 will under-

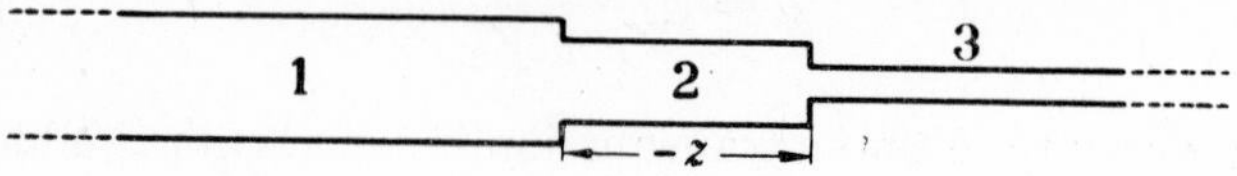

Fig. 21

go no reflection provided that we make the impedance (6-58) equal to Z_1. Hence we shall have the condition

$$Z_1 = Z_2 \frac{-iZ_2 \sin k_2 z + Z_3 \cos k_2 z}{Z_2 \cos k_2 z - iZ_3 \sin k_2 z}. \tag{6 59}$$

The simplest way to satisfy (6-59) is to make $z = -\lambda/4$ where λ represents the wavelength of the line 2. Then (6-59) by virtue of (6-48) becomes

$$Z_2^2 = Z_1 Z_3. \tag{6-60}$$

This means that Z_2 must be the geometric mean of Z_1 and Z_3. Since we have assumed that Z_2 is real this is possible only if Z_1 and Z_3 have equal and opposite arguments, in particular if they are real. We shall restrict ourselves to this case which is interesting in practice.

The above argument shows that the impedances of two lines 1 and 3 may be matched by means of a length $\lambda/4$ of lossless line having a characteristic impedance equal to the geometric mean of the other two. Physically this fact may be interpreted as follows. The incident wave is partially reflected at the junction 1, 2; the transmitted wave is again partially reflected at the junction 2, 3. In travelling from 1, 2 to 2, 3 and coming back the wave covers a distance equal to $\lambda/4 + \lambda/4 = \lambda/2$. Hence the wave reflected by 2, 3 has opposite phase with respect to that reflected by 1, 2. As the two reflected waves have (approximately) equal amplitudes they cancel with one another. As a net result there is no reflected wave. Naturally all the power arriving from 1 is transferred to 3, because 2 is lossless.

This line of reasoning, though elegant, is only approximate

because actually one should deal with multiple reflections. The wave reflected by 2, 3 will again be reflected by 1, 2, then again by 2, 3 and so on.

Stationary Waves, Resonance

§ 19. Consider now a lossless line short-circuited at $z = 0$, i.e., having a vanishing load impedance. The incident and reflected waves will have the same amplitude, because $r_I = -r_V = 1$. It will be

$$V(z) = V \exp[-ikz] - V \exp[ikz],$$
$$I(z) = I \exp[-ikz] + I \exp[ikz],$$

with $V/I = Z$. One may also write

$$\text{(6-61)} \qquad \begin{cases} V(z) = -2iV \sin kz, \\ I(z) = 2I \cos kz. \end{cases}$$

There results an interesting fact. The phases of the voltage and current are constant along the whole line (provided in this case we allow the amplitude to be both positive or negative). The amplitude varies, however, with a sine law. This is the well-known phenomenon of the *stationary* or *standing waves* of elementary physics. Both voltage and current present zeros (nodes) and maxima (anti-nodes) in fixed positions on the line (Fig. 22). The anti-

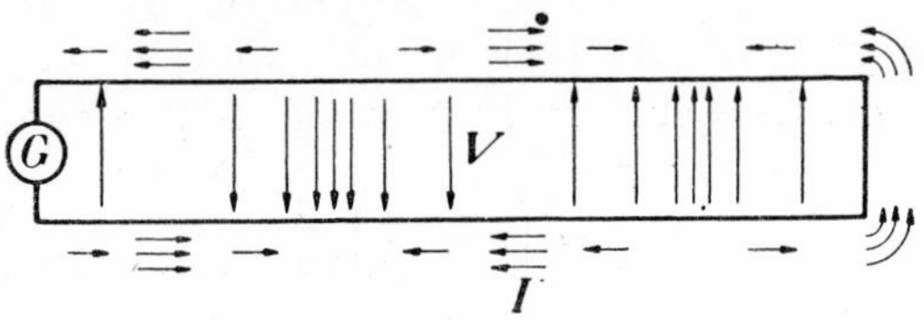

Fig. 22

nodes of the voltage coincide with the nodes of the current and vice versa. The end of the line is a node of the voltage and an anti-node of the current. The spacing between two successive nodes or anti-nodes is a half wavelength.

Let us now investigate what happens at the generator. It is

evident that if the generator is located in the vicinity of a node of the voltage it will supply a small voltage and a large current. If the generator is located exactly at a voltage node no voltage will be required from it; the generator in this case can simply be dispensed with and all we have to do is to short-circuit the line also on the left. The stationary waves will go on indefinitely by themselves (in the present approximation where losses have been neglected). The line has turned into a resonant circuit.

The condition for resonance is that the length l of the line be a multiple of half-wavelength

$$l = n\frac{\lambda}{2}. \tag{6-62}$$

Conversely if the length l is fixed, resonance conditions may be attained by varying the frequency. Taking into account that $\omega = 2\pi v/\lambda$, (6-62) yields the condition

$$\omega_n = n\pi\frac{v}{l}, \tag{6-63}$$

There are an infinity of resonance frequencies, all multiples of a *fundamental frequency* $\omega_1 = \pi v/l$. To each frequency there corresponds a *mode* of oscillation for the circuit; in particular to the fundamental frequency there corresponds the *fundamental mode.*

If the generator is in the vicinity of a voltage anti-node it will supply a large voltage and a small current. If the generator is placed exactly at the anti-node it will supply no current. This is a condition of anti-resonance. In place of (6-62) we shall now have

$$l = \left(n + \frac{1}{2}\right)\frac{\lambda}{2},$$

and in place of (6-63)

$$\omega_n = \left(n + \frac{1}{2}\right)\pi\frac{v}{l} \tag{6-64}$$

Perfectly similar arguments could be carried out if the line were open instead of short-circuited at its end. All we should have to do would be to interchange the nodes and anti-nodes of the voltage with those of the current and resonances with anti-resonances.

A circuit of the type just investigated is said to have *distributed constants*, because the resistance, the inductance and the capacitance are not localized in well-defined impedances but are distributed all along the line.

§ 20. Another instructive way to consider the facts presented in the foregoing section consists in evaluating the admittance Y_l presented to a generator by a short-circuited line. From (6-61) we obtain

$$Y_l = \frac{I(-l)}{V(-l)} = -iY \cot kl,$$

Y_l being the characteristic admittance.

For the sake of generality we will assume that the line is slightly lossy so that $\mathscr{R}$ and $\mathscr{G}$ are very small but do not vanish. In this case the propagation constant will present also a real part instead of being only ik. As a consequence we must replace ik by h or, what amounts to the same, k by $-ih$. Hence we get

$$Y_l = iY \cot ihl. \tag{6-65}$$

By taking into account the well-known series expansion

$$\cot x = \frac{1}{x} - \sum_1^\infty {}_n \frac{2x}{(n\pi)^2 - x^2},$$

(6-65) may be written in the form

$$Y_l = \frac{Y}{hl} + \sum_1^\infty {}_n \frac{2Yhl}{(n\pi)^2 + (hl)^2}.$$

This equation shows that the actual circuit is equivalent to an infinite number of circuits connected in parallel; the admittances of the component circuits are added to give the overall admittance.

Let us consider the circuit represented by the n-th term of the sum. Its admittance is

$$Y_n = \frac{2Yhl}{(n\pi)^2 + (hl)^2}.$$

Recalling (6-41) we obtain

$$Y_n = \frac{2\mathscr{Y}l}{(n\pi)^2 + \mathscr{Y}\mathscr{Z}l^2} = \frac{2(\mathscr{G} + i\omega\mathscr{C})l}{(n\pi)^2 + (\mathscr{G} + i\omega\mathscr{C})(\mathscr{R} + i\omega\mathscr{L})l^2},$$

By hypothesis $\mathscr{R}$ and $\mathscr{G}$ are very small; we may then neglect $\mathscr{G}$ in the numerator and the product $\mathscr{R}\mathscr{G}$ in the denominator, obtaining (divide both numerator and denominator by $i\mathscr{L}\mathscr{C}$)

$$Y_n = \frac{2\omega l/\mathscr{L}}{\omega\left(\dfrac{\mathscr{R}}{\mathscr{L}} + \dfrac{\mathscr{G}}{\mathscr{C}}\right)l^2 + i\left(\omega^2 l^2 - \dfrac{n^2\pi^2}{\mathscr{L}\mathscr{C}}\right)}. \tag{6-66}$$

The imaginary part of the denominator vanishes when ω assumes the value

$$\omega_n = \frac{n\pi}{l\sqrt{\mathscr{L}\mathscr{C}}}. \tag{6-67}$$

This equation, by (6-50) coincides with (6-63). We thus find the resonance frequencies; they correspond to maximum admittance (no more to infinite admittance as was found in the previous section without taking into account losses).

Let us set now by analogy with (6-32)

$$Q_{\mathscr{R}} = \frac{\omega_n \mathscr{L}}{\mathscr{R}}, \tag{6-68}$$

and by analogy with (6-36)

$$Q_{\mathscr{G}} = \frac{\omega_n \mathscr{C}}{\mathscr{G}}. \tag{6-69}$$

Further we put

$$\frac{1}{Q} = \frac{1}{Q_{\mathscr{R}}} + \frac{1}{Q_{\mathscr{G}}}. \tag{6-70}$$

Taking into account (6-67) we may transform (6-66) into

$$Y_n = \frac{2\omega Q/\mathscr{L}l}{\omega\omega_n + iQ(\omega^2 - \omega_n^2)}. \tag{6-71}$$

By analogy with (6-34) one may write $\omega = \omega_n(1 + \delta)$ and substitute into (6-71) with the assumption that δ is very small with respect to unity. In this way one readily obtains

$$Y_n = \frac{2}{\left(\mathscr{R} + \dfrac{\mathscr{L}}{\mathscr{C}}\mathscr{G}\right) l} \frac{1}{1 + 2iQ\delta}. \tag{6-72}$$

The dependence of the admittance on δ is identical with that given by (6-35) for a resonant circuit. We conclude that the line considered behaves like an infinite number of circuits joined in parallel, each presenting its resonance frequency (6-67) and its Q (6-70).

§ **21.** Instead of the admittance Y_l of the line section we may consider its impedance Z_l. From (6-65) is obtained

$$Z_l = -iZ \tan ihl. \tag{6-73}$$

Then the series expansion

$$\tan x = \sum_0^\infty {}_n \frac{2x}{\left(\dfrac{2n+1}{2}\pi\right)^2 - x^2}$$

is utilized with the result

$$Z_l = \sum_0^\infty {}_n \frac{2Zhl}{\left(\dfrac{2n+1}{2}\pi\right)^2 + (hl)^2},$$

The line is equivalent to an infinite number of circuits joined in series; their impedances are added to give the overall impedance.

The n-th circuit has the impedance

$$Z_n = \frac{2Zhl}{\left(\dfrac{2n+1}{2}\pi\right)^2 + (hl)^2}.$$

By a procedure similar to that of the previous section we find the analog of (6-66)

$$(6\text{-}74)\quad Z_n = \frac{2\omega l/\mathscr{C}}{\omega\left(\dfrac{\mathscr{R}}{\mathscr{L}}+\dfrac{\mathscr{G}}{\mathscr{C}}\right)l^2 + i\left[\omega^2 l^2 - \left(n+\dfrac{1}{2}\right)^2\dfrac{\pi^2}{\mathscr{L}\mathscr{C}}\right]}.$$

The imaginary part of the denominator vanishes at the anti-resonance frequency

$$(6\text{-}75)\qquad \omega_n = \left(n+\frac{1}{2}\right)\frac{\pi}{l\sqrt{\mathscr{L}\mathscr{C}}},$$

which coincides with that of (6-64). By applying the just seen transformations (6-74) is readily transformed into

$$(6\text{-}76)\qquad Z_n = \frac{2}{\left(\mathscr{R}\dfrac{\mathscr{L}}{\mathscr{C}}+\mathscr{G}\right)l}\,\frac{1}{1+2iQ\delta}.$$

Thus the line section considered may be replaced, as it were, by an infinite number of anti-resonant circuits joined in series, each having its anti-resonance frequency (6-75) and its Q still given by (6-70).

CHAPTER 7

Homogeneous Media and Plane Waves

Electric Admittivity

§ 1. The behavior of an isotropic medium with respect to direct current may be specified by means of its conductivity γ (possibly a function of position if the medium is not homogeneous). But when dealing with an alternating current this is not sufficient and one has to consider what may be termed a specific impedance.

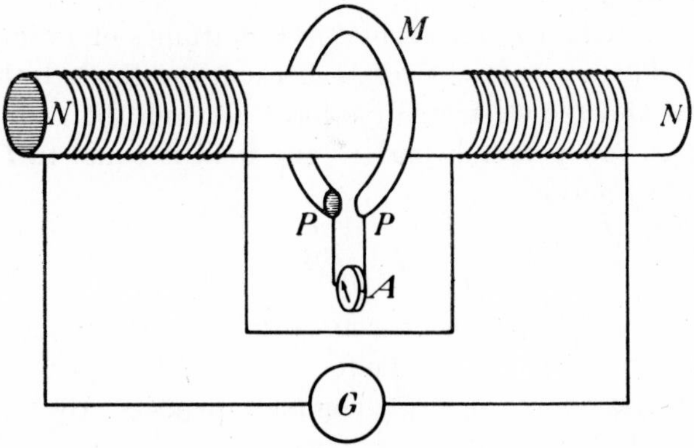

Fig. 23

To measure this quantity one might set up the following experiment which, however, has only a conceptual value and is practically unrealizable at a very high frequency (†). Let us consider a torus M of the homogeneous material to be investigated (Fig. 23) placed around an iron core NN carring a known alternating magnetic flux. An inductive electromotive force will arise along M. The electromotive force will in turn give rise to a current which

(†) The whole setup must be small with respect to the wavelength, which is absurd at optical frequencies.

is collected by the metal plates PP and measured by the instrument A, which gives the amplitude and the phase.

The experiment shows that M behaves like an impedor having the electric impedance (†) Z_e. If the cross section Σ of the torus is sufficiently small, Z_e turns out to be inversely proportional to it and directly proportional to the length l of the circuit M. Hence we write

$$Z_e = \zeta_e \frac{l}{\Sigma}. \tag{7-1}$$

The constant ζ_e is called the *specific electric impedance* and is measured in *ohm · meters*. Its reciprocal $\eta_e = 1/\zeta_e$ will be termed the *electric admittivity* of the medium M. The unit of η_e will be the *mho/meter*.

It is evident that η_e represents the admittance of an impedance constituted by a cubic meter of M. The current through this cubic meter is $\boldsymbol{J}$ and the electromotive force between the two opposite faces which are perpendicular to the field is equal to $\boldsymbol{E}$. There follows the relation

$$\boldsymbol{J} = \eta_e \boldsymbol{E}, \tag{7-2}$$

perfectly similar to (2-9). Of course in (7-2) $\boldsymbol{J}$ and $\boldsymbol{E}$ represent complex amplitudes and the factor exp $(i\omega t)$ is to be understood.

The electric admittance is a complex quantity. By separating the real and the imaginary part we write

$$\eta_e = \gamma_e + i\beta_e, \tag{7-3}$$

We will term γ_e the *electric conductivity* and β_e the *specific electric susceptance* (††).

(†) In the following we shall define also the magnetic impedance; for this reason it is convenient to give the name of electric impedance to the ordinary impedance. But in nearly all cases this specification may be omitted without causing any confusion.

(††) It would be rational to call this quantity the *electric susceptivity*. But unfortunately this name has already been given to another quantity (see 2-§11) and we want to avoid confusion.

Main Causes of Admittivity

§ 2. The electric admittivity depends on a number of physical factors, of which the main ones will now be reviewed in a very sketchy way.

First of all the material will present the ordinary conductivity γ which may be measured by means of a direct current ($\omega = 0$). If it is a good conductor γ will predominate over all other causes of admittivity and we shall have with a great approximation $\eta_e = \gamma$. The corresponding current will be $\boldsymbol{J}_c = \gamma \boldsymbol{E}$.

Another portion of the current will be represented by the displacement current of empty space (ignoring for a moment the atomic particles which constitute M). This current will be $\boldsymbol{J}_0 = $ $= \varepsilon_0 \partial \boldsymbol{E}/\partial t \rightarrow i\omega\varepsilon_0 \boldsymbol{E}$.

One must consider also a polarization current (see 2-§11). This current, as already illustrated, is due to the relative displacement of the charged elementary particles which constitute the molecules of M.

Let us analyze the nature of the polarization current a little closer in a typical case which is very instructive. Each molecule of M contains several electrons 1, 2, 3, . . . with different degrees of freedom. It is expedient to consider several electronic clouds 1, 2, 3, . . ., each constituted by the corresponding electrons of the molecules of M. The electrons are bound to the atomic nuclei, which will be assumed to be fixed, by restoring forces of an elastic (†) type; on the other hand, they present some inertia and their motion is hindered by a sort of friction. The physical nature of this friction will be investigated later.

Let $\boldsymbol{s}_1$ represent the displacement of cloud 1 from its equilibrium position and $\boldsymbol{v}_1$ its velocity. We shall have $\boldsymbol{s}_1 = \boldsymbol{v}_1/i\omega$, while the acceleration will be given by $i\omega\boldsymbol{v}_1$. If ϱ_1 designates the electric charge density of the cloud and m_1 its physical density (mass per

(†) As is well known, the electrons are bound to the nuclei by forces of the Coulomb type. According to the classical representation each electron describes an orbit along which the attraction and the centrifugal force are in equilibrium. A small displacement from this dynamic equilibrium requires a force which is proportional to the displacement. Hence we may speak of elastic forces.

unit volume) we may write the equation ($\boldsymbol{F} = m\boldsymbol{a}$)

$$\varrho_1 \boldsymbol{E} - \alpha \frac{\boldsymbol{v}_1}{i\omega} - \beta \boldsymbol{v}_1 = m_1 i\omega \boldsymbol{v}_1,$$

α being the coefficient of the restoring force and β that of the friction (†). By writing $\varrho_1 \boldsymbol{v}_1 = \boldsymbol{J}_1$ and

$$\frac{\varrho_1^2}{\alpha} = C_1, \quad \frac{\beta}{\varrho_1^2} = R_1, \quad \frac{m_1}{\varrho_1^2} = L_1, \tag{7-4}$$

the last equation becomes

$$\boldsymbol{J}_1 = \eta_{e1} \boldsymbol{E},$$

with

$$\eta_{e1} = \frac{1}{R_1 + i\left(\omega L_1 - \dfrac{1}{\omega C_1}\right)} \tag{7-5}$$

One may verify that η_{e1} turns out formally identical to the admittivity (6-22) of a circuit with resistance, capacitance and inductance in series.

The total current carried by M will be the sum of the currents due to all the causes investigated and we shall have

$$\boldsymbol{J} = \boldsymbol{J}_c + \boldsymbol{J}_0 + \boldsymbol{J}_1 + \boldsymbol{J}_2 + \ldots = (\gamma + i\omega\varepsilon_0 + \eta_{e1} + \eta_{e2} + \ldots)\boldsymbol{E}.$$

By comparing with (7-2) we derive the electric admittivity of M

$$\eta_e = \gamma + i\omega\varepsilon_0 + \eta_{e1} + \eta_{e2} + \ldots. \tag{7-6}$$

The situation is the same as when a number of circuits are connected in parallel and their admittances must be added to give the total admittance.

Equation (7-2) with η_e given by (7-6) represents a generalization of Ohm's law. The current $\boldsymbol{J}$ is a generalization of the conduction

(†) Strictly speaking the electrons are not acted upon by the electric field strength $\boldsymbol{E}$ alone. Each molecule is embedded in the polarization field produced by the surrounding molecules (*internal field*). The present discussion is valid only for a very rarified medium like a gas. However the consideration of the internal field would not bring about a great difference from a qualitative standpoint.

current because it is composed by all the currents caused by the electric force of the field. But it cannot include the impressed current, which, if present, must be taken into account separately.

§ **3.** To begin with let us suppose that ω is very small. The dominant term in the denominator of the right side of (7-5) will be $1/\omega C_1$ and it will be convenient to write

$$\eta_{e1} = \frac{i\omega C_1}{1 + i\omega C_1 R_1 - \omega^2 L_1 C_1}. \tag{7-7}$$

By a series expansion in powers of ω we get

$$\eta_{e1} = i\omega C_1 + \omega^2 C_1 R_1 + i\omega^3 C_1^2 (L_1 - C_1 R_1) + \dots.$$

And for the total admittivity there will result

$$\eta_e = \gamma + i\omega(\varepsilon_0 + \sum C_k) + \\ + \omega^2 \sum C_k^2 R_k + i\omega^3 \sum C_k^2 (L_k - C_k R_k^2) + \dots. \tag{7-8}$$

Note that the total displacement current inside M, as defined in 2-§8 is $\boldsymbol{J} = \partial \boldsymbol{D}/\partial t = \varepsilon \partial \boldsymbol{E}/\partial t \rightarrow i\omega\varepsilon \boldsymbol{E}$. By comparing with (7-8) one finds

$$\varepsilon = \varepsilon_0 + \sum C_k, \tag{7-9}$$

in perfect correspondence with (2-26). Equation (7-8) shows that the conductance and displacement currents which are present at low frequencies do not constitute the whole current carried by M. At high frequencies there appear other terms that must be taken into account. For example, if one takes into account also the terms in ω^2, the total electric conductivity resulting from (7-3, 8) is

$$\gamma_e = \gamma + \omega^2 \sum C_k^2 R_k. \tag{7-10}$$

The electric admittivity of empty space will be $\eta_{e0} = i\omega\varepsilon_0$, as is evident.

Magnetic Admittivity

§ **4.** The magnetic current may be dealt with in an essentially similar way. Consider the homogeneous and isotropic material M

bent to form a torus (Fig. 24). If an alternating magnetomotive force is applied to M, an alternating magnetic current will arise which is proportional to the magnetomotive force (†). The coefficient of proportionality Z_m will be termed the *magnetic impedance.*

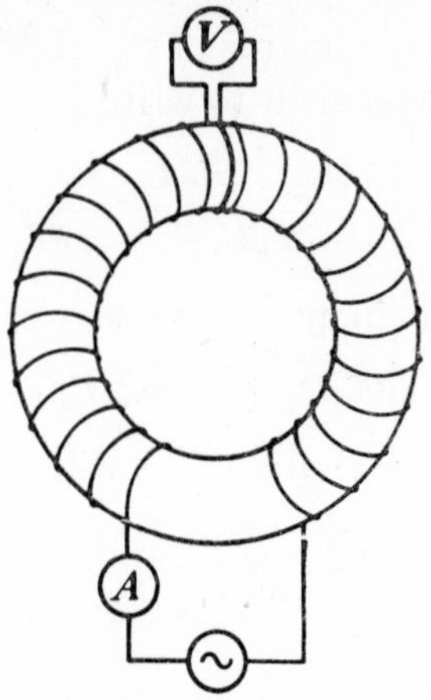

Fig. 24

Of course no conduction current will be present at low frequencies but there will be the displacement current of empty space plus the polarization current of M.

The density of magnetic current will turn out proportional to $\boldsymbol{H}$ and the coefficient of proportionality η_m will be termed the *magnetic admittivity*. It may be readily verified that η_m is measured in *ohms/meter*.

Generally speaking η_m will be a complex quantity and we shall write

$$\eta_m = \gamma_m + i\beta_m, \tag{7-11}$$

where γ_m represents the *magnetic conductivity* (vanishing for $\omega=0$) and β_m the *specific magnetic susceptance*. In empty space $\eta_m = i\omega\mu_0$ so that the admittivity reduces to a pure susceptance.

In material substances the magnetic admittivity will be $i\omega\mu$ plus a number of terms containing higher powers of ω as in (7-8).

(†) Ferromagnetic materials will be excluded.

In most cases these terms may be disregarded (a conclusion drawn from experience) and one may simply assume $\eta_m = i\omega\mu$. But it will be born in mind that this relation has not a completely general validity and that η_m may depend on ω in the same way as η_e.

Polarazition of Radiation

§ **5.** The meaning of the complex amplitudes $\boldsymbol{E}$ and $\boldsymbol{H}$ of the foregoing sections is readily understood. In the experiments discussed $\boldsymbol{E}$ and $\boldsymbol{H}$ each maintained a fixed direction and consequently were given by the product of a complex number and a unit vector in that direction. In other words $\boldsymbol{E}$ and $\boldsymbol{H}$ were given each by the sum of a real and an imaginary vector *mutually parallel*. But in the general case the last restriction is not necessary, so that the complex vectors $\boldsymbol{E}$ and $\boldsymbol{H}$ will have the form

$$\text{(7-12)} \qquad \begin{cases} \boldsymbol{E} = \boldsymbol{E}_r + i\boldsymbol{E}_i\,, \\ \boldsymbol{H} = \boldsymbol{H}_r + i\boldsymbol{H}_i\,, \end{cases}$$

$\boldsymbol{E}_r$, $\boldsymbol{E}_i$, $\boldsymbol{H}_r$, $\boldsymbol{H}_i$ being any four real vectors.

As an example let us consider the electric force. By multiplying by exp $(i\omega t)$ and taking the real part, one will obtain for the actual physical quantity the law of variation with time

$$\text{(7-13)} \qquad \boldsymbol{E}(t) = \boldsymbol{E}_r \cos \omega t - \boldsymbol{E}_i \sin \omega t.$$

The resultant vector $\boldsymbol{E}$ is always parallel to the plane of $\boldsymbol{E}_r$ and $\boldsymbol{E}_i$ so that if we picture it as a radius vector, its end will describe a plane curve which is closed and completely contained within a finite region.

From (7-13) one may derive

$$E_x^2 = E_{rx}^2 \cos^2 \omega t - 2E_{rx}E_{ix} \cos \omega t \sin \omega t + E_{ix}^2 \sin^2 \omega t,$$

and two similar equations for E_y^2 and E_z^2. By adding to these equations the identity $1 = \cos^2 \omega t + \sin^2 \omega t$ a system of four linear equations is obtained in the three unknowns $\cos^2 \omega t$, $\cos \omega t \sin \omega t$, $\sin^2 \omega t$. Hence the determinant must vanish

$$\begin{vmatrix} E_x^2 & E_{rx}^2 & -2E_{rx}E_{ix} & E_{ix}^2 \\ E_y^2 & E_{ry}^2 & -2E_{ry}E_{iy} & E_{iy}^2 \\ E_z^2 & E_{rz}^2 & -2E_{rz}E_{iz} & E_{iz}^2 \\ 1 & 1 & 0 & 1 \end{vmatrix} = 0.$$

This represents a second order equation for the coordinates E_x, E_y, E_z of the end of vector $\boldsymbol{E}$. Consequently the closed curve described is an ellipse. The electric field strength in the point considered is said to have *elliptic polarization.*

In order to find the axes of the ellipse we write down the square modulus of $\boldsymbol{E}$

$$E^2 = E_r^2 \cos^2 \omega t - 2\boldsymbol{E}_r \cdot \boldsymbol{E}_i \sin \omega t \cos \omega t + E_i^2 \sin^2 \omega t,$$

or

$$E^2 = \frac{1}{2}(E_r^2 + E_i^2) + \frac{1}{2}(E_r^2 - E_i^2) \cos 2\omega t - \boldsymbol{E}_r \cdot \boldsymbol{E}_i \sin 2\omega t.$$

The last two terms, as is well known, represent together a harmonic oscillation with the amplitude $\sqrt{(E_r^2 - E_i^2)^2/4 + (\boldsymbol{E}_r \cdot \boldsymbol{E}_i)^2}$. Consequently the lengths a, b of the two half-axes of the ellipse are given by

$$\begin{matrix} a^2 \\ b^2 \end{matrix} = \frac{1}{2}(E_r^2 + E_i^2) \pm \sqrt{(E_r^2 - E_i^2)^2/4 + (\boldsymbol{E}_r \cdot \boldsymbol{E}_i)^2}.$$

If $\boldsymbol{E}$ again designates the complex amplitude, the foregoing equation may be written as

$$\text{(7-14)} \qquad \begin{matrix} a^2 \\ b^2 \end{matrix} = \frac{1}{2}[\boldsymbol{E} \cdot \boldsymbol{E}^* \pm \sqrt{(\boldsymbol{E} \cdot \boldsymbol{E})(\boldsymbol{E}^* \cdot \boldsymbol{E}^*)}].$$

Two particular and important cases of elliptic polarization are to be noted. The first is the case of the *linear* polarization which occurs when the ellipse degenerates into a straight line. This requires $b = 0$. This condition is satisfied when $\boldsymbol{E}_r$ and $\boldsymbol{E}_i$ are parallel, as is seen from (7-13). In conclusion linear polarization will be present if the relation

$$\text{(7-15)} \qquad \boldsymbol{E} \wedge \boldsymbol{E}^* = 0.$$

is satisfied.

Another particular case is that of *circular* polarization which occurs when the ellipse is a circle. This will happen for $a = b$, which, by virtue of (7-14) is equivalent to

$$E \cdot E = 0. \tag{7-16}$$

It will be noted that this apparently queer relation does not imply $\boldsymbol{E} = 0$ but $\boldsymbol{E}_r \cdot \boldsymbol{E}_i = 0$ and $E_r = E_i$.

Maxwell's Equations for Alternating Fields

§ 6. Henceforth, unless stated to the contrary, all electric and magnetic quantities of the field will represent complex amplitudes.

The two circuit relations (2-19, 22), upon division by exp $(i\omega t)$ will still be written in the form

$$U = I, \qquad V = -K. \tag{7-17}$$

In order to pass to the differential Maxwell equations one must bear in mind that, as stated above, the density of the total electric current due to the field is $\eta_e \boldsymbol{E}$ and the density of the magnetic current is $\eta_m \boldsymbol{H}$. By applying (7-17) to infinitesimal circuits, as was done in 2-§§9, 10, one obtains

$$\text{curl}\, \boldsymbol{H} = \eta_e \boldsymbol{E} + \boldsymbol{J}^i, \tag{7-18}$$

$$\text{curl}\, \boldsymbol{E} = -\eta_m \boldsymbol{H}, \tag{7-19}$$

where $\boldsymbol{J}^i$ represents the impressed current (not due to the field). By taking the divergence of both sides of both equations and recalling the equation of continuity (2-8) (which will now be written as $\text{div}\, \boldsymbol{J} + i\omega\varrho = 0$) we find

$$\text{div}\, \eta_e \boldsymbol{E} = i\omega\varrho^i, \qquad \text{div}\, \eta_m \boldsymbol{H} = 0,$$

where ϱ^i is the density of the impressed charges. These equations replace now (2-3, 5). In a homogeneous medium where no impressed charges or currents are present it follows $\text{div}\, \boldsymbol{E} = 0$, $\text{div}\, \boldsymbol{H} = 0$.

Energy Relations

§ 7. Let us now transfer to the case of alternating fields the considerations developed in Chapters 2 and 3 about the energy and its flow. For a moment we shall apply those formulas as they were found, ignoring the fact that the classical definitions of ε and μ are valid only for static fields. Later we shall derive a formula which is more general and more consistent with the characterization given above for the electromagnetic properties of material media.

The electric and magnetic energies stored in the unit volume are given by (2-31, 32). For instance, by utilizing (7-13) one finds for the electric energy

$$U_e = \frac{1}{2}\varepsilon(\boldsymbol{E}_r \cos \omega t - \boldsymbol{E}_i \sin \omega t)^2 =$$

$$= \frac{1}{2}\varepsilon(E_r^2 \cos^2 \omega t + E_i^2 \sin^2 \omega t - 2\boldsymbol{E}_r \cdot \boldsymbol{E}_i \cos \omega t \sin \omega t) =$$

$$= \frac{1}{4}\varepsilon(E_r^2 + E_i^2) + \frac{1}{4}\varepsilon[(E_r^2 - E_i^2) \cos 2\omega t - 2\boldsymbol{E}_r \cdot \boldsymbol{E}_i \sin 2\omega t].$$

The terms appearing in the square brackets are oscillating and their time average vanishes. Therefore the mean energy stored in the unit volume is

$$\frac{1}{4}\varepsilon(E_r^2 + E_i^2) = \frac{1}{4}\varepsilon\boldsymbol{E} \cdot \boldsymbol{E}^*,$$

as one readily finds by applying the first equation (7-12). A similar argument is valid for the magnetic field so that in conclusion we may write

$$\bar{U}_e = \frac{1}{4}\varepsilon\boldsymbol{E} \cdot \boldsymbol{E}^*, \qquad \bar{U}_m = \frac{1}{4}\mu\boldsymbol{H} \cdot \boldsymbol{H}^*, \tag{7-20}$$

where $\bar{U}_e$ and $\bar{U}_m$ represent the mean energies stored in the unit volume.

By a similar line of reasoning applied to (2-12) one finds that the mean power dissipated in the unit volume by Joule effect is

$$\overline{W}_e = \frac{1}{2}\gamma \boldsymbol{E} \cdot \boldsymbol{E}^*.$$

The flow of electromagnetic energy is represented by Poynting's vector (3-11). Introducing the expression (7-13) we have

$$\boldsymbol{S}(t) = (\boldsymbol{E}_r \cos \omega t - \boldsymbol{E}_i \sin \omega t) \wedge (\boldsymbol{H}_r \cos \omega t - \boldsymbol{H}_i \sin \omega t) =$$
$$= (\boldsymbol{E}_r \wedge \boldsymbol{H}_r) \cos^2 \omega t + (\boldsymbol{E}_i \wedge \boldsymbol{H}_i) \sin^2 \omega t - (\boldsymbol{E}_r \wedge \boldsymbol{H}_i + \boldsymbol{E}_i \wedge \boldsymbol{H}_r) \sin \omega t \cos \omega t =$$
$$= \frac{1}{2}(\boldsymbol{E}_r \wedge \boldsymbol{H}_r + \boldsymbol{E}_i \wedge \boldsymbol{H}_i) + \frac{1}{2}[(\boldsymbol{E}_r \wedge \boldsymbol{H}_r - \boldsymbol{E}_i \wedge \boldsymbol{H}_i) \cos 2\omega t -$$
$$- (\boldsymbol{E}_r \wedge \boldsymbol{H}_i + \boldsymbol{E}_i \wedge \boldsymbol{H}_r) \sin 2\omega t].$$

The terms in the square brackets are oscillating and their time average vanishes. Consequently the mean energy flow reduces to the expression

$$\overline{\boldsymbol{S}} = \frac{1}{2}(\boldsymbol{E}_r \wedge \boldsymbol{H}_r + \boldsymbol{E}_i \wedge \boldsymbol{H}_i).$$

If we now introduce the complex Poynting vector

$$\boldsymbol{S} = \frac{1}{2}\boldsymbol{E} \wedge \boldsymbol{H}^*, \tag{7-21}$$

we may write simply

$$\overline{\boldsymbol{S}} = \mathcal{R}e\boldsymbol{S}. \tag{7-22}$$

One may readily see the analogy with the considerations developed in 6-§15 regarding the energy carried by a transmission line.

An argument perfectly similar to that seen in the case of $\boldsymbol{S}$ may be applied to (2-15) (changing the vector product into a scalar product) with the conclusion that the time average $\overline{W}^i$ of the impressed power is the real part of the complex power

$$W^i = -\frac{1}{2}\boldsymbol{E} \cdot \boldsymbol{J}^{i*}, \tag{7-23}$$

also in the case when $\boldsymbol{E}$ or $\boldsymbol{J}^i$ present elliptic polarization.

We are now in a position to derive a general relation for the energy similar to (3-13). By multiplying scalarly the complex conjugate of (7-18) by $\boldsymbol{E}$ and (7-19) by $\boldsymbol{H}^*$ and subtracting the first equation from the second we obtain

$$\boldsymbol{H}^* \cdot \text{rot}\, \boldsymbol{E} - \boldsymbol{E} \cdot \text{rot}\, \boldsymbol{H}^* = -\, \eta_m \boldsymbol{H} \cdot \boldsymbol{H}^* - \eta_e^* \boldsymbol{E} \cdot \boldsymbol{E}^* - \boldsymbol{E} \cdot \boldsymbol{J}^{i*}$$

making use of (M1-28) and of (7-21, 23) we may write

$$\text{(7-24)} \qquad W^i - \text{div}\, \boldsymbol{S} = \frac{1}{2}\, \eta_m \boldsymbol{H} \cdot \boldsymbol{H}^* + \frac{1}{2}\, \eta_e^* \boldsymbol{E} \cdot \boldsymbol{E}^*.$$

Taking the real part of both sides we get

$$\overline{W}^i - \text{div}\, \overline{\boldsymbol{S}} = \frac{1}{2}\, \gamma_m \boldsymbol{H} \cdot \boldsymbol{H}^* + \frac{1}{2} \gamma_e \boldsymbol{E} \cdot \boldsymbol{E}^*.$$

The left side shows the mean power impressed in the unit volume and the mean power entering by radiation; the two terms of the right side represent respectively the power dissipated by the electric and magnetic Joule effect. The energy balance is apparent.

It is of interest also to examine the imaginary part of (7-24); we have

$$Im\, W^i - Im\, \text{div}\, \boldsymbol{S} = \frac{1}{2}\, \beta_m \boldsymbol{H} \cdot \boldsymbol{H}^* - \frac{1}{2} \beta_e \boldsymbol{E} \cdot \boldsymbol{E}^*.$$

The meaning of the right side is readily found on the basis of (7-20) by remembering that for a small value of ω the coefficients β_m and β_e reduce respectively to $\omega\mu$ and $\omega\varepsilon$. In this case we shall have $\beta_m \boldsymbol{H} \cdot \boldsymbol{H}^*/2 = 2\omega \overline{U}_m$ and $\beta_e \boldsymbol{E} \cdot \boldsymbol{E}^*/2 = 2\omega \overline{U}_e$. It is natural to assume that these relations be valid in general so that the preceding equation becomes

$$Im W^i - Im\, \text{div}\, \boldsymbol{S} = 2\omega(\overline{U}_m - \overline{U}_e).$$

In conclusion if we call $\overline{W}_m$ and $\overline{W}_e$ respectively the magnetic and electric Joule heat we arrive at the interesting formula

$$\text{(7-25)} \qquad W^i - \text{div}\, \boldsymbol{S} = \overline{W}_m + \overline{W}_e + 2i\omega(\overline{U}_m - \overline{U}_e),$$

which is similar to (6-28).

Plane Waves

§ 8. Let the medium be homogeneous and unbounded and assume that the field depends only on the rectangular coordinate z. Let no impressed current be present.

Writing (7-18, 19) in rectangular components one finds

$$-\frac{dH_y}{dz}\boldsymbol{i}+\frac{dH_x}{dz}\boldsymbol{j}=\eta_e(E_x\boldsymbol{i}+E_y\boldsymbol{j}+E_z\boldsymbol{k}),$$

$$-\frac{dE_y}{dz}\boldsymbol{i}+\frac{dE_x}{dz}\boldsymbol{j}=-\eta_m(H_x\boldsymbol{i}+H_y\boldsymbol{j}+H_z\boldsymbol{k}).$$

By equating corresponding components in both sides of each equation one finds in the first place

(7-26) $$E_z=0, \qquad H_z=0;$$

secondly

(7-27) $$\begin{cases}\dfrac{dE_x}{dz}=-\eta_m H_y,\\[2ex] \dfrac{dH_y}{dz}=-\eta_e E_x,\end{cases}$$

and finally

(7.28) $$\begin{cases}\dfrac{dE_y}{dz}=\eta_m H_x,\\[2ex] \dfrac{dH_x}{dz}=\eta_e E_y.\end{cases}$$

The two systems (7-27) and (7-28) are independent of one another so that their solutions may simply be added without interference.

§ 9. To begin with let us put the solutions of (7-28) equal to zero and investigate the solutions of (7-27). By taking into account also (7-26) we may conclude that the only non-vanishing components of the field are E_x and H_y. These components obey (7-27). But these equations are formally identical to the differential equations (6-37, 38) of a transmission line. There E_x is replaced by V, H_y by I, η_m by $\mathscr{Z}$ and η_e by $\mathscr{Y}$. As regards dimensions, the first quantities are obtained from the second ones by dividing by *meters*: V is measured in *volts* and E_x in *volts/meter*, I in *amperes* and H_y in *amperes/meter*, η_m and $\mathscr{Z}$ in *ohms/meter* and η_e and $\mathscr{Y}$ in *mhos/meter*.

We may then utilize the results found in the case of a transmission line, applying them to the solution of (7-27). These solutions represent both progressive and regressive waves traveling along the z axis. The progressive waves are given by

$$E_x = ZH_y = A \exp[-\alpha x] \exp[-ikz], \tag{7-29}$$

where A is a constant (*volts/meter*) and

$$Z = \sqrt{\frac{\eta_m}{\eta_e}} \quad (\mathscr{R}e\, Z > 0), \tag{7-30}$$

$$h = \alpha + ik = \sqrt{\eta_m \eta_e} \quad (\mathscr{R}e\, h \geqq 0,\ \mathscr{I}m\, h > 0). \tag{7-31}$$

Equations (7-29) represent *plane waves* because the surfaces of constant phase which are termed the *wave surfaces* are planes perpendicular to the z axis. These waves are *transverse* because $\boldsymbol{E}$ and $\boldsymbol{H}$ are perpendicular to the direction of propagation $\boldsymbol{k}$ (†). Further $\boldsymbol{E}$, $Z\boldsymbol{H}$, $\boldsymbol{k}$ form a direct triad (meaning that $Z\boldsymbol{H} = \boldsymbol{k} \wedge \boldsymbol{E}$). To express the fact that both the electric and magnetic vectors are transverse these waves are said to be *transverse electromagnetic* or briefly *TEM*.

The constant Z given by (7-30) is termed the *intrinsic impedance* of the medium and is equal to the quotient E_x/H_y. It is measured in *ohms*. Its reciprocal quantity $Y = 1/Z$ is termed the *intrinsic admittance* and is measured in *mhos*. Putting $Z = R + iX$ and $Y = G + iB$ we may define the intrinsic resistance, reactance, conductance and susceptance.

The wavelength λ and the phase velocity v are related to the wave number k by the usual relations

$$\lambda = \frac{2\pi}{k}, \qquad v = \frac{\omega}{k}. \tag{7-32}$$

(†) It is evident that the wave number k has nothing to do with the unit vector $\boldsymbol{k}$ of the z axis.

The regressive waves do not present anything new except for the reversal of the sign of the ratio E_x/H_y which is now equal to $-Z$ as follows from (6-42). This is equivalent to changing the sign of H_y so we may again conclude that $\boldsymbol{E}$, $Z\boldsymbol{H}$ and the direction of propagation which is now $-\boldsymbol{k}$ form a direct triad.

§ 10. Let us examine (7-28). If we reverse the sign of H_x these equations become formally identical to (6-37, 38). Therefore they too represent both progressive and regressive waves, the progressive ones being given by

$$E_y = -ZH_x = B \exp[-\alpha z] \exp[-ikz]. \tag{7-33}$$

This solution represents nothing new and can be deduced from the preceding one by a 90° rotation about the z axis. A similar remark may be made for the regressive waves.

It is evident that (7-29, 33) represent plane waves linearly polarized. Actually they both satisfy (7-15). The electric and magnetic vectors remain each parallel to itself for all values of t and z. Due to historical reasons the plane containing $\boldsymbol{H}$ and the direction of propagation is called the *plane of polarization* (†).

In general we shall consider a superposition of both solutions (7-29, 33). Setting $A\boldsymbol{i} + B\boldsymbol{j} = \boldsymbol{A}$ we write

$$\begin{cases} \boldsymbol{E} = \boldsymbol{A} \exp[-\alpha z] \exp[-ikz], \\ \boldsymbol{H} = Y\boldsymbol{k} \wedge \boldsymbol{E}. \end{cases} \tag{7-34}$$

Since $\boldsymbol{A}$ may be any complex vector in the plane x, y, there will be in general elliptic polarization. By applying (7-15, 16) it is found that the condition of linear polarization is $\boldsymbol{A} \wedge \boldsymbol{A}^* = 0$ and the condition of circular polarization is $\boldsymbol{A} \cdot \boldsymbol{A} = 0$ independent of z. Substituting the first equation (7-34) into (7-14) it is found also that the *ellipticity* of the polarization, i.e., the ratio of the two half-axes of the ellipse does not vary along the z axis. A plane wave while traveling does not change the form of its polarization.

(†) However, people who are not directly concerned with optics tend more and more to give this name to the plane containing $\boldsymbol{E}$ and the direction of propagation. One must be careful to avoid confusion.

In Fig. 25 the xy plane is represented, the z axis being toward the reader. In this plane the electric force as a function of time will be given by

$$\boldsymbol{E}(t) = \boldsymbol{A}_r \cos \omega t - \boldsymbol{A}_i \sin \omega t.$$

For $t = 0$ we get $\boldsymbol{E} = \boldsymbol{A}_r$, and the end of the vector $\boldsymbol{E}$ will be at C. Then it will move downwards. An observer will note that the ellipse is run clockwise and the polarization is said to be *right-handed*. This happens when $\boldsymbol{A}_r$, $\boldsymbol{A}_i$ and $\boldsymbol{k}$ form a direct triad as in the figure. In the opposite case the polarization is said to be *left-handed*.

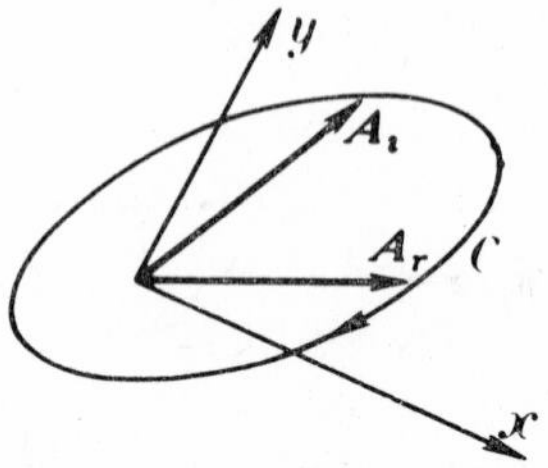

Fig. 25

To find the energy carried by a plane wave one has to form the complex Poynting vector (7-21) with the expressions (7-34). One obtains

$$\text{(7-35)} \quad \boldsymbol{S} = \frac{1}{2} Y^* \boldsymbol{A} \wedge (\boldsymbol{k} \wedge \boldsymbol{A}^*) \exp\,[-2\alpha z] = \frac{1}{2} \boldsymbol{k} Y^* \boldsymbol{A} \cdot \boldsymbol{A}^* \exp\,[-2\alpha z].$$

The real part $\overline{\mathbf{S}}$ turns out positive because $\mathcal{R}eZ > 0$ and consequently also $\mathcal{R}eY > 0$. The attenuation constant for the energy flow is 2α.

If Z is real $\boldsymbol{S}$ is real too so that in this case we may conclude by (7-25) that the magnetic and electric energies stored in the field are equal.

By adding the two solutions (7-29, 33) we have constructed a wave with elliptic polarization as a superposition of two waves linearly polarized at right angles. Conversely it is always possible (in an infinity of ways) to split an elliptically polarized wave into two linearly polarized waves at right angles. The particular case is interesting when the phases of these two components are in quadrature. With reference to (7-34) this occurs when $\boldsymbol{A}_r$ and $\boldsymbol{A}_i$ are mutually perpendicular. It is readily seen from (7-14) that in this case $\boldsymbol{A}_r$ and $\boldsymbol{A}_i$ represent the two half-axes of the ellipse in the plane $z = 0$.

Symmetry of Maxwell's Equations

§ 11. When the medium is homogeneous and does not present impressed currents the introduction of the two constants (7-30, 31) namely of the intrinsic impedance and of the propagation constant allows us to give a very useful form to the Maxwell equations. One may verify that in this case (7-18, 19) can be written in the following way

$$\begin{cases} \text{curl } (Z\boldsymbol{H}) = h\boldsymbol{E}, \\ \text{curl } \boldsymbol{E} = -\, h(Z\boldsymbol{H}). \end{cases} \tag{7-36}$$

It is readily noted that this system of equations shows a particular sort of symmetry. It remains unaltered if $\boldsymbol{E}$ is replaced by $Z\boldsymbol{H}$ and $Z\boldsymbol{H}$ by $-\boldsymbol{E}$. This fact gives the possibility of writing two different solutions as soon as one is found. For instance the two solutions (7-29, 33) are in this condition with respect to one another.

It is readily verified that if Z is real the complex Poynting vectors $\boldsymbol{S} = \boldsymbol{E} \wedge \boldsymbol{H}^*/2$ and $\boldsymbol{S}^* = \boldsymbol{E}^* \wedge \boldsymbol{H}/2$ of the two solutions are one the conjugate of the other. As a consequence the energy flow is the same in the two cases while the difference between the energies stored by the electric and by the magnetic fields has opposite sign.

Non-dispersive Dielectrics

§ 12. After these general considerations it is convenient to examine the behavior of the different materials with respect to electromagnetic waves.

We shall begin by investigating dielectric media.

It is a result of experience (and may be theoretically justified by atomic physics) that the electronic clouds which are most responsible for the admittivity possess very small resistances R and inductances L, so that when the frequency is not too high all terms beyond the first power of ω may be neglected in the series (7-8). Of course this approximation breaks down when a resonance frequency of an electronic cloud is approached. However, since the resonance frequencies are very great, the approximation holds good in the domain of radio waves and some times also in the domain of optical waves.

A more accurate investigation will be developed later; for the moment we shall consider the important case, when one can simply put $\eta_e = \gamma + i\omega\varepsilon$. A dielectric in which this approximation is valid is said to be *non-dispersive*. As regards the magnetic admittivity we can put it equal to $i\omega\mu$ or in practice to $i\omega\mu_0$ (non-ferromagnetic materials) as was explained in §4.

Let us first investigate the case of a *perfect* or *lossless* dielectric, where we have exactly $\gamma = 0$.

Equation (7-30) yields then

$$Z = \sqrt{\frac{\mu}{\varepsilon}} \quad \textit{ohms}. \tag{7-37}$$

The intrinsic impedance is real or a pure resistance. For the plane waves investigated above (7-37) gives $\sqrt{\varepsilon}E = \sqrt{\mu}H$ as was found in (3-8) for a discontinuity wave front. By applying (7-20) one finds that the electric and magnetic energies stored in the medium are equal; this conclusion can also be derived by noting that since Z is real, $\boldsymbol{S}$ given by (7-35) is also real so that by (7-25) $\overline{U}_m = \overline{U}_e$. As a consequence the total energy stored in the unit volume may be written in either of the two forms

$$\overline{U} = \frac{1}{2}\varepsilon \boldsymbol{E} \cdot \boldsymbol{E}^* = \frac{1}{2}\mu \boldsymbol{H} \cdot \boldsymbol{H}^*. \tag{7-38}$$

From (7-31) we find

$$\alpha = 0, \qquad k = \omega\sqrt{\varepsilon\mu}, \tag{7-39}$$

and by (7-32) the phase velocity will be given by

$$v = \frac{1}{\sqrt{\varepsilon\mu}}. \tag{7-40}$$

This equation is identical to (3-7) which is valid for the propagation of discontinuities.

The first equation (7-39) shows that in a dielectric of the type considered there is no attenuation. Such dielectric is *transparent* to electromagnetic radiation. The energy flow (7-35) does not depend on z. Thus we have shown that a perfect and non-dispersive dielectric is also lossless.

It is of interest to compare (7-37, 40) respectively with (6-51, 50) which were found in the case of a lossless line.

§ 13. Empty space is a particular case of a perfect and lossless dielectric as is made evident by experience. Its intrinsic impedance is

$$Z_0 = \sqrt{\frac{\mu_0}{\varepsilon_0}} = 377 \qquad \textit{ohms}. \tag{7-41}$$

For the phase velocity we have

$$c = \frac{1}{\sqrt{\varepsilon_0\mu_0}} = 2.998 \cdot 10^8 \qquad \textit{meters/second}. \tag{7-42}$$

In the case of a material dielectric the name of *refractive index* is given to the quotient

$$n = \frac{c}{v}, \tag{7-43}$$

of the phase velocity in vacuum by that in the dielectric. From (7-40, 42) and (7-37, 41) it is readily found

$$n = \sqrt{\varepsilon_r\mu_r} \cong \sqrt{\varepsilon_r} = \frac{Z_0}{Z}, \tag{7-44}$$

because $\mu_r \cong 1$. The refractive index is a pure number nearly always greater than 1.

From (7-32) is seen that, for a given frequency, λ is proportional to v; as a consequence if we designate by λ the wavelength in vacuum, the wavelength in the dielectric will be

$$\lambda = \frac{\lambda_0}{n}, \tag{7-45}$$

always smaller than in vacuum. The formula $n = k/k_0$ is also valid.

§ 14. Perfect dielectrics are only an idealization. In practice the conductivity γ will never vanish exactly and the dielectric even if non-dispersive will give rise to some dissipation of energy.

It is of interest to investigate the case when γ although not vanishing, is very small. The propagation constant may then be represented approximately by

$$h = \sqrt{(\gamma + i\omega\varepsilon)i\omega\mu} = i\omega\sqrt{\varepsilon\mu}\sqrt{1 + \frac{\gamma}{2i\omega\varepsilon}} = \frac{1}{2}\gamma\sqrt{\frac{\mu}{\varepsilon}} + i\omega\sqrt{\varepsilon\mu}.$$

Thus there appears an attenuation constant

$$\alpha = \frac{1}{2}\gamma\sqrt{\frac{\mu}{\varepsilon}}, \tag{7-46}$$

while the wave number $k = \omega\sqrt{\varepsilon\mu}$ and the phase velocity are not affected by the conductivity.

The attenuation is due to the fact that while the wave travels a part of its energy is dissipated by Joule effect. By analogy with what we said in Chapter 6 in the case of a circuit we shall define the Q of a dielectric so that ω/Q be equal to the ratio of the energy lost per unit time and the stored energy. Recalling (7-38) we have

$$\frac{\omega}{Q} = \frac{\frac{1}{2}\gamma \boldsymbol{E} \cdot \boldsymbol{E}^*}{\frac{1}{2}\varepsilon \boldsymbol{E} \cdot \boldsymbol{E}^*},$$

or

$$Q = \frac{\omega\varepsilon}{\gamma}. \tag{7-47}$$

It is of interest to compare this equation with (6-36) which is valid for a parallel circuit, remembering that ε is measured in *farads/meter* and γ in *mhos/meter*. By virtue of (2-14) one may also write

$$Q = 2\pi \frac{\tau}{T},$$

τ being the relaxation time and T the period of the oscillation. For a good dielectric and for the electromagnetic waves which are practically realisable τ is much larger than T so that Q turns out to have a very great value.

Let us now evaluate the intrinsic impedance, cutting off the series expansion after the first two terms. We get

$$Z = \sqrt{\frac{i\omega\mu}{\gamma + i\omega\varepsilon}} = \sqrt{\frac{\mu}{\varepsilon}} \sqrt{\frac{1}{1 + \dfrac{\gamma}{i\omega\varepsilon}}} = \sqrt{\frac{\mu}{\varepsilon}} \left(1 + i \frac{1}{2} \frac{\gamma}{\omega\varepsilon}\right).$$

The intrinsic resistance $R = \sqrt{\mu/\varepsilon}$ is the same as that of the perfect dielectric but there appears in addition an intrinsic reactance. Consequently E and H are no more perfectly in phase as in a lossless dielectric. However, it will be noted that by (7-47) the foregoing equation may be written in the following way

$$Z = R\left(1 + i\frac{1}{2Q}\right).$$

This shows that for a good dielectric the intrinsic reactance is very small with respect to the intrinsic resistance and in most cases may be disregarded.

Finally we call attention to the interesting relation

(7-48) $$\alpha = \frac{1}{2} \frac{\omega}{Qv},$$

which is derived from (7-40, 46, 47).

Dispersive Dielectrics

§ 15. We now go back to the study of perfect dielectrics, namely, to those having $\gamma = 0$. We have investigated their behavior when they do not present dispersion. In reality all dielectrics are dispersive and when the frequency is not negligible as compared with the resonance frequency one cannot simply put $\eta_e = i\omega\varepsilon$. We must go back to the consideration of (7-7). The resistance R is always extremely small and may be neglected everywhere except in the very vicinity of a resonance frequency. Then we may write for the l-th electronic cloud

$$\eta_{el} = \frac{i\omega C_l}{1 - \omega^2 L_l C_l} = \frac{i\omega\omega_l^2 C_l}{\omega_l^2 - \omega^2},$$

$\omega_l = 1/\sqrt{L_l C_l}$ being the resonance frequency. For the total admittivity of the medium we shall have

$$\eta_e = i\omega\left[\varepsilon_0 + \sum \frac{\omega_l^2 C_l}{\omega_l^2 - \omega^2}\right], \tag{7-49}$$

the sum being extended to all the electronic clouds. By applying (7-31) one readily gets $\alpha = 0$ and

$$k^2 = \omega^2\mu_0\left[\varepsilon_0 + \sum \frac{\omega_l^2 C_l}{\omega_l^2 - \omega^2}\right]. \tag{7-50}$$

It is concluded that the dielectric is still transparent (the attenuation constant vanishes) but the wave number (and consequently also the phase velocity $v = \omega/k$) turn out to be dependent on the frequency. This is termed *dispersion.*

The refractive index may still be defined by (7-43). Since $n = k/k_0$ we find

$$n^2 = 1 + \frac{1}{\varepsilon_0}\sum \frac{\omega_l^2 C_l}{\omega_l^2 - \omega^2}. \tag{7-51}$$

There follows that the refractive index is always an increasing function of the frequency. This is confirmed by experience.

The ratio C_l/ε_0 represents, so to speak, the contribution to the relative dielectric constant due to the electronic cloud l. By analogy with (7-44) we may define a partial refractive index $n_l = \sqrt{C_l/\varepsilon_0}$. Then (7-51) becomes

$$n^2 = 1 + \sum n_l^2 \frac{\omega_l^2}{\omega_l^2 - \omega^2}. \tag{7-52}$$

§ 16. In the vicinity of a resonance frequency (7-52) ceases to be valid. Suppose for example that the frequency is in the vicinity of ω_1. In the expression (7-7) of η_{e1} one has to retain also the term R_1, otherwise the denominator vanishes. It will be noted that in the vicinity of ω_1 only η_{e1} will be subject to a rapid variation while the other η will show much slower variations. For this reason we are justified in assuming that all the other η_e be represented by expressions like those appearing in (7-49) with the substitution of ω_1 in place of ω in the denominators. From (7-31) we shall get

$$(\alpha + ik)^2 = -\omega^2\mu_0\left(\varepsilon_0 + \sum_{l \neq 1} \frac{\omega_l^2 C_l}{\omega_l^2 - \omega_1^2} + \frac{C_1}{1 - \omega^2 L_1 C_1 + i\omega C_1 R_1}\right),$$

where the sum does not include the term with $l = 1$.

Now replace ω with $(1 + \delta)\omega_1$ and make the approximation $(1 + \delta)^2 = 1 + 2\delta$ (see 6-§11). Next replace ω_1 with $1/\sqrt{L_1C_1}$; finally put $Q_1 = \omega_1 L_1/R_1 = (\sqrt{L_1/C_1})/R_1$. Thus the following equation is arrived at

$$(\alpha + ik)^2 = -\omega^2\mu_0\left(\varepsilon_0 + \sum \frac{\omega_l^2 C_l}{\omega_l^2 - \omega_1^2} - i\frac{C_1 Q_1}{1 + (2iQ + 1)\delta}\right).$$

Another admissible simplification is that of neglecting unity with respect to Q in the last denominator, Q being always a very large number. By separating the real and imaginary parts we get

$$\text{(7-53)} \quad \begin{cases} k^2 - \alpha^2 = \omega^2\mu_0\left(\varepsilon_0 + \sum \dfrac{\omega_l^2 C_l}{\omega_l^2 - \omega_1^2} - \dfrac{2Q_1^2 C_1 \delta}{1 + 4Q_1^2\delta^2}\right) \\[2ex] 2\alpha k = \omega^2\mu_0 \dfrac{Q_1 C_1}{1 + 4Q_1^2\delta^2}. \end{cases}$$

From these equations the constants α and k may be evaluated. However for those frequencies which allow an experimental measurement to be made, α is very small in comparison to k; otherwise the wave would be practically extinguished after a few wavelengths and the medium would be opaque. We shall accordingly neglect α^2 relatively to k^2 in (7-53). Dividing the first equation by $k_0^2 = \omega^2\mu_0\varepsilon_0$ and introducing the partial refractive indices we finally obtain

$$(7\text{-}54)\quad \begin{cases} n^2 = 1 + \sum n_i^2 \dfrac{\omega_i^2}{\omega_i^2 - \omega_1^2} - n_1^2 \dfrac{2Q_1^2\delta}{1 + 4Q_1^2\delta^2}, \\ 2\alpha = k_0 \dfrac{n_1}{n} \dfrac{Q_1}{1 + 4Q_1^2\delta^2} \end{cases}$$

From the last equations one may derive the behavior of n^2 and α in the vicinity of a resonance frequency. As is shown by Fig. 26,

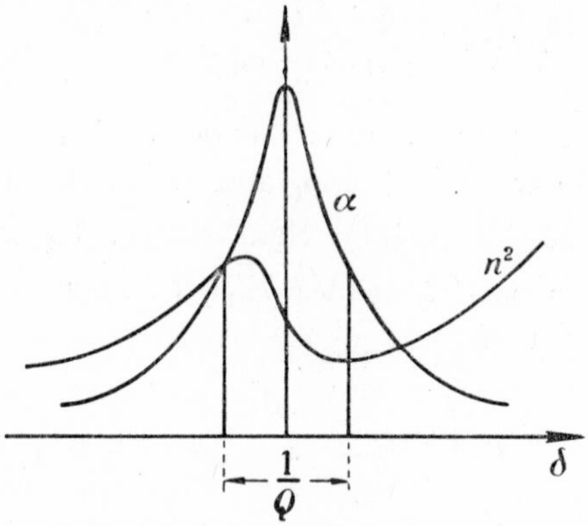

Fig. 26

the resonance frequencies are characterized by a strong attenuation. In the language of spectroscopy it is common to speak of *absorption lines*. In correspondence of an absorption line the refractive index stops being an increasing function and presents a descending interval (*anomalous dispersion*).

The width of the absorption line defined as in 6-§11 is again represented by $1/Q_1$ as is shown by the second equation (7-54). For this reason Q_1 represents a measure of the *monochromaticity* of the line.

§ 17. The considerations of the preceding sections do not completely cover the field of dispersive dielectrics. First of all we call again attention to the fact that inside a condensed substance one should take into account also the internal field which we have neglected in our discussion.

In the second place it will be noted that in some cases (for instance in the case of water) the admittance is given not only by the displacement of electronic clouds relative to fixed nuclei but also (and mainly) by the rotation of the molecules which possess a permanent dipole moment (*dipolar molecules*) and tend to orient themselves in the direction of the field. The considerable moment of inertia of the molecules does not allow them to follow too rapid oscillations of the field; for this reason the dipolar admittance tends to vanish at very high frequencies. For example in the case of water we have $\sqrt{\varepsilon_r} \cong 9$ while the refractive index for visible radiation becomes as low as about 1.33.

Further, even in the case when it may be assumed that the nuclei are fixed and the admittivity is purely electronic, the description of the preceding section requires a small correction on account of the thermal agitation of the molecules. The frequency of the field as seen from a moving system is influenced by the veloctiy of the system (Doppler effect) so that the effective frequency is different for the different molecules; besides, the mutual collisions of the molecules disturb the harmonic motions of the electrons (†).

Anyhow a dielectric at given temperature and pressure is perfectly characterized when its admittivity is known as a function of the frequency; this knowledge may be derived experimentally.

Good Conductors

§ 18. As was already shown, in a conducting medium the electrical admittivity includes also the conductivity γ so that generally speaking the intrinsic impedance Z will be complex and the attenuation constant α will not vanish. This means that a conducting medium absorbs radiation.

We shall now study good conductors or metallic conductors. In these media the conductivity presents very great values and is

(†) It is clear that a rigorous treatment of dispersion should involve quantum mechanics. But the above classical discussion is sufficient for representing very well qualitative features.

so much more important than all the other sources of admittivity that one may simply put $\eta_e = \gamma$, neglecting in (7-8) all the terms but the first. To justify this simplification we note that the quotient of the second by the first term is in absolute value given by $\omega\varepsilon/\gamma = 2\pi\tau/T$, where τ represents the relaxation time (2-14) and T the period of the oscillation. And, since τ for a good conductor was shown to be of the order of 10^{-19} *seconds* while T for visible radiation is about 10^{-15} *seconds*, said quotient turns out less than one thousandth; and a still smaller value will be obtained for radio waves.

With this simplification one gets from (7-30, 31)

$$h = \sqrt{i\omega\mu_0\gamma}\,, \qquad Z = \sqrt{\frac{i\omega\mu_0}{\gamma}}. \tag{7-55}$$

Remembering that $\sqrt{i} = (1 + i)/\sqrt{2}$, it is derived from the first equation

$$\alpha = k = \sqrt{\omega\mu_0\gamma/2}. \tag{7-56}$$

As a result the wave number and the attenuation constant are equal. For $\gamma = 6 \cdot 10^7$ *mhos/meter* and $T = 2 \cdot 10^{-15}$ *seconds* (visible radiation) their common value will be about $3 \cdot 10^8$ *meters*$^{-1}$. The attenuation constant attains an enormous value, so that a very small thickness of metal is sufficient to extinguish completely an electromagnetic wave. Good conductors are practically opaque. It will be noted that the attenuation diminishes with the frequency.

The refractive index is obtained by dividing k by $k_0 = \omega\sqrt{\varepsilon_0\mu_0}$ and results

$$n = \sqrt{\frac{\gamma}{2\omega\varepsilon_0}}. \tag{7-57}$$

Substituting the numerical values used above there results a refractive index greater than 30, much larger than that of any dielectric. For radio waves it becomes enormous.

Let us now consider the second equation (7-55). First of all, since the argument of $\sqrt{i}$ is $\pi/4$ we see that $\boldsymbol{H}$ has a phase retardation of $\pi/4$ relative to $\boldsymbol{E}$. Next by separating the real and imaginary parts of Z we find $R = X = \sqrt{\omega\mu_0/2\gamma}$. The intrinsic resistance and reactance are equal. The intrinsic admittance is readily found to be $Y = 1/Z = (1-i)\sqrt{\gamma/2\omega\mu_0}$.

Substituting into (7-35) we find the only non-vanishing component of $\boldsymbol{S}$

$$S_z = \frac{1}{2}(1+i)\sqrt{\frac{\gamma}{2\omega\mu_0}}\, AA^* \exp[-2\alpha z].$$

From this equation taking into account (7-56) it may be derived

$$\mathscr{I}m(-\operatorname{div}\boldsymbol{S}) = -\mathscr{I}m\frac{dS_z}{dz} = \alpha\sqrt{\frac{\gamma}{2\omega\mu_0}}\, AA^* \exp[-2\alpha z] =$$

$$= \frac{1}{2}\gamma AA^* \exp[-2\alpha z].$$

By recalling (7-25) it is seen that the difference $\overline{U}_m - \overline{U}_e$ is positive so that the magnetic energy stored is greater than the electric energy.

The last results may be derived also by the following argument. Putting as before $\gamma = 6 \cdot 10^7$ and $T = 2 \cdot 10^{-15}$, the modulus of Z turns out to be about 7 *ohms*. This value is much smaller than that of empty space. For a given value of $\boldsymbol{H}$ the value of $\boldsymbol{E}$ is much smaller than in empty space; for this reason the magnetic energy is larger than the electric energy.

The intrinsic impedance diminishes with the frequency, so that for micro-waves and radio waves it becomes absolutely negligible.

To simplify the mathematical treatment of some problems involving metal screens it is a standard practice to consider the metal as a *perfect conductor* putting $\gamma = \infty$. The intrinsic impedance of a perfect conductor vanishes. Inside such conductor the electric field vanishes even if the magnetic field does not vanish.

Evanescent Waves

§ 19. Consider now a homogeneous dielectric free of both dispersion and losses. A plane wave of the type (7-34) may be represented by

$$\boldsymbol{E} = \boldsymbol{A}\exp[-ik(P-Q)\cdot\boldsymbol{k}], \qquad Z\boldsymbol{H} = \boldsymbol{k}\wedge\boldsymbol{E}, \qquad (\boldsymbol{A}\cdot\boldsymbol{k} = 0)$$

P being the variable field point and Q the origin. We may assume that the direction of propagation instead of being the z axis is a general direction specified by the unit vector $\boldsymbol{s}$. In this case we shall write

$$(7\text{-}58)\quad \boldsymbol{E} = \boldsymbol{A} \exp\left[-ik(P-Q)\cdot\boldsymbol{s}\right], \quad Z\boldsymbol{H} = \boldsymbol{s}\wedge\boldsymbol{E}, \quad (\boldsymbol{A}\cdot\boldsymbol{s} = 0)$$

$\boldsymbol{A}$ being a complex vector perpendicular to $\boldsymbol{s}$.
Sometimes it is useful to introduce the Cartesian coordinates x, y, z of P and the components (direction cosines) of $\boldsymbol{s}$ writing

$$(7\text{-}59)\quad \boldsymbol{E} = \boldsymbol{A} \exp\left[-ik(s_x x + s_y y + s_z z)\right].$$

To simplify the discussion we may suppose that $\boldsymbol{s}$ is parallel to the xz plane. We shall have then $s_y = 0$, $s_x = \sin\theta$ and $s_z = \cos\theta$ if θ represents the angle made by $\boldsymbol{s}$ with the z axis. If the value of s_x is made to increase, the value of θ increases also eventually attaining the value $\pi/2$ for $s_x = 1$. If s_x is further increased the angle becomes imaginary, but (7-58) still gives a solution of Maxwell's equations provided that $s_x^2 + s_z^2 = 1$. The last relation shows that in this case s_z is purely imaginary and equal to $\pm i\sqrt{s_x^2 - 1}$. If we choose the lower sign and substitute into (7-59) we get

$$(7\text{-}60)\quad \boldsymbol{E} = \boldsymbol{A} \exp\left[-kz\sqrt{s_x^2 - 1}\right] \exp\left[-iks_x x\right].$$

This represents a wave traveling along the x axis. The wave surfaces are planes perpendicular to the x-axis, yet they are not ordinary plane waves. The first exponential shows that the amplitude is attenuated in the direction of the z axis namely in a direction perpendicular to that of propagation. The wave is said to be *evanescent.*

It will be noted that the propagation constant is ks_x which is greater than k. As a consequence the velocity of propagation is s_x times smaller than that of ordinary plane waves. The same remark will be made for the wave length.

We have now $\boldsymbol{s} = s_x\boldsymbol{i} - i\sqrt{s_x^2 - 1}\,\boldsymbol{k}$ so that the orthogonality condition $\boldsymbol{A}\cdot\boldsymbol{s} = 0$ becomes

$$(7\text{-}61)\quad A_x s_x - A_z i\sqrt{s_x^2 - 1} = 0.$$

The evanescent waves are not necessarily transverse since (7-61) does not require $A_x = 0$. It is also of interest to note that this equation does not set any condition for A_y which remains perfectly arbitrary.

§ **20.** To begin with let us assume $A_y = 0$. In this case $\boldsymbol{E}$ is in the xz plane. From (7-61) it is derived that E_x and E_z are in quadrature of phase. The electric field is elliptically polarized in the xz plane. The axes of the ellipse are parallel respectively to x and z and their ratio is the fixed number $s_x/\sqrt{s_x^2 - 1}$. It is clear that one may set $A_x = Ai\sqrt{s_x^2 - 1}$, $A_z = As_x$, thus automatically satisfying (7-61). It will be then

$$\text{(7-62)} \quad \boldsymbol{E} = A(i\sqrt{s_x^2 - 1}\,\boldsymbol{i} + s_x\boldsymbol{k}) \exp(-kz\sqrt{s_x^2 - 1}) \exp(-iks_x x).$$

On the other hand from $\boldsymbol{H} = Y\boldsymbol{s} \wedge \boldsymbol{E}$ it is readely obtained

$$\text{(7-63)} \quad \boldsymbol{H} = -YA\boldsymbol{j} \exp(-kz\sqrt{s_x^2 - 1}) \exp(-iks_x x).$$

Consequently the magnetic field is linearly polarized and perpendicular to the direction of propagation, or transverse. For this reason this type of waves is said to be *transverse magnetic* or briefly *TM*.

The complex Poynting vector is found from (7-62, 63)

$$\text{(7-64)} \quad \boldsymbol{S} = \frac{1}{2}\boldsymbol{E} \wedge \boldsymbol{H}^* = \frac{1}{2}Y^*AA^*(s_x\boldsymbol{i} - i\sqrt{s_x^2 - 1}\,\boldsymbol{k})\exp(-kz\sqrt{s_x^2 - 1}) =$$

$$= \frac{1}{2}Y^*AA^*\boldsymbol{s} \exp(-kz\sqrt{s_x^2 - 1}).$$

Assuming Y to be real we conclude that the real power flows in the direction of the x axis, the density of flow being

$$\text{(7-65)} \quad \bar{S} = \frac{1}{2}YAA^*s_x \exp(-kz\sqrt{s_x^2 - 1}).$$

Further from (7-64) we derive in the case of a real Y

$$\text{(7-66)} \quad -\mathscr{I}m \operatorname{div} \boldsymbol{S} = -\frac{1}{2}YAA^*k(s_x^2 - 1) \exp(-kz\sqrt{s_x^2 - 1}).$$

This equation by virtue of (7-25) shows that the electric energy stored is larger than the magnetic energy.

An evanescent wave of the *transverse electric* type or TE may be obtained from (7-62, 63) by interchanging $\boldsymbol{E}$ with $Z\boldsymbol{H}$ and $Z\boldsymbol{H}$ with $-\boldsymbol{E}$ (see 7-§11). By this procedure we get

$$(7.67)\quad \begin{cases} \boldsymbol{E} = A\boldsymbol{j}\exp\left(-kz\sqrt{s_x^2-1}\right)\exp\left(-iks_x x\right), \\ \boldsymbol{H} = YA\left(i\sqrt{s_x^2-1}\,\boldsymbol{i}+s_x\boldsymbol{k}\right)\exp\left(-kz\sqrt{s_x^2-1}\right)\exp\left(-iks_x x\right). \end{cases}$$

If Z is real the vector $\boldsymbol{S}$ of the new solution is conjugate to that of the preceding solution. Therefore the density of the energy flow is still represented by (7-65). The right side of (7-66) presents instead an inversion of sign, meaning that the magnetic energy stored is larger than the electric energy.

The most general type of evanescent wave is represented by a superposition of TE and TM waves.

The Family of Electromagnetic Waves

§ 21. The reader may ask himself why in the present investigation harmonic oscillations have been selected from among all the possible types of dependence on the time variable.

The answer to this question might be of a purely mathematical character. One might remark that by means of a Fourier series or integral (see M3) any function of time may be pictured as a sum of a number of sine-wave oscillations. And it is easier to investigate the behavior of these simple components than to tackle the study of the resultant field.

This mathematical argument is certainly right. But there are some physical reasons which are still more important and justify the privileged position given to the harmonic oscillations and to the resulting sine-wave propagation. All the known systems of production and reception of the electromagnetic field, whether natural or artificial, show a considerable tendency to be selective, that is to send out or to reveal each a well determined frequency of harmonic oscillations, or at least a narrow band of frequencies in the vicinity of a fundamental frequency. We have seen some examples represented by the resonant circuits, the antiresonant circuits and by the electronic oscillators; a number of other examples will be illustrated in the following chapters. Quantum physics confirms in a suggestive manner the basic importance and the individuality which must be attributed to each harmonic component (†).

This is the reason why in most cases, instead of speaking of the electromagnetic field in general, it is customary to speak of electromagnetic waves. The frequency or the wavelength is then assumed as a fundamental parameter.

This parameter has an astonishing large range of variation (theoretically infinite) giving rise to the family of the known electromagnetic waves. The longest waves are those employed in classic radio transmission (Hertzian waves) going from the order of magnitude of some ten kilometers to the order of magnitude of some ten meters (with a subdivision into very long waves, long waves, medium waves, short waves and very short waves). Next we find the waves between ten meters and a centimeter which are used in the most modern applications as frequency modulation, television, radar etc. The shortest waves produced artificially, going approximately from a meter to a millimeter, are called the microwaves. There follow the infrared radiations down to the wavelength of about $8 \cdot 10^{-5}$ cm; beyond this limit we find the radiations which are capable of stimulating the human retina (visible radiations). Below $4 \cdot 10^{-5}$ cm the radiations are again invisible and are given the name of ultra-violet down to about 10^{-6} cm. Next there come the X-rays down to about 10^{-9} cm and finally the γ rays which are produced in nuclear reactions. The respective wavelength ranges of all these different types of radiations partially overlap on one another so that there is no empty space.

(†) In quantum theory of fields, even a static field is formed by a number of virtual traveling waves (*virtual photons*).

CHAPTER 8

General Waves in Continuous Media

Radiation of an Electric Dipole

§ 1. Beside the plane waves studied in the preceding chapter there exist other types of waves of well-defined shapes. A very important class is that of *spherical waves.* There are several kinds of spherical waves. The fundamental type is represented by the spherical wave emitted by an electric dipole. We shall study this case with the assumption that the medium is a homogeneous dielectric free from dispersion and losses.

We have already started this investigation in 4-§12 where a localized electric dipole was considered having an electric moment $\boldsymbol{L}(t)$. Naturally we shall now specialize the kind of time dependence by writing $\boldsymbol{L}\exp(i\omega t)$ in place of $\boldsymbol{L}(t)$ and $i\omega\boldsymbol{L}\exp(i\omega t)$ in place of $\boldsymbol{L}'(t)$. Substituting into (4-32) and dividing by $\exp(i\omega t)$ we get

$$\text{(8-1)}\qquad \begin{aligned} \boldsymbol{E}(Q) &= \frac{1}{4\pi\varepsilon}\operatorname{curl}_Q\operatorname{curl}_Q\left[\frac{\exp(-ikr)}{r}\boldsymbol{L}\right],\\ \boldsymbol{H}(Q) &= \frac{i\omega}{4\pi}\operatorname{curl}_Q\left[\frac{\exp(-ikr)}{r}\boldsymbol{L}\right], \end{aligned}$$

where r designates the distance between point P where the dipole is located and point Q where we want to evaluate the field. Let us introduce Green's function

$$\text{(8-2)}\qquad G(r) = G(P, Q) = \frac{\exp(-ikr)}{4\pi r}.$$

Then we may write

$$\text{(8-3)}\qquad \boldsymbol{E}(Q) = \frac{1}{\varepsilon}\operatorname{curl}_Q\operatorname{curl}_Q(G\boldsymbol{L}),\qquad \boldsymbol{H}(Q) = i\omega\operatorname{curl}_Q(G\boldsymbol{L}).$$

If we take into account that $\boldsymbol{L}$ is a constant vector, we have by

(M1-29) and (M2-41)

$$\text{(8-4)} \qquad \operatorname{curl}_Q (G\boldsymbol{L}) = \operatorname{grad}_Q G \wedge \boldsymbol{L} = G'(r)\boldsymbol{s} \wedge \boldsymbol{L},$$

$\boldsymbol{s}$ being a unit vector parallel to $Q - P$. Next we note that from (M2-31, 39, 40) there follows

$$\operatorname{curl}_Q (\boldsymbol{s} \wedge \boldsymbol{L}) = - \boldsymbol{L} \operatorname{div}_Q \boldsymbol{s} + (\operatorname{grad}_Q \boldsymbol{s}) \cdot \boldsymbol{L} =$$
$$= - \frac{2}{r} \boldsymbol{L} + \frac{1}{r} \boldsymbol{L} \cdot (\boldsymbol{U} - \boldsymbol{ss}) = - \frac{1}{r} \boldsymbol{L} \cdot (\boldsymbol{U} + \boldsymbol{ss}).$$

Taking into account this and the preceding equation we get

$$\text{(8-5)} \quad \operatorname{curl}_Q \operatorname{curl}_Q (G\boldsymbol{L}) = \operatorname{curl}_Q [G'(r)\boldsymbol{s} \wedge \boldsymbol{L}] = G'(r) \operatorname{curl}_Q (\boldsymbol{s} \wedge \boldsymbol{L}) +$$
$$+ \operatorname{grad}_Q G'(r) \wedge (\boldsymbol{s} \wedge \boldsymbol{L}) = - \frac{1}{r} G'(r) \boldsymbol{L} \cdot (\boldsymbol{U} + \boldsymbol{ss}) + G''(r)\boldsymbol{s} \wedge (\boldsymbol{s} \wedge \boldsymbol{L}),$$

or

$$\operatorname{curl}_Q \operatorname{curl}_Q (G\boldsymbol{L}) = - \boldsymbol{L} \cdot \left\{ \left[\frac{1}{r} G'(r) + G''(r) \right] \boldsymbol{U} + \left[\frac{1}{r} G'(r) - G''(r) \right] \boldsymbol{ss} \right\}.$$

Putting

$$\text{(8-6)} \quad \boldsymbol{K}(P, Q) = - \left(\frac{1}{r} G' + G'' \right) \boldsymbol{U} - \left(\frac{1}{r} G' - G'' \right) \boldsymbol{ss},$$

we get

$$\text{(8-7)} \qquad \operatorname{curl}_Q \operatorname{curl}_Q (G\boldsymbol{L}) = \boldsymbol{K} \cdot \boldsymbol{L},$$

because $\boldsymbol{K}$ is a symmetrical tensor. In conclusion from (8-3, 4, 7) we get

$$\text{(8-8)} \qquad \boldsymbol{E}(Q) = \frac{1}{\varepsilon} \boldsymbol{K} \cdot \boldsymbol{L}, \qquad \boldsymbol{H}(Q) = i\omega G' \boldsymbol{s} \wedge \boldsymbol{L}.$$

These equations represent very concise expressions of the field radiated by a dipole.

Dipolar Spherical Waves

§ 2. Having derived the mathematical expression (8-8) we shall present some simpler but approximate formulas with a view to discovering a more immediate physical meaning. The field radiated by a dipole acquires a particularly simple form at a great distance from the dipole. We note that $\boldsymbol{E}$ and $\boldsymbol{H}$ are represented each by the sum of terms containing different powers of $1/r$. At a great distance we shall retain only the lowest power, which amounts to the same as putting $G' \cong - ik \exp(-ikr)/4\pi r$ and $G'' \cong - k^2 \exp(-ikr)/4\pi r$ in (8-4, 5). Substituting into (8-3) we thus get, up to terms of order $1/r$,

$$(8\text{-}9) \qquad \begin{cases} \boldsymbol{E}(Q) = - \omega k Z \dfrac{\exp(-ikr)}{4\pi r} \boldsymbol{s} \wedge (\boldsymbol{s} \wedge \boldsymbol{L}), \\ \\ \boldsymbol{H}(Q) = \omega k \dfrac{\exp(-ikr)}{4\pi r} \boldsymbol{s} \wedge \boldsymbol{L}. \end{cases}$$

It is readily seen that the wave surfaces have the equation $r =$ *constant* and are spheres centered on the dipole. These spherical waves are sent out by the dipole with the velocity $v = \omega/k$ characteristic of the medium.

The amplitudes of $\boldsymbol{E}$ and $\boldsymbol{H}$ are inversely proportional to r. Both vectors are perpendicular to the direction of propagation $\boldsymbol{s}$ and are also perpendicular to one another. Thus in this approximation the waves are *TEM*.

If $\boldsymbol{L}$ is linearly polarized and its direction is assumed as polar axis, $\boldsymbol{H}$ is tangent to the parallels of the wave surfaces and $\boldsymbol{E}$ is parallel to the meridians. The polarization in this case is linear also for $\boldsymbol{E}$ and $\boldsymbol{H}$. The amplitudes are proportional to the sine of the angle θ made by $\boldsymbol{s}$ with the polar axis. One may verify that the relation

$$Z\boldsymbol{H} = \boldsymbol{s} \wedge \boldsymbol{E},$$

holds good as in the case of plane waves.

Equations (8-9) may also serve to evaluate the radiated power, because the power radiated by the dipole equals the power crossing any spherical surface containing the dipole. The density of the energy flow is

$$\overline{\boldsymbol{S}} = - \frac{1}{2} \mathcal{R}e \frac{\omega^2 k^2}{16\pi^2 r^2} Z[\boldsymbol{s} \wedge (\boldsymbol{s} \wedge \boldsymbol{L}] \wedge (\boldsymbol{s} \wedge \boldsymbol{L}^*).$$

Expanding the products it is readily obtained in the case of linear polarization

$$\overline{S} = \frac{\omega^2 k^2}{32\pi^2 r^2} ZLL^* \sin^2 \theta \ \boldsymbol{s}. \tag{8-10}$$

To evaluate the radiated power $\overline{W}$ one has to integrate over a whole sphere having an elementary area represented by $r^2 \sin\theta \, d\theta \, d\varphi$. Taking into account that

$$\int_0^{2\pi} d\varphi \int_0^{\pi} \sin^3 \theta \, d\theta = \frac{8\pi}{3},$$

one gets

$$\overline{W} = \frac{\omega^2 k^2}{12\pi} ZLL^* = \frac{1}{3} \pi \frac{\omega^2}{\lambda^2} ZLL^*. \tag{8-11}$$

As is natural, the radiated power does not depend on r.

Radiation of a Magnetic Dipole

§ 3. Similar considerations may be made in the case of a magnetic dipole. The starting point will be (4-33) instead of (4-32). Thus we get in place of (8-3)

$$\boldsymbol{H}(Q) = \frac{1}{\mu} \operatorname{curl}_Q \operatorname{curl}_Q (G\boldsymbol{N}), \qquad \boldsymbol{E}(Q) = - i\omega \operatorname{curl}_Q (G\boldsymbol{N}), \tag{8-12}$$

$\boldsymbol{N}$ representing the dipole moment. A comparison with (8-3) shows that $\boldsymbol{N}$ has replaced $\boldsymbol{L}$, $\boldsymbol{E}$ has replaced $-\boldsymbol{H}$ and $\mu\boldsymbol{H}$ has replaced $\varepsilon\boldsymbol{E}$. By carrying out these interchanges we get from (8-8)

$$\boldsymbol{E} = - i\omega G' \boldsymbol{s} \wedge \boldsymbol{N}, \qquad \boldsymbol{H}(Q) = \frac{1}{\mu} \boldsymbol{K} \cdot \boldsymbol{N}. \tag{8-13}$$

The spherical wave at a great distance from the dipole is in turn obtained by carrying out the same interchanges in (8-9)

$$\begin{cases} \boldsymbol{E} = - \omega k \dfrac{\exp(-ikr)}{4\pi r} \boldsymbol{s} \wedge \boldsymbol{N}, \\ \boldsymbol{H} = - \omega k Y \dfrac{\exp(-ikr)}{4\pi r} \boldsymbol{s} \wedge (\boldsymbol{s} \wedge \boldsymbol{N}). \end{cases} \tag{8-14}$$

As a result $\boldsymbol{E}$ is tangent to the parallels and $\boldsymbol{H}$ to the meridians.

Figure 27 shows a comparison of the fields radiated by an electric and a magnetic dipole respectively.

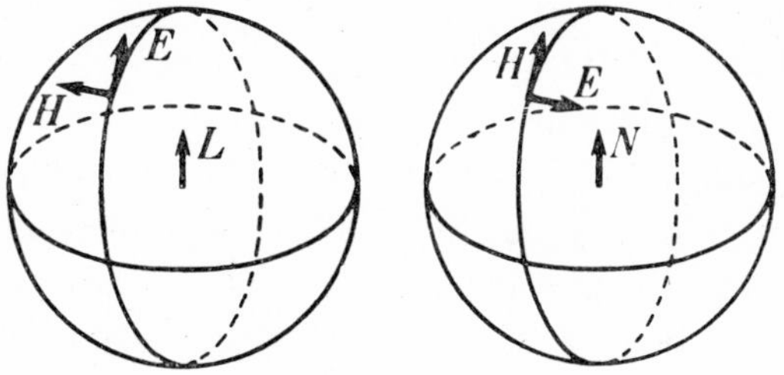

Fig. 27

In any case we have $Z\boldsymbol{H} = \boldsymbol{s} \wedge \boldsymbol{E}$ and the power radiated by a magnetic dipole is readily found to be given by

$$\overline{W} = \frac{1}{3}\pi\frac{\omega^2}{\lambda^2}YNN^*. \tag{8-15}$$

It is of interest to note the analogy of this equation with (8-11).

Radiation Resistance of a Dipole

§ 4. An electric dipole may be realized practically as in Fig. 28. A two-wire line carries the current to two small spheres placed at a distance $\boldsymbol{l}$ apart from one another. Such distance will be assumed

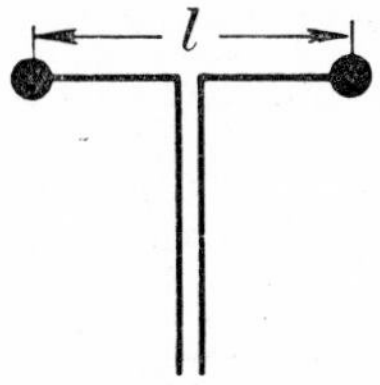

Fig. 28

to be very small with respect to the wavelength, so that the dipole may be imagined as concentrated in a point. If I designates the current flowing in the line it may be said that I *coulombs* arrive every second on each sphere. The corresponding charge will be positive for one sphere and negative for the other. The electric moment will increase by $\boldsymbol{Il}$ units per second. Then we write

$$i\omega \boldsymbol{L} = \boldsymbol{Il}. \tag{8-16}$$

Substituting this expression into (8-11) we obtain

$$\overline{W} = \frac{1}{3}\pi\left(\frac{l}{\lambda}\right)^2 ZII^*. \tag{8-17}$$

It is clear that this energy is supplied by the generator feeding the dipole and then is radiated. As far as the generator is concerned the situation is the same as if in place of the dipole there were a resistance R absorbing this energy. In such case the power dissipated would be represented by $\mathscr{R}e VI^*/2 = RII^*/2$. By comparing with (8-17) we find

$$R = \frac{2}{3}\pi\left(\frac{l}{\lambda}\right)^2 Z \qquad \textit{ohms}. \tag{8-18}$$

For obvious reasons this resistance is called the *radiation resistance.*

§ 5. To show how a magnetic dipole may be realized in practice we shall recall (4-27) expressing the vector potential produced by a current. Replacing $\boldsymbol{J}(P, t)$ with $\boldsymbol{J}(P) \exp(i\omega t)$ we find

$$\boldsymbol{A}(Q) = \mu \iiint\limits_V \boldsymbol{J}(P) G(P, Q) \mathrm{d}V_P.$$

In the case of a thin wire of cross section Σ_0 carring a solenoidal current I we have $J\Sigma_0 = I$ and consequently $\boldsymbol{J}\mathrm{d}V = \boldsymbol{J}\Sigma_0 \mathrm{d}l = J\Sigma_0 \mathrm{d}\boldsymbol{l} = I\mathrm{d}\boldsymbol{l}$. A first integration over the cross section Σ_0 yields

$$\boldsymbol{A}(Q) = \mu I \int\limits_l G(P, Q) \mathrm{d}P, \tag{8-19}$$

$\mathrm{d}P = \mathrm{d}\boldsymbol{l}$ being the line element of the wire at P and the integration being extended over the whole wire.

Consider now a two-wire line (Fig. 29) ending in a loop. The integral (8-19) extended over the feeding line will give a null result provided that the two wires are sufficiently close to one another (because two corresponding $\mathrm{d}P$ are equal and opposite). There remains to evaluate the contribution of the loop.

Let O be an arbitrary point inside the loop. If the loop has a sufficiently small size we may write

$$G(P, Q) = G(O, Q) + (\mathrm{grad}_O\, G) \cdot (P - O).$$

Introducing this expression into (8-19) we have by (M2-13)

$$\boldsymbol{A}(Q) = \mu I G(O, Q) \int_l \mathrm{d}P + \mu I\, \mathrm{grad}_O\, G(O, Q) \cdot \int_l (P - O)\mathrm{d}P.$$

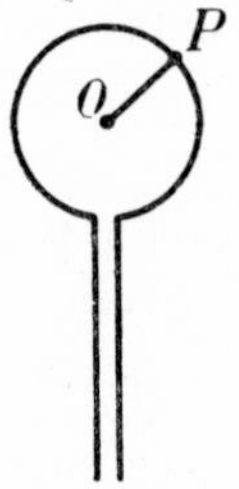

Fig. 29

The first integrand is an exact differential and yields a null result when integrated around the close circuit represented by the loop. The second integrand is a dyad and may be written in the following way

$$(P - O)\mathrm{d}P = \frac{1}{2}[(P - O)\mathrm{d}P + \mathrm{d}P(P - O)] + \\ + \frac{1}{2}[(P - O)\mathrm{d}P - \mathrm{d}P(P - O)] = \\ = \frac{1}{2}\mathrm{d}[(P - O)(P - O)] + \frac{1}{2}[(P - O)\mathrm{d}P - \mathrm{d}P(P - O)].$$

The first term in the right-hand side is also an exact differential and yields a vanishing contribution. There remains therefore, recalling (M2-15)

$$\boldsymbol{A}(Q) = \frac{1}{2}\mu I\, \mathrm{grad}_O\, G(O, Q) \cdot \int_l [(P - O)\mathrm{d}P - \mathrm{d}P(P - O)] = \\ = \frac{1}{2}\mu I \left[\int_l (P - O) \wedge \mathrm{d}P\right] \wedge \mathrm{grad}_O\, G(O, Q).$$

We shall assume now the loop to be plane; the unit normal to the plane will be indicated by $\boldsymbol{n}$ and the area of the loop by Σ. The last integral turns out to be equal to $2\Sigma\boldsymbol{n}$ so that finally we obtain

$$\boldsymbol{A}(Q) = \mu\Sigma I\boldsymbol{n} \wedge \text{grad}_O\, G(O, Q) = -\,\mu\Sigma I\boldsymbol{n} \wedge \text{grad}_Q\, G(O, Q).$$

With the position

$$(8\text{-}20) \qquad \mu\Sigma I\boldsymbol{n} = \boldsymbol{N} \qquad \textit{weber} \cdot \textit{meters},$$

we may also write by (M1-29)

$$\boldsymbol{A}(Q) = \text{curl}_Q\,(G\boldsymbol{N}).$$

The scalar potential vanishes (or is a constant) because there is no accumulation of charge. From (4-9) it is then derived

$$(8\text{-}21) \quad \boldsymbol{E}(Q) = -\,i\omega\,\text{curl}_Q\,(G\boldsymbol{N}), \qquad \boldsymbol{H}(Q) = \frac{1}{\mu}\,\text{curl}_Q\,\text{curl}_Q\,(G\boldsymbol{N}).$$

These equations coincide with (8-12). This shows that the loop is equivalent to a magnetic dipole having the moment $\boldsymbol{N}$ given by (8-20).

To evaluate the radiation resistance R of the magnetic dipole constituted by the loop one has to substitute the expression (8-20) of $\boldsymbol{N}$ into (8-15) and to equate the resulting power to $RII^*/2$. Thus one finds after some simplification

$$(8\text{-}22) \qquad R = \frac{8}{3}\pi^3\left(\frac{\sqrt{\Sigma}}{\lambda}\right)^4 Z \qquad \textit{ohms}.$$

A comparison of this formula with (8-18) shows that if the dimensions of the radiating system are very small with respect to the wavelength, as was supposed here, the radiation resistance of the loop magnetic dipole is of lesser order of magnitude than that of the electric dipole. An electric dipole carrying the same current radiates much more.

Radiation Resistance of an Electronic Cloud

§ 6. In 7-§2 the capacitance C and the inductance L of an electronic cloud were introduced with a reasonable justification, while no physical meaning was ascribed to the resistance R. We are now in a position to understand the main cause of this resistance.

An electron oscillating under the influence of the field constitutes an electric dipole; its radiation resistance introduces a real component in the admittivity and is therefore responsible for some loss.

In order to set up a quantitative argument we can no more assume the charge to be distributed with continuity; we shall instead picture the electrons as being sufficiently distant form one another. To utilize our formulas we shall assume that the electronic cloud considered contains N electrons per unit volume. Each electron will be so far apart from all the other electrons that it may be considered to be placed in empty space. The inductance $L = m/\varrho^2$ defined in 7-§2 will now be given by

$$L = \frac{Nm}{(Ne)^2} = \frac{m}{Ne^2}, \tag{8-23}$$

where m represents the mass of the electron and e its charge.

If $\boldsymbol{el}$ indicates the electric moment of an electron we shall derive from (8-11) (†) the power radiated by N electrons

$$\overline{W} = \frac{N}{3}\pi\frac{\omega^2}{\lambda_0^2}Z_0 e^2 ll^*.$$

The total electric moment of the unit volume or the polarization is given by $\boldsymbol{P}^e = N\boldsymbol{el}$. On the other hand we know that $\boldsymbol{J} = i\omega\boldsymbol{P}^e = i\omega N\boldsymbol{el}$ so that $\boldsymbol{el} = \boldsymbol{J}/i\omega N$. Substituting into the preceding equation we get

$$\overline{W} = \frac{1}{3N}\pi\frac{Z_0}{\lambda_0^2}JJ^*.$$

But $\overline{W}$ is given also by $RII^*/2$ so that

$$R = \frac{2}{3N}\pi\frac{Z_0}{\lambda_0^2}. \tag{8-24}$$

λ_0 and Z_0 referring to empty space.

(†) It will be noted that in (8-11) L indicates the modulus of the dipole moment while in the present section it stands for the induction (8-23).

Having evaluated L and R we can now derive the value of the width of an absorption line as introduced in 7-§16. This quantity depends on $Q = \omega_0 L/R$ if by ω_0 we indicate the resonance frequency. Utilizing (8-23, 24) and putting $\omega_0 = 2\pi/T_0$ we obtain

$$Q = 3Y_0 \frac{\lambda_0^2}{T_0} \frac{m}{e^2}.$$

The presence of R is felt only in the vicinity of resonance so that one may put $\lambda_0 = cT_0$; thus one finally obtains

$$Q = 3Y_0 T_0 \frac{mc^2}{e^2} \tag{8-25}$$

and it is readily verified that this represents a pure number.

If we put $T_0 = 2 \cdot 10^{-15}$ (visible radiation), $m = 9.1 \cdot 10^{-31}$ *kilograms* (electron mass) and $e = 1.6 \cdot 10^{-19}$ *coulombs* (electron charge) there follows $Q = 5 \cdot 10^7$. We conclude that the *natural width* of an electronic absorption line is extremely small.

In reality one must take into account thermal agitation which through Doppler effect and molecular collisions increases the width and reduces the monochromaticity.

Further it will be noted that the present classical treatment cannot give exact results in a field where quantum techniques are necessary.

Waves of General Shape in a Non-homogeneous Medium

§ 7. Plane waves and spherical waves are only particular solutions of the Maxwell equations, which are valid in a homogeneous medium. One may ask whether in a continuous medium, no matter whether homogeneous or not, there may exist solutions representing a wave propagation with wave surfaces of arbitrary shape. This is a rather involved problem which can be completely solved only in the case where the wavelength is small in comparison with all the other relevant lengths of the problem (radii of curvature of the wave surfaces, intervals within which the characteristics of the medium undergo appreciable variation).

Suppose that the medium is a continuous dielectric free from dispersion and losses where ε is a function of position P. We shall inquire whether there exist solutions of Maxwell's equations of the type

$$E = A(P) \exp[-ik_0\varphi(P)], \quad H = B(P) \exp[-ik_0\varphi(P)], \tag{8-26}$$

k_0 being the wave number in vacuum ($k_0 = 2\pi/\lambda_0 = \omega\sqrt{\varepsilon_0\mu_0}$), A and B two unknown complex vectors (†) and $\varphi(P)$ a scalar function of position. The wave surfaces will be represented by $\varphi(P) = constant$.

Let us substitute (8-26) into Maxwell's equations (7-18, 19) which in the present case take the form curl $H = i\omega\varepsilon E$, curl $E = - i\omega\mu H$; we obtain by (M1-29, 26)

$$\text{curl}\, B - ik_0 \,\text{grad}\, \varphi \wedge B = i\omega\varepsilon A,$$
$$\text{curl}\, A - ik_0 \,\text{grad}\, \varphi \wedge A = - i\omega\mu B.$$

Dividing by ik_0 we may write

$$\begin{aligned} \text{grad}\, \varphi \wedge B + \varepsilon c A &= \frac{1}{ik_0} \text{curl}\, B, \\ \text{grad}\, \varphi \wedge A - \mu c B &= \frac{1}{ik_0} \text{curl}\, A. \end{aligned} \tag{8-27}$$

If λ_0 is very small, k_0 is very great so that the right-hand side may be neglected writing

$$\begin{cases} \text{grad}\, \varphi \wedge B + \varepsilon c A = 0, \\ \text{grad}\, \varphi \wedge A - \mu c B = 0. \end{cases} \tag{8-28}$$

It is readily seen from this equation that A and B are both perpendicular to grad φ or to the normal to the wave surface. In this approximation we get *TEM* waves. Further A, B and grad φ form in this order a direct triad and the same may be said of E, H and grad φ.

(†) For the sake of simplicity we shall assume the polarization to be linear so that A and B are both represented by the product of a complex number and a real vector.

Substituting into the first equation (8-28) the expression of $\boldsymbol{B}$ derived from the second it is readily obtained

$$(\text{grad}\ \varphi)^2 = n^2, \tag{8-29}$$

where n represents the local value of the refractive index. Making the vector product of the first equation (8-28) and $\boldsymbol{B}$ and of the second equation and $\boldsymbol{A}$ one obtains

$$B^2 \text{grad}\ \varphi = \varepsilon c\boldsymbol{A} \wedge \boldsymbol{B},$$
$$A^2 \text{grad}\ \varphi = \mu c\boldsymbol{A} \wedge \boldsymbol{B},$$

whence

$$\frac{A^2}{B^2} = \frac{\mu}{\varepsilon} = Z^2,$$

and finally

$$E = ZH, \tag{8-30}$$

Z being the local value of the intrinsic impedance of the dielectric.

§ 8. If we want to follow the evolution of a wave surface with time we have to complete (8-26) by the factor exp $(i\omega t)$. It is then readily found that any given wave surface is governed by the equation

$$k_0\varphi(P) - \omega t = \text{constant}$$

or

$$\varphi(P) - ct = \text{constant} \tag{8-31}$$

For an infinitesimal displacement dP in the direction of grad φ (normal to the wave surface) we have $\mathrm{d}\varphi = |\text{grad}\ \varphi|\ |\mathrm{d}P|$ so that by differentiating (8-31) and calling v the normal velocity $|\mathrm{d}P|/\mathrm{d}t$ of displacement of the wave surface we obtain $|\text{grad}\ \varphi|\ v = c$. Then by (8-29)

$$v = \frac{c}{n}. \tag{8-32}$$

Note now that (8-29, 30, 32) are respectively identical to (3-10, 8, 7). Hence we conclude that wave propagation, when the wavelength is very small, is governed by the same laws as the propagation of discontinuities. In particular one may introduce the rays which in a homogeneous medium are straight lines.

The many deductions which are derived from these laws are said to constitute *geometrical optics*. We shall deal with this subject in a later chapter.

It is worth noticing that the value of φ so far as (8-26) is concerned is rather arbitrary. One could put $\varphi(P) + \varphi_1(P)$ in place of $\varphi(P)$ provided that $\boldsymbol{A}$ is replaced by $\boldsymbol{A} \exp (ik_0\varphi_1)$ and $\boldsymbol{B}$ by $\boldsymbol{B} \exp (ik_0\varphi_1)$. But then curl $\boldsymbol{A}$ and curl $\boldsymbol{B}$ appearing at the right-hand side of (8-27) would contain also terms of the same order as ik_0 and our approximation would break down. Hence we may say that the value of φ derived from (8-29) is that corresponding to a variation of $\boldsymbol{A}$ and $\boldsymbol{B}$ sufficiently small to make the right-hand sides of (8-27) negligible.

The W.K.B. Approximation

§ **9.** The approximation of the foregoing section sets only the condition that $\boldsymbol{A}$, $\boldsymbol{B}$ and the ray are mutually perpendicular and fixes the ratio of the magnitudes of $\boldsymbol{A}$ and $\boldsymbol{B}$. But the same approximation is not sufficient for deriving the law of variation of the magnitude of $\boldsymbol{A}$ (or $\boldsymbol{B}$) along the ray. To this end it is necessary to set up a further approximation by retaining in the solution of (8-27) also the terms containing the first power of $1/ik_0$ and disregarding higher order terms.

We will retain (8-29), as is always possible on account of the arbitrariness of φ. If by $\boldsymbol{s}$ we represent the unit vector in the direction of the ray we shall have

$$\text{grad}\, \varphi = n\boldsymbol{s}. \tag{8-33}$$

Next we go back to (8-27); we derive $\boldsymbol{B}$ from the second and substitute its expression into the first, neglecting the term in $(1/ik_0)^2$. We shall obtain

$$\frac{n}{\mu c}\boldsymbol{s} \wedge \left[(n\boldsymbol{s} \wedge \boldsymbol{A}) - \frac{1}{ik_0} \,\text{curl}\, \boldsymbol{A} \right] + \varepsilon c \boldsymbol{A} - \frac{1}{ik_0} \text{curl} \left(\frac{n}{\mu c}\, \boldsymbol{s} \wedge \boldsymbol{A} \right) = 0.$$

Note that we have $n/\mu c = \sqrt{\varepsilon/\mu} = Y$ and $nY = c\sqrt{\varepsilon\mu}\sqrt{\varepsilon/\mu} = \varepsilon c$

so that expanding the double vector product and simplifying we get

$$(8\text{-}34) \quad \varepsilon c(\boldsymbol{s} \cdot \boldsymbol{A})\boldsymbol{s} - \frac{1}{ik_0}[Y\boldsymbol{s} \wedge \operatorname{curl} \boldsymbol{A} + \operatorname{curl}(Y\boldsymbol{s} \wedge \boldsymbol{A})] = 0.$$

In the approximation of the preceding section $\boldsymbol{s}$ and $\boldsymbol{A}$ are mutually perpendicular. Hence $\boldsymbol{s} \cdot \boldsymbol{A}$ is at least of the order of $1/k_0$. Taking this into account and multiplying scalarly (8-34) by $\boldsymbol{A}$ we find, up to terms of the first order in $1/k_0$

$$[Y\boldsymbol{s} \wedge \operatorname{curl} \boldsymbol{A} + \operatorname{curl}(Y\boldsymbol{s} \wedge \boldsymbol{A})] \cdot \boldsymbol{A} = 0.$$

dividing by Y and recalling (M1-29) and (M2-30, 31) the left side may be expanded in the following way

$$\Big[\boldsymbol{s} \cdot \operatorname{grad} \boldsymbol{A} - (\operatorname{grad} \boldsymbol{A}) \cdot \boldsymbol{s} + \boldsymbol{s} \operatorname{div} \boldsymbol{A} - \boldsymbol{A} \operatorname{div} \boldsymbol{s} + (\operatorname{grad} \boldsymbol{s}) \cdot \boldsymbol{A} -$$
$$- (\operatorname{grad} \boldsymbol{A}) \cdot \boldsymbol{s} + \frac{\operatorname{grad} Y}{Y} \wedge (\boldsymbol{s} \wedge \boldsymbol{A})\Big] \cdot \boldsymbol{A} = 0.$$

Since the expression within square brackets appears in (8-34) multiplied by $1/ik_0$ we may now neglect $\boldsymbol{s} \cdot \boldsymbol{A}$; thus with some easy considerations and ordering in a different way we find

$$(8\text{-}35) \quad - A^2 \operatorname{div} \boldsymbol{s} - A^2 \frac{\partial \log Y}{\partial s} - \frac{\partial A^2}{\partial s} + (\boldsymbol{s} \cdot \operatorname{grad} \boldsymbol{A}) \cdot \boldsymbol{A} +$$
$$+ [(\operatorname{grad} \boldsymbol{s}) \cdot \boldsymbol{A}] \cdot \boldsymbol{A} = 0.$$

The last term may transform in this way: $\boldsymbol{A} \cdot [(\operatorname{grad} \boldsymbol{s}) \cdot \boldsymbol{A}] = (\boldsymbol{A} \cdot \operatorname{grad} \boldsymbol{s}) \cdot \boldsymbol{A}$ as may readily be verified; then by (M2-29) the last two terms of (8-35) become

$$(\boldsymbol{s} \cdot \operatorname{grad} \boldsymbol{A} + \boldsymbol{A} \cdot \operatorname{grad} \boldsymbol{s}) \cdot \boldsymbol{A} = [\operatorname{grad}(\boldsymbol{s} \cdot \boldsymbol{A})] \cdot \boldsymbol{A} = 0.$$

owing to the orthogonality of $\boldsymbol{s}$ and $\boldsymbol{A}$. In conclusion (8-35) yields

$$(8\text{-}36) \quad \frac{\partial}{\partial s} \log A^2 Y = - \operatorname{div} \boldsymbol{s}.$$

Consider now (Fig. 30) a tube of flow of $\boldsymbol{s}$ (or a bundle of rays) and a portion of it limited by two bases placed at a distance ds apart from one another and having respectively the areas Σ and $\Sigma + d\Sigma$. The outward flux of $\boldsymbol{s}$ will obviously be given by $\Sigma + d\Sigma - \Sigma = d\Sigma$. Dividing by the volume of that portion of the tube we shall obtain by definition the divergence of $\boldsymbol{s}$. The volume

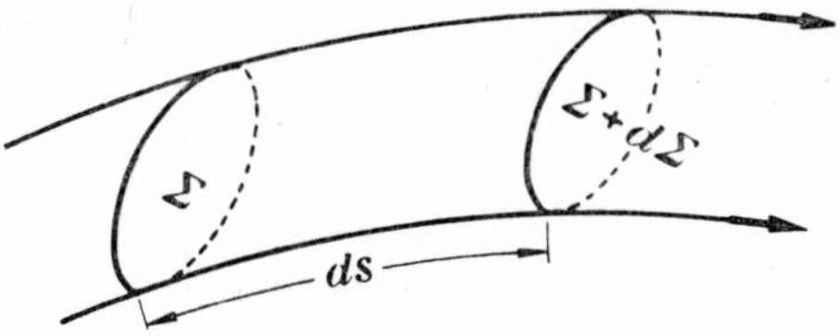

Fig. 30

(apart from higher order infinitesimals) equals Σds so that we may write

$$\operatorname{div} \boldsymbol{s} = \frac{d\Sigma}{\Sigma ds} = \frac{\partial \log \Sigma}{\partial s}.$$

Substituting this expression into (8-36) the differential equation can be integrated with the result

$$A^2 \Sigma Y = A_0^2, \tag{8-37}$$

A_0 being constant along the ray (but not necessarily equal for all rays).

§ 10. We have thus found the law governing the variation of the amplitude along a given ray. On the other hand the equation $\operatorname{grad} \varphi = n\boldsymbol{s}$ when integrated yields

$$\varphi = \int^s n \, ds.$$

Then taking into account (8-26, 37) one obtains

$$E = A_0 \sqrt{\frac{Z}{\Sigma}} \exp\left(- ik_0 \int^s n \, ds\right), \tag{8-38}$$

still with the condition $B = YA$.

In a non-dispersive dielectric Z and n are inversely proportional to one another, hence in this case (8-38) may also be written in the form

$$E = \frac{A_0}{\sqrt{n\Sigma}} \exp\left(-ik_0 \int^{s} n\,ds\right). \tag{8-39}$$

The type of approximation illustrated, specially in the one-dimensional case, is often indicated by *W. K. B.* after the names of Wentzel, Kramers, and Brillouin, who investigated it in the scalar case of wave mechanics (†).

It is interesting to evaluate the magnitude of Poynting's vector $\bar{S} = \mathcal{R}e(1/2)EH^*$. In our case we readily get

$$\bar{S}\Sigma = \frac{1}{2} A_0^2 .$$

As a consequence the energy flow is the same through all successive cross sections of the bundle of rays. Energy propagation is solenoidal; ray bundles represent tubes of flow and rays represent lines of flow of the energy.

Interference

§ 11. So far we have considered the propagation of a single wave. But in general two or more waves with the same wavelength may be superimposed in the same region of space. There arise then the so-called phenomena of *interference*.

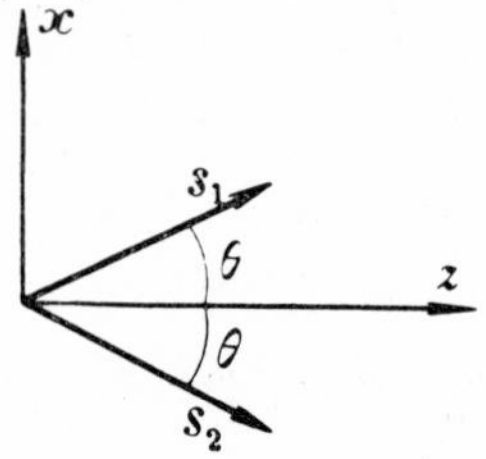

Fig. 31

We shall investigate the particularly simple case of the interference of two plane waves in a homogeneous and dispersionless

(†) However, the same type of approximation was known a long time before.

dielectric. Let the two directions of propagation $\boldsymbol{s}_1$, $\boldsymbol{s}_2$ be in the xz plane symmetrically oriented with respect to the z axis (Fig. 31). We shall put $s_{1x} = - s_{2x} = \sin\theta$ and $s_{1z} = s_{2z} = \cos\theta$.

We assume now that the two waves have the same amplitude and are both linearly polarized with the electric vector perpendicular to the xz plane. We shall put $\boldsymbol{A}_1 = \boldsymbol{A}_2 = A\boldsymbol{j}$ and write by (7-59)

$$\boldsymbol{E}_1 = A\boldsymbol{j} \exp\left[- ik(x \sin\theta + z\cos\theta)\right],$$
$$\boldsymbol{E}_2 = A\boldsymbol{j} \exp\left[- ik(- x \sin\theta + z\cos\theta)\right],$$

while from $Z\boldsymbol{H} = \boldsymbol{s} \wedge \boldsymbol{E}$ we find

$$Z\boldsymbol{H}_1 = (-A\cos\theta\,\boldsymbol{i} + A\sin\theta\,\boldsymbol{k}) \exp\left[-ik(x\sin\theta + z\cos\theta)\right],$$
$$Z\boldsymbol{H}_2 = (-A\cos\theta\,\boldsymbol{i} - A\sin\theta\,\boldsymbol{k}) \exp\left[-ik(-x\sin\theta + z\cos\theta)\right].$$

By adding the complex amplitudes of both waves we get

$$\text{(8-40)} \quad TE \begin{cases} \boldsymbol{E} = 2A\boldsymbol{j}\cos(kx\sin\theta)\exp(-ikz\cos\theta), \\ Z\boldsymbol{H} = 2A[-\boldsymbol{i}\cos\theta\cos(kx\sin\theta) - \\ \qquad - i\boldsymbol{k}\sin\theta\sin(kx\sin\theta)]\exp(-ikz\cos\theta). \end{cases}$$

As is seen from this equation, we get a special type of plane waves which are perpendicular to the z axis and travel with a velocity $v/\cos\theta$ greater than the ordinary phase velocity in the medium. These waves are not TEM like ordinary plane waves but only TE owing to the longitudinal component of $\boldsymbol{H}$. Furthermore the amplitude is not constant over a whole wave surface but is a harmonic function of x.

The corresponding TM waves can be obtained by interference of two plane waves having the magnetic vectors perpendicular to the xz plane. Replacing $\boldsymbol{E}$ by $Z\boldsymbol{H}$ and $Z\boldsymbol{H}$ by $-\boldsymbol{E}$ (see 7-§11) it is most readily found

$$\text{(8-41)} \quad TM \begin{cases} Z\boldsymbol{H} = 2A\boldsymbol{j}\cos(kz\sin\theta)\exp(-ikz\cos\theta). \\ \boldsymbol{E} = 2A[\boldsymbol{i}\cos\theta\cos(kx\sin\theta) + \\ \qquad + i\boldsymbol{k}\sin\theta\sin(kx\sin\theta)]\exp(-ikz\cos\theta). \end{cases}$$

In both *TE* and *TM* cases the mean Poynting vector is given by

$$\overline{\mathbf{S}} = 2YAA^* \cos\theta \cos^2 (kx \sin\theta)\boldsymbol{k}, \tag{8-42}$$

and is directed parallel to the z axis. We see that the energy flow is a maximum in certain planes $x = constant$ and vanishes on intermediate planes. The former are given the name of *anti-nodal planes* while the latter are given the name of *nodal planes*. The spacing between two successive nodal or anti-nodal planes is $\lambda/2 \sin\theta$. If we are dealing with light waves the intersection of the nodal and antinodal planes with a screen perpendicular to the z axis gives rise to *interference fringes* that is to a number of equispaced stripes alternatively dark and bright. The period of the fringes is given by

$$p = \frac{\lambda}{2 \sin\theta}. \tag{8-43}$$

The illumination (light flux per unit surface) on the axis of a bright fringe is four times the illumination that would be given by one only of the two waves. This paradox may be explained by noting that the excess energy which is found in a bright fringe is missing from the next dark fringe.

Of course, when there are more than two waves or they are not plane, the interference phenomena are more complicated.

CHAPTER 9

Reflection, Refraction, Geometrical Optics

Reflection, Refraction, Diffraction

§ 1. The free propagation in a continuous medium which is illustrated in the preceding chapter is of fundamental importance for a description of electromagnetic waves, but is extremely idealized. In reality the media in which the propagation of electromagnetic waves takes place ordinarily are continuous only in finite and bounded regions separated from one another by surfaces of discontinuity. In passing across one of these surfaces, the medium presents a sudden change in characteristics.

It is customary to classify the different phenomena which may take place at a surface of discontinuity according to a distinction of substantially historical meaning which, however, in most cases corresponds to an actual difference of qualitative appearances.

Let a surface Σ separate the homogeneous medium M from the homogeneous medium M'. Suppose an electromagnetic wave of general shape coming from medium M is incident onto Σ. Suppose also that Σ is either plane and unbounded or curved with radii of curvature which are everywhere much greater than the wave length. Experience shows that in this case the incident wave will be split at Σ into two waves, one going back into medium M (*reflected wave*) and the other passing into medium M' (*refracted* or *transmitted wave*). These phenomena are called respectively *reflection* and *refraction.*

If the radii of curvature of Σ are somewhere comparable with the wavelength, a more complicated phenomenon will take place which is termed the *diffraction*. Instead of a single wave reflected and a single wave refracted there will appear an infinite number of such waves. An electromagnetic field will result from the interference of all these waves.

Finally we may mention that a particular case of propagation in the presence of surfaces of discontinuity is represented by the so-called *guided propagation* which will be dealt with in Chapter 11.

In the present chapter we shall be concerned with reflection and refraction.

Laws of Reflection and Refraction

§ 2. In order to derive the quantitative laws of reflection and refraction we shall begin with the case when the surface Σ is plane and the media M and M' are perfect and dispersionless dielectrics. We shall indicate with n and n' respectively the two refractive indices and with Z and Z' the two intrinsic inpedances.

Let a plane wave be incident onto Σ coming from medium M. We shall see that also the reflected and transmitted waves are both plane in agreement with experience. We shall distinguish by the superscripts i, r, t respectively the quantities referring to the incident, reflected and transmitted waves. The wave numbers in the first and in the second media will be given respectively by $k = nk_0$ and $k' = n'k_0$, so that recalling (7-58) we may write

$$(9\text{-}1)\qquad \begin{cases} \boldsymbol{E}^i = \boldsymbol{A}^i \exp\,[-\,ink_0\boldsymbol{s}^i \cdot (P - O)], & Z\boldsymbol{H}^i = \boldsymbol{s}^i \wedge \boldsymbol{E}^i, \\ \boldsymbol{E}^r = \boldsymbol{A}^r \exp\,[-\,ink_0\boldsymbol{s}^r \cdot (P - O)], & Z\boldsymbol{H}^r = \boldsymbol{s}^r \wedge \boldsymbol{E}^r, \\ \boldsymbol{E}^t = \boldsymbol{A}^t \exp\,[-\,in'k_0\boldsymbol{s}^t \cdot (P - O)], & Z'\boldsymbol{H}^t = \boldsymbol{s}^t \wedge \boldsymbol{E}^t. \end{cases}$$

We already know that the tangential components of $\boldsymbol{E}$ and $\boldsymbol{H}$ are continuous across Σ (see 3-§2). A necessary condition for this to happen over the whole surface is that the arguments of the three exponentials be equal when P is on Σ. This requires that the tangential components of $n\boldsymbol{s}^i$, $n\boldsymbol{s}^r$ and $n'\boldsymbol{s}^t$ be equal. Therefore we shall write

$$(9\text{-}2)\qquad \boldsymbol{s}^i \wedge \boldsymbol{k} = \boldsymbol{s}^r \wedge \boldsymbol{k}, \qquad n\boldsymbol{s}^i \wedge \boldsymbol{k} = n'\boldsymbol{s}^t \wedge \boldsymbol{k},$$

having represented by $\boldsymbol{k}$ the unit normal to the surface.

Formulas (9-2) represent the well-known laws of reflection and refraction. They summarize the condition that the normal, the incident ray and the reflected (or refracted) ray be in the same plane, and the conditions for the angles. Denoting by θ the angle made by a ray with the normal, we readily get from (9-2) (†)

$$\theta^i = \pi - \theta^r, \qquad n \sin \theta^i = n' \sin \theta^t. \tag{9-3}$$

It is well known that the quantity $n'/n = N$ is called the *relative refractive index* of the second medium with respect to the first. One may write $\sin \theta^i / \sin \theta^t = N$.

Oblique Impedance

§ 3. In order to evaluate the amplitudes of the reflected and transmitted waves one has to consider the impedances of both media. It is expedient to introduce an oblique impedance. The ordinary intrinsic impedance considered so far gives the ratio of the electric and magnetic forces normal to the direction of propagation. One may also be interested in defining the ratio of the projections of the electric and magnetic forces on a plane different from the plane normal to the direction of propagation.

Let us assume that the unit vector $\boldsymbol{s}$ parallel to the direction of propagation is in the xz plane and makes the angle θ with the z axis. The corresponding plane wave will be represented by the expression

$$\boldsymbol{E} = \boldsymbol{A} \exp\left[-ik(x \sin \theta + z \cos \theta)\right], \qquad Z\boldsymbol{H} = \boldsymbol{s} \wedge \boldsymbol{E}.$$

As is readily seen by inspection, one may also say that a plane wave is traveling in the direction of the z axis with the propagation constant $k \cos \theta$ and amplitude $\boldsymbol{A} \exp(-ikx \sin \theta)$ variable with x. The impedance will be now represented by the ratio of the transverse components of $\boldsymbol{E}$ and $\boldsymbol{H}$ with respect to the z axis.

It is convenient to distinguish the TE and TM cases. Suppose that the polarization is linear and $\boldsymbol{E}$ is in the xz plane (Fig. 32). This represents the TM case, since $\boldsymbol{H}$ does not show a longitudinal component relative to the z-axis. The field components which are transverse to z will have the magnitudes $E \cos \theta$ and H respectively. Their ratio $Z \cos \theta$ gives the oblique impedance.

(†) Of course, we cannot write $\theta^i = \theta^r$ since in this case the reflected and incident waves would coincide.

The TE case is represented in Fig. 33 and it is clear that in this case the oblique impedance will be found to be $Z/\cos\theta$.

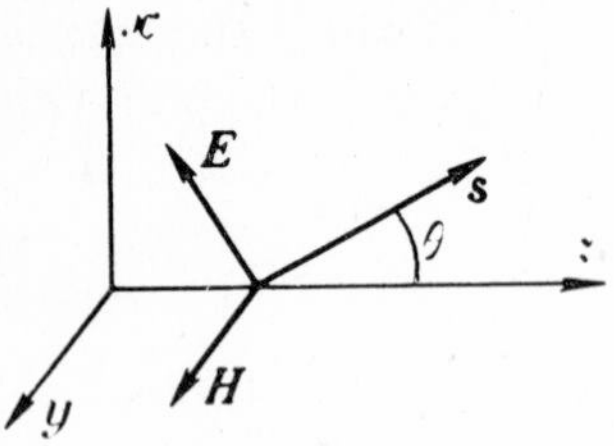

Fig. 32

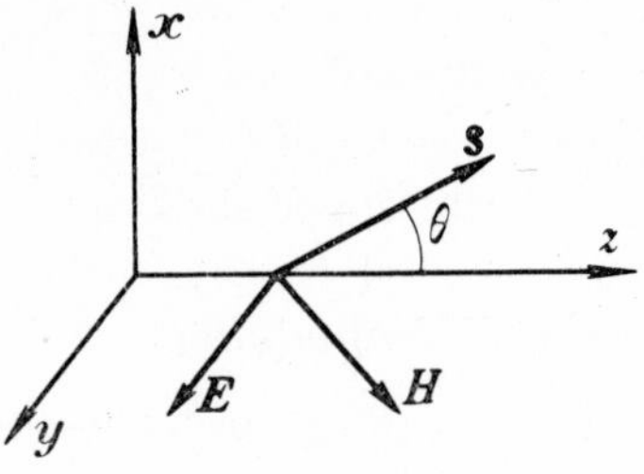

Fig. 33

To distinguish progressive from regressive waves a sign must be ascribed to the oblique impedance. We shall make the convention that the sign is plus when $\boldsymbol{E}, \boldsymbol{H}, \boldsymbol{k}$ constitute a direct (non-orthogonal) triad and minus in the opposite case. Then referring to Figs. 32, 33 (progressive waves) the oblique impedances will both be positive, while if the waves were regressive with respect to z the oblique impedances would be negative. This follows also by considering that for regressive waves θ is either in the second or in the third quadrant.

Fresnel's Formulas

§ 4. Let us go back now to the case of reflection at a plane surface which will be assumed coincident with the xy plane. Equations (3-1, 2) require the continuity of the tangential components of $\boldsymbol{E}$ and $\boldsymbol{H}$; hence the tangential component of $\boldsymbol{E}^i + \boldsymbol{E}^r$ must equal the tangential component of $\boldsymbol{E}^t$ and the tangential component of $\boldsymbol{H}^i + \boldsymbol{H}^r$ must equal the tangential component of $\boldsymbol{H}^t$. On the other hand the oblique impedances require the ratio of the tangential part of $\boldsymbol{E}$ and $\boldsymbol{H}$ to have a well-determined value for each of the three waves. We recall now the results illustrated in 6-§16; one will readily see that the present case is perfectly similar to that of the transition from a given transmission line to another transmission line of different characteristic impedance. One has only to replace V by the tangential part of $\boldsymbol{E}$, I by the tangential part of $\boldsymbol{H}$ and the characteristic impedance by the oblique impedance. By this procedure the reflection coefficients (i.e., the ratios of the reflected and the incident tangential amplitudes) will be found immediately from (6-55, 56) (†)

$$\text{(9-4)} \quad \begin{cases} TM \quad r_H = \dfrac{H^r}{H^i} = \dfrac{Z \cos\theta^i - Z' \cos\theta^t}{Z \cos\theta^i + Z' \cos\theta^t}, \\[2ex] TE \quad r_E = \dfrac{E^r}{E^i} = \dfrac{Z'/\cos\theta^t - Z/\cos\theta^i}{Z'/\cos\theta^t + Z/\cos\theta^i}. \end{cases}$$

Introducing the refractive indices of both dielectrics which by (7-44) are inversely proportional to the respective intrinsic impedances we may also write

$$\text{(9-5)} \quad \begin{cases} TM \quad r_H = \dfrac{n' \cos\theta^i - n \cos\theta^t}{n' \cos\theta^i + n \cos\theta^t}, \\[2ex] TE \quad r_E = \dfrac{n \cos\theta^i - n' \cos\theta^t}{n \cos\theta^i + n' \cos\theta^t}. \end{cases}$$

To find the amplitude of the transmitted wave one has to write $H^i + H^r = H^t$ in the TM case and $E^i + E^r = E^t$ in the TE case and to take into account (9-5). In this way one readily finds

$$\text{(9-6)} \quad \begin{cases} TM \quad \varkappa_H = \dfrac{H^t}{H^i} = \dfrac{2n' \cos\theta^i}{n' \cos\theta^i + n \cos\theta^t}, \\[2ex] TE \quad \varkappa_E = \dfrac{E^t}{E^i} = \dfrac{2n \cos\theta^i}{n \cos\theta^i + n' \cos\theta^t}, \end{cases}$$

where $\varkappa_E$ and $\varkappa_E$ represent the *transmission coefficients*.

Equations (9-5, 6) are known as the *Fresnel formulas*.

We may remark now that on account of (9-3) n and n' are proportional respectively to $\sin\theta^t$ and $\sin\theta^i$. Hence in the Fresnel

(†) It will be clear why in the TM case we consider r_H and in the TE case we consider r_E. In the first case $\boldsymbol{H}$ coincides with its tangential component while in the second case this property is presented by $\boldsymbol{E}$. It is also readily seen that either r_H or r_E are sufficient to specify completely the reflected wave.

formulas the refractive indices may be replaced by the sines, obtaining for the reflection coefficients the expressions

$$(9\text{-}7)\quad \begin{cases} TM \quad r_H = \dfrac{\sin 2\theta^i - \sin 2\theta^t}{\sin 2\theta^i + \sin 2\theta^t} = \dfrac{2\cos(\theta^i+\theta^t)\sin(\theta^i-\theta^t)}{2\sin(\theta^i+\theta^t)\cos(\theta^i-\theta^t)} = \\ \qquad\qquad = \dfrac{\tan(\theta^i-\theta^t)}{\tan(\theta^i+\theta^t)}, \\ TE \quad r_E = \dfrac{\sin(\theta^t-\theta^i)}{\sin(\theta^t+\theta^i)}. \end{cases}$$

In the first expression a well-known formula of trigonometry has been applied.

To evaluate the reflection factor ϱ (i.e., the ratio of the reflected energy and the incident energy) one may remark that the energy flow for a plane wave is given in our case by $EH^*/2 = ZHH^*/2 = YEE^*/2$. In this way it is readily found that in both the TM and the TE cases the following relation holds:

$$(9\text{-}8)\qquad \varrho = rr^*.$$

Of course, in the TM case one has to take for r the first expression (9-4), and in the TE case the second.

§ 5. In the case of normal incidence we have $\theta^i = \theta^t = 0$ and from (9-5, 6) we may derive

$$(9\text{-}9)\qquad TEM \quad r_H = -r_E = \frac{n'-n}{n'+n}, \quad \varkappa_H = \frac{n'}{n}\varkappa_E = \frac{2n'}{n'+n}.$$

We see that in this case if $n' \neq n$ the reflected wave cannot be absent; the intrinsic impedances of both media are not matched to one another.

From (9-7) it is also concluded that in the TE case the reflected wave is always present. On the contrary the TM case can be free from reflection provided that $\theta^i + \theta^t = \pi/2$. By the law of refraction (9-3) it follows immediately for this case

$$(9\text{-}10)\qquad \tan\theta^i = \frac{n'}{n}.$$

The angle θ^i thus defined is known as the *Brewster angle.* For this angle of incidence the impedances of both media are matched in the TM case.

To study the reflection of a wave polarized linearly or elliptically one has to divide the wave into a TM wave and a TE wave. This is always possible because, as already noted, any vector amplitude can be split into two complex amplitudes which are perpendicular to one another (as well as to the direction of propagation).

Total Reflection

§ 6. When n is less than n' (9-3) yields a real angle of refraction whatever the angle of incidence θ^i. But when the first medium has a refractive index greater than that of the second, θ^t becomes imaginary as soon as θ^i attains a value greater than arc sin (n'/n) which is called the *critical angle.*

If the angle of incidence is greater than the critical angle we have $\cos\theta^t = \pm i\cdot\sqrt{n^2\sin^2\theta^i/n'^2 - 1}$, so that both the first and the second equations (9-5) give $\varrho = 1$. For this reason it is customary to speak of *total reflection.*

As the whole energy goes back with the reflected wave, one may ask what happens to the refracted wave. It is evident that this wave will be evanescent (see 7-§19), the sine of the angle of refraction being greater than 1 and the cosine being imaginary. The amplitude is attenuated exponentially in the direction of the z-axis; the greater the absolute value of $\cos\theta$ or the greater the value of the angle of incidence, the more attenuated will be the wave.

Recalling what was said in 7-§19 one may readily conclude that the evanescent wave will present the same TM or TE character as the incident wave.

There is no steady flow of energy from M to M' because in the latter medium the energy is confined to a layer adjacent to Σ; in the stationary case under consideration the energy per unit surface in the layer is a constant. The energy flows only along Σ as was shown in 7-§20.

Reflection at a Metal Surface

§ 7. When medium M is a perfect dispersionless dielectric and medium M' is a conductor the phenomena are slightly more complicated than those discussed above. They present some interest in optics as a means of investigation. However, for microwaves and radiowaves the discussion may be simplified because good conductors are in this case nearly perfect conductors. We shall begin by this case which presents a great interest in modern applications.

A perfect conductor (see 7-§18) has a refractive index which tends to infinity and an intrinsic impedance which tends to vanish. When the refractive index tends to infinity, the identity of the arguments in the exponentials (9-1) everywhere on Σ is obtained with an $\boldsymbol{s}^t$ which tends to be normal to Σ. Whatever the angle of incidence, the angle of refraction is approximately zero and the refracted wave travels in a direction normal to Σ. The attenuation caused by conductivity is also in a direction perpendicular to Σ. Consequently we may conclude that the amplitude of the refracted wave is constant over the whole surface Σ. By the argument outlined in 9-§4 one may again arrive at (9-4) where Z' tends to vanish. In this way,

$$r_H = -r_E = 1. \tag{9-11}$$

Hence the reflection is always total. This is a consequence of the fact that the electromagnetic field does not penetrate perfect conductors.

Equation (9-11) states that for $z = 0$ the tangential part of $\boldsymbol{H}^r$ equals that of $\boldsymbol{H}^i$, while the tangential part of $\boldsymbol{E}^r$ has the same magnitude as that of $\boldsymbol{E}^i$, but with opposite sign.

In conclusion the tangential part of the magnetic force over Σ will be equal to twice that of the incident wave while the tangential part of the electric force will vanish.

The last condition gives at the surface of any perfect conductor

$$\boldsymbol{n} \wedge \boldsymbol{E} = 0, \tag{9-12}$$

$\boldsymbol{n}$ being the unit normal to the surface directed inside the conductor. Remembering that curl $\boldsymbol{E} = -\eta_m \boldsymbol{H}$ one has only to apply

Stokes' theorem to any arbitrary loop on the surface of the conductor to derive from (9-12) the other condition

$$\boldsymbol{n} \cdot \boldsymbol{H} = 0. \tag{9 13}$$

Hence the normal component of the magnetic force at the surface of a perfect conductor vanishes. From (9-12) and curl $\boldsymbol{H} = \eta_e \boldsymbol{E}$ there follows immediately

$$\boldsymbol{n} \wedge \frac{\partial \mathbf{H}}{\partial n} = 0. \tag{9-14}$$

Hence the normal derivative of the tangential projection of $\boldsymbol{H}$ vanishes too.

Note that, since the electromagnetic field vanishes inside the conductor, the tangential projection of $\boldsymbol{H}$ presents a discontinuity across the surface. Then, recalling (3-1), one finds that there must exist a surface current induced by the field having the density

$$\boldsymbol{\iota} = \boldsymbol{n} \wedge (\boldsymbol{H}^{+} - \boldsymbol{H}^{-}) = - \boldsymbol{n} \wedge \boldsymbol{H}, \tag{9-15}$$

where $\boldsymbol{H}^{-} = \boldsymbol{H}$ represents the magnetic force in the dielectric. As the conductivity is infinite, this current does not absorb any energy. We note that (9-12) is merely a consequence of the vanishing of $\boldsymbol{E}$ inside the conductor. Hence (9-12) as well as (9-13, 14), which are derived from (9-12), present a great generality and do not depend on the assumption that the incident wave is plane.

§ 8. A second approximation taking into account the finite (but very great) conductivity of metals may be obtained as follows.

The value of $\boldsymbol{H}$ is not very much influenced by the conductivity being finite. Over Σ the tangential projection of $\boldsymbol{H}$ will still be twice that of $\boldsymbol{H}^i$. But the tangential projection of $\boldsymbol{E}$ will be obtained from it by a rotation of $\pi/2$ about k and a multiplication by Z' which though very small in absolute value does not vanish.

In the *TM* case the tangential projection of $\boldsymbol{H}$ is represented by $2\boldsymbol{H}^i$ so that the tangential projection of $\boldsymbol{E}$ will have the magnitude $2Z'H^i$.

The mean flow of energy across the unit surface of Σ will be given by

$$\bar{S}_z = 2\mathcal{Re}\, Z'H^iH^{i*} = 2R'H^iH^{i*},$$

where $R' = \sqrt{\omega\mu/2\gamma}$ represents the intrinsic resistance of the conductor (see 7-§18). On the other hand the incident power on a unit surface equals $ZH^iH^{i*} \cos\theta^i/2$ so that the fraction of the incident power which is absorbed equals $4R'/Z \cos\theta^i$. The reflection factor will then be given by

$$\varrho_{TM} = 1 - \frac{4R'}{Z\cos\theta^i}. \tag{9-16}$$

In the TE case the tangential projection of $\boldsymbol{H}$ equals $2H^i \cos\theta^i$ so that the tangential projection of $\boldsymbol{E}$ will be $2Z'H^i \cos\theta^i$ and the power crossing a unit surface of Σ will be represented by

$$\bar{S}_z = 2\mathcal{Re} Z'H^iH^{i*} \cos^2\theta^i = 2R'H^iH^{i*} \cos^2\theta^i.$$

The fraction of the incident power which is absorbed equals $4R' \cos\theta^i/Z$, and the reflection factor will be given by

$$\varrho_{TE} = 1 - \frac{4R'\cos\theta^i}{Z}. \tag{9-17}$$

For good conductors (9-16, 17) represent excellent approximations up to the region of infra-red. For visible radiation they are in general unsufficient.

Of course (9-16) cannot be applied in the case of grazing incidence. However for large values of the angle of incidence our approximation breaks down.

If the first medium is vacuum and the second medium presents a conductivity $\gamma = 6 \cdot 10^7$, the reflection factor for normal incidence and the frequency of 10^6 *cycles/second* turns out $\varrho = 1 - 2{,}7 \cdot 10^{-6}$. Hence one may conclude that for radio waves good conductors are practically perfect reflectors.

Real conductors present a certain difference from perfect conductors also as regards the inside electromagnetic field. In the former conductors the field does not exactly vanish showing instead a little penetration with an attenuation α which though very great is not infinite.

The length $d = 1/\alpha$ represents the distance which is traveled by the waves before their amplitudes are reduced in the ratio $1/e$. This length is assumed by convention to represent the depth of the surface film of a conductor which is influenced by the external field. For this reason d is called the *skin depth*. Recalling (7-56) we have

$$d = \sqrt{\frac{2}{\omega\mu_0\gamma}}. \tag{9-18}$$

Hence it is seen that the greater the frequency the smaller the skin depth. For example in the case of copper and for a frequency of 10^6 *cycles/second* the formula gives $d = 7 \cdot 10^{-5}$ *meters*. For light waves the skin depth becomes practically zero.

In conclusion we may say that good conductors are excellent screens as far as electromagnetic radiation is concerned.

Anti-reflecting Coatings

§ 9. Sometimes it is wished that an electromagnetic radiation may pass from one dielectric to another with the smallest possible amount of reflection. This case is presented for example by photographic lenses with many elements in so far as the many surfaces of separation between air and glass cause a large amount of the incident light to be lost.

It is then customary to have recourse to a device similar to that discussed for transmission lines (see 6-§18). Each surface is coated by a special *anti-reflecting layer*. In its simplest form such layer is homogeneous, its thickness is a quarter wavelength and its refractive index equals the geometric mean of the indices of the two adjoining media. As the refractive indices are inversely proportional to the intrinsic impedances, one may conclude on the basis of the discussion of the above mentioned section that the reflection coefficient vanishes at normal incidence.

Of course, this is not valid for an oblique incidence. However one may note that oblique impedances depend on the factor $\cos\theta^i$

so that the growth of reflection with increasing θ^i is very slow and may be disregarded up to about 30°.

A more serious difficulty is represented by the fact that a coating which is appropriate for one wavelength is not exactly appropriate for other wavelengths. It is customary to design the coating for the mean wavelength of the interesting band. For this reason a lens coated with an anti-reflective layer shows ordinarily a purple hue; this is because the layer does not reflect yellow but reflects red and violet.

Geometrical Optics

§ 10. Strictly speaking, the formulas which were found in the preceding section for reflection and refraction are valid only for the case of plane waves and plane surfaces of separation. In the theory of optical instruments one has to deal with more general types of waves and surfaces (in most cases they are spherical); a rigorous investigation is then much more involved.

It is customary to have recourse to a type of approximation which is valid when the radii of curvature of both waves and surfaces of separation are very great in comparison with the wave length. It will be clear that such approximation is particularly appropriate in the case of a very small wavelength namely in optics.

The procedure consists in dividing the incident wave surface into several elements which are small in comparison with the radii of

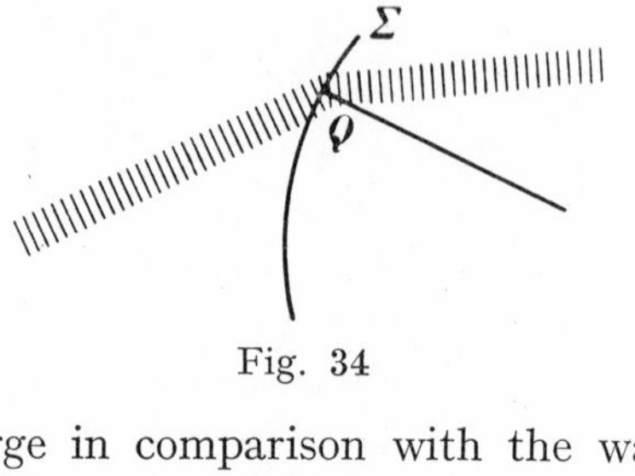

Fig. 34

curvature but large in comparison with the wavelength. Each surface element may be considered as plane; it travels in the direction of its normal (Fig. 34) and impinges onto the refracting surface Σ. In the region interested by the element the surface is also practically plane, consequently one may apply (9-2) and Fresnel's formulas.

It is clear that this procedure amounts to considering the rays instead of the wave surfaces; each ray is reflected or refracted according to (9-2). Everything reduces now to a set of relations between geometrical entities (namely rays and surface normals). For this reason it is customary to speak of geometrical optics.

The Malus-Dupin Theorem

§ 11. If the procedure of geometrical optics is to be useful, it is clearly necessary that all the elements of the incident wave, after reflection or refraction, may join to form a single wave (reflected or refracted wave). It is by no means obvious that this is possible, so that the problem requires a careful investigation.

The rays belonging to the incident wave form a *normal set* of straight lines. This means that they are not a general double infinity of lines inasmuch as they admit of an inifnite number of normal surfaces (†) (the wave surfaces). For the reflected or refracted elements to be united into a single wave, it is clearly required that their normals form again a normal set.

To investigate this question we shall begin by deriving the mathematical condition for a set of rays to be normal. Let us cut the set of rays with a surface Σ. Each point Q of Σ is crossed by a ray. This allows the rays of the set to be specified by means of the two curvilinear coordinates u, v of Q on Σ. Let P indicate a point on a wave surface. We may write

$$P = Q + r\mathbf{s},$$

$\mathbf{s}$ representing a unit vector parallel to the ray through Q and r the distance $| P - Q |$. Taking the derivatives with respect to u and v we obtain

$$\frac{\partial P}{\partial u} = \frac{\partial Q}{\partial u} + \frac{\partial r}{\partial u}\mathbf{s} + r\frac{\partial \mathbf{s}}{\partial u}, \qquad \frac{\partial P}{\partial v} = \frac{\partial Q}{\partial v} + \frac{\partial r}{\partial v}\mathbf{s} + r\frac{\partial \mathbf{s}}{\partial v}. \tag{9-19}$$

(†) It may be shown that, if the set admits one normal surface, it necessarily admits an infinite number of such surfaces.

The two vectors $\partial P/\partial u$ and $\partial P/\partial v$ are tangent to the wave surface and, as a consequence, normal to $\boldsymbol{s}$. Multiplying scalarly (9-19) by $\boldsymbol{s}$ we get then

$$\frac{\partial Q}{\partial u} \cdot \boldsymbol{s} + \frac{\partial r}{\partial u} = 0, \qquad \frac{\partial Q}{\partial v} \cdot \boldsymbol{s} + \frac{\partial r}{\partial v} = 0. \tag{9-20}$$

Taking the derivative of the first equation with respect to v and the derivative of the second equation with respect to u and eliminating the mixed second derivative of r we obtain the condition of integrability

$$\frac{\partial Q}{\partial u} \cdot \frac{\partial \boldsymbol{s}}{\partial v} = \frac{\partial Q}{\partial v} \cdot \frac{\partial \boldsymbol{s}}{\partial u}.$$

Since u and v may be any pair of curvilinear coordinates the last equation may be written as

$$\mathrm{d}Q \cdot \delta \boldsymbol{s} = \delta Q \cdot \mathrm{d}\boldsymbol{s}, \tag{9-21}$$

where $\mathrm{d}Q$ and δQ represent two infinitesimal and independent displacements of Q along Σ and $\mathrm{d}\boldsymbol{s}$ and $\delta\boldsymbol{s}$ the corresponding variations of $\boldsymbol{s}$. Equation (9-21) represents a necessary and sufficient condition for the set to be normal. We have already demonstrated that it is necessary; to show that it is also sufficient one has only to remark that, if (9-21) is satisfied, (9-20) may be integrated and r may be derived as a function of u, v. This allows an actual wave surface to be constructed (or an infinite number of equispaced wave surfaces since r is determined apart from an arbitrary additive constant).

§ **12.** Now let the incident set $\boldsymbol{s}$ be normal; (9-21) will hold. To find the refracted set $\boldsymbol{s}'$ we apply the second equation (9-2) (reflection is only a particular case):

$$(n'\boldsymbol{s}' - n\boldsymbol{s}) \wedge \boldsymbol{N} = 0, \tag{9-22}$$

where $\boldsymbol{N}$ represents the unit normal to Σ at Q. By differentiation we get

$$(n'\mathrm{d}\boldsymbol{s}' - n\mathrm{d}\boldsymbol{s}) \wedge \boldsymbol{N} + (n'\boldsymbol{s}' - n\boldsymbol{s}) \wedge \mathrm{d}\boldsymbol{N} = 0,$$

and making the vector product with δQ (which is normal to $\boldsymbol{N}$) we find

$$(9\text{-}23)\quad [(n'\mathrm{d}\boldsymbol{s}' - n\mathrm{d}\boldsymbol{s})\cdot\delta Q]\boldsymbol{N} - (n'\boldsymbol{s}' - n\boldsymbol{s})(\mathrm{d}\boldsymbol{N}\cdot\delta Q) + \\ + [(n'\boldsymbol{s}' - n\boldsymbol{s})\cdot\delta Q]\mathrm{d}\boldsymbol{N} = 0.$$

The last term in square brackets vanishes by virtue of (9-22) because $n'\boldsymbol{s}' - n\boldsymbol{s}$ is normal to Σ. Interchanging d with δ in (9-23) and subtracting the first equation from the second, there results

$$[(n'\delta\boldsymbol{s}' - n\delta\boldsymbol{s})\cdot\mathrm{d}Q - (n'\mathrm{d}\boldsymbol{s}' - n\mathrm{d}\boldsymbol{s})\cdot\delta Q]\boldsymbol{N} - \\ - (n'\boldsymbol{s}' - n\boldsymbol{s})(\delta\boldsymbol{N}\cdot\mathrm{d}Q - \mathrm{d}\boldsymbol{N}\cdot\delta Q) = 0.$$

The last term vanishes because $\boldsymbol{N}$ belongs to a normal set, as is obvious. Hence taking into account (9-21) we are simply left with

$$\mathrm{d}Q\cdot\delta\boldsymbol{s}' = \delta Q\cdot\mathrm{d}\boldsymbol{s}',$$

which proves that the refracted set is normal.

This is the so-called *Malus-Dupin theorem* which justifies the procedure of geometrical optics.

Fermat's Principle

§ 13. Consider a ray from point P of medium n (Fig. 35) which is incident on Σ at Q and after refraction goes to point P' of me-

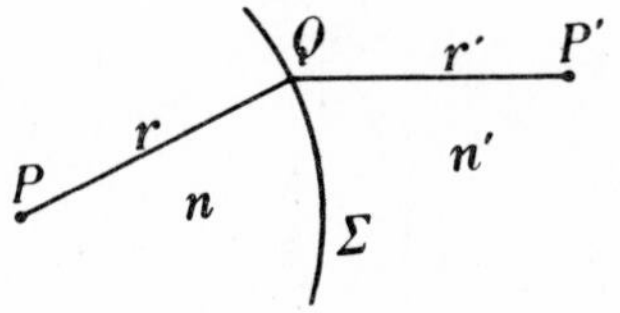

Fig. 35

dium n'. If r represents the distance from Q to P and r' the distance from P' to Q the sum

$$(9\text{-}24)\qquad l = nr + n'r'.$$

is termed the *optical path* from P to P'.

Let us give a small displacement $\mathrm{d}Q$ to the point of incidence with the assumption that the incident and refracted rays still pass through P and P' respectively. The increment dl of the optical path will be found in the following way

$$dl = \text{grad}_Q\, l \cdot dQ = (n\, \text{grad}_Q\, r + n'\, \text{grad}_Q\, r') \cdot dQ,$$

and by (M2-36)

$$dl = (n\mathbf{s} - n'\mathbf{s}') \cdot dQ.$$

The right side of this equation vanishes when $\mathbf{s}$ and $\mathbf{s}'$ are subject to the law of refraction. Hence we derive *Fermat's principle* according to which in going from one point to another, light follows a stationary path as compared with all possible paths in a small neighborhood. We have demonstrated this principle in the particular case of one refracting surface but it would be easy to generalize it to the case of several successive surfaces and then at the limit to the case of non-homogeneous media.

Images

§ 14. Let Σ represent a spherical surface of radius R separating two media of indices n and n' respectively. Let P, P' (Fig. 36) represent two points located in medium n and in medium n' respectively on the same diameter POP' of the sphere. The abscissas of

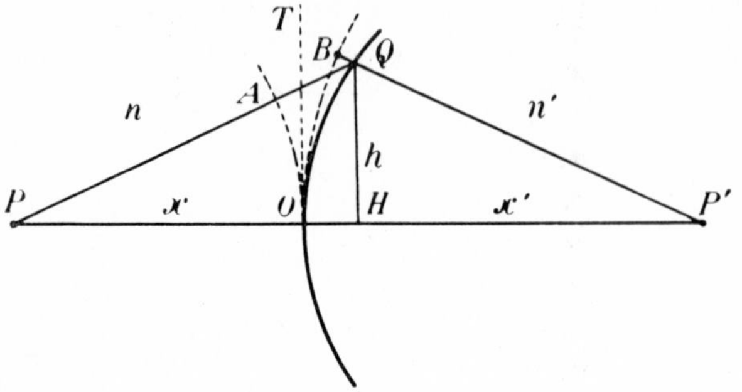

Fig. 36

P and P' with respect to O will be indicated by x and x' (in the figure x is negative). The optical path from P to P′ is obviously equal to $-nx + n'x'$. We want to evaluate the increment of this optical path for a ray PQP'. We have only to consider the two spheres through O having their centers at P and P' respectively. The increment dl of the optical path will be $n\overline{AQ} - n'\overline{BQ}$.

Let us now assume that the height h of Q on H is very small. In a first approximation we may consider AQ and PQ as horizontal utilizing the well-known expression of the distance of a circle from the tangent OT at height h. Such distance is given approximately by h^2 divided by twice the radius (as is readily derived substituting for the circle its osculating parabola at O). By this way it is found

$$dl = n\left(-\frac{h^2}{2x} + \frac{h^2}{2R}\right) - n'\left(\frac{h^2}{2R} - \frac{h^2}{2x'}\right). \tag{9-25}$$

The proportionality of the increment to the square of h shows that the optical path along POP' is stationary as we already knew. But from (9-25) we derive also another interesting consequence. If x and x' satisfy the relation

$$\frac{n'}{x'} - \frac{n}{x} = \frac{n' - n}{R}, \tag{9-26}$$

the optical path does not depend on h. This means that every path PQP' passing in the vicinity of O is stationary and consequently represents an actual ray. All these rays start from P and go to P'. It is customary to say that P' is the image of P. The formula of the spherical surface (9-26) relates the distance of the image with the distance of the object.

By properly combining two spherical surfaces one obtains a *lens* as is known from elementary physics. The image formed by the first surface represents the object for the second. The second surface forms the final image. Hence a lens is a device capable of forming images.

A spherical mirror may be obtained as a particular case of spherical refracting surface putting $n/n' = -1$.

Finally by combining several lenses and mirrors an extensive class of optical instruments is obtained which is illustrated in textbooks on optics.

CHAPTER 10

Diffraction

Typical Problems of Diffraction

§ 1. It has already been mentioned in the preceding chapter that, when the radii of curvature of the surface Σ separating different media are comparable with the wavelength, one can no longer speak of a single reflected or refracted wave, not even as a first approximation. There takes place instead a rather involved process known as the *diffraction.*

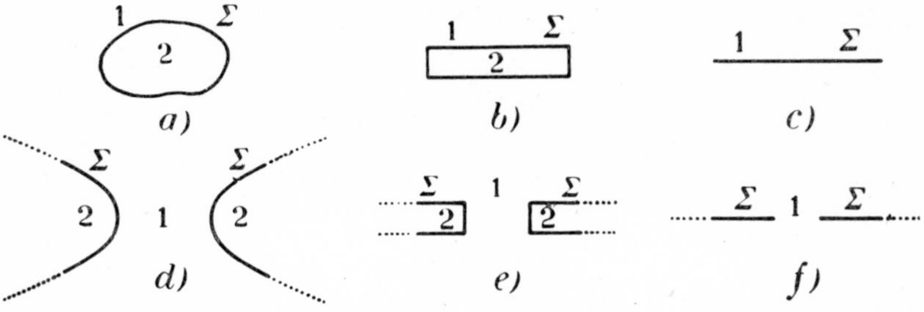

Fig. 37

Some typical cases which are dealt with in the theory of diffraction are represented in Fig. 37. In (*a*) medium 2 fills a bounded region and the radii of curvature of Σ are everywhere comparable with the wavelength. In (*b*) Σ results from a number of plane or cylindrical portions with possibly small curvatures but presents some lines along which a radius of curvature vanishes (corners). In (*c*) medium 2 degenerates into a infinitely thin layer. In (*d*), (*e*), (*f*) the so-called *complementary* cases of the first ones are presented.

Ordinarily the elementary theory of diffraction deals with the ideal cases (*c*) and (*f*) where medium 2 is a good conductor (metallic screens, diaphragms with apertures). Even so, the mathematical problem is considerably complicated and still more complicated is the general case.

Due to these difficulties the exact treatment is often given up in favor of an approximate procedure. The approximation is based on some *principle,* namely on some rule of a half-empirical and half-mathematical character which in a number of cases may lead to a result perfectly in agreement with experience.

Huygens' Principle in the Form of the Helmholtz-Kirchhoff Formulas

§ 2. Consider now a closed surface Σ (Fig. 38) embedded in a homogeneous and lossless medium and a distribution of sources located outside the surface. We want to evaluate the electromagnetic field at an internal point Q. This problem may be solved

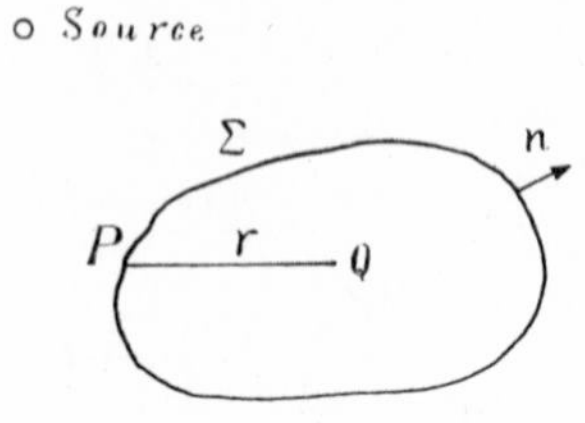

Fig. 38

either directly or by first evaluating the field existing on Σ and then deriving from it the field at Q. We shall follow the latter method which is of great historical significance.

We may apply Kirchhoff's formula (4-25). To show this we note that within Σ both the electromagnetic potentials and the Hertz or Fitzgerald vectors obey the homogeneous d'Alembert equation. Since the medium is homogeneous, this same equation will be satisfied also by $\boldsymbol{E}$ and $\boldsymbol{H}$ which are derived from the above-mentioned quantities by means of differentiation. Therefore, representing by f any rectangular component of $\boldsymbol{E}$ or $\boldsymbol{H}$, we may derive from (4-25)

$$(10\text{-}1)\quad f(Q,t)=\frac{1}{4\pi}\iint_{\Sigma}\left\{\frac{1}{r}\frac{\partial f(P,t)}{\partial n}+\left[\frac{1}{r^2}f(P,t)+\frac{1}{vr}\frac{\partial f(P,t)}{\partial t}\right]\frac{\partial r}{\partial n}\right\}_{t=t_r}\mathrm{d}\Sigma_P,$$

where P is a variable point on Σ, n the outward normal of Σ, $t_r = t - v/r$ the retarded time and $r = |Q - P|$. In order to make use of the complex notation one has to replace $f(P, t)$ by $f(P) \exp(i\omega t)$ and $\partial f/\partial t$ by $i\omega f(P) \exp(i\omega t)$. Carrying out these substitutions in (9-1) and introducing the retarded time into the exponentials, one obtains upon division by $\exp(i\omega t)$

$$f(Q)=\frac{1}{4\pi}\iint_\Sigma\left\{\frac{1}{r}\frac{\partial f(P)}{\partial n}\exp(-ikr)+\left[\frac{1}{r^2}f(P)+\frac{ik}{r}f(P)\right]\exp(-ikr)\frac{\partial r}{\partial n}\right\}d\Sigma_P.$$

Making use of the Green function introduced with (8-2), one may also write

$$(10\text{-}2)\qquad f(Q) = \iint_\Sigma\left[G(P, Q)\frac{\partial f(P)}{\partial n} - f(P)\frac{\partial}{\partial n}G(P, Q)\right]d\Sigma_P\,.$$

This represents the *Helmholtz formula,* which is a particular case of Kirchhoff's formula. We have a mathematical expression of *Huygens' principle* stating that each point which is reached by a light wave becomes in turn an *elementary source* and sends out a spherical wave. Equation (10-2) shows that the value of f at Q

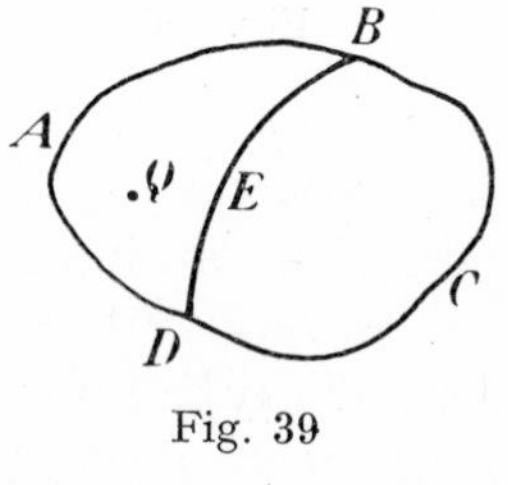

Fig. 39

may be calculated by adding (or bringing to interference, as was made clear by Fresnel) all the contributions sent out by the elementary sources P of Σ; besides, (10-2) states in what way an elementary source sends out radiation.

We may remark that (10-2) applies only if Q is inside Σ. If Q is outside we would obtain a vanishing result. To show this let us refer to Fig. 39. If we take $ABCD$ to represent the surface Σ, point Q is inside, and from (10-2) we get $f(Q)$. The same result would obviously be obtained if the surface had been taken to be $ABED$. Hence BED and BCD yield two identical contributions. If now the surface Σ is taken to be $BCDE$ the portion BED will have a normal opposite to that of the preceding cases; the corresponding contribution will have the sign reversed and will exactly cancel with the contribution of BCD. As a consequence (10-2) gives for f at point Q (which is now external) a vanishing value.

Kirchhoff's Method in Diffraction

§ 3. Formula (10-2) has been often applied to solve diffraction problems. We shall confine ourselves to the classical problems which are represented by Fig. 37(c) and (f).

Let S (Fig. 40) represent a light source and Σ an opaque un-

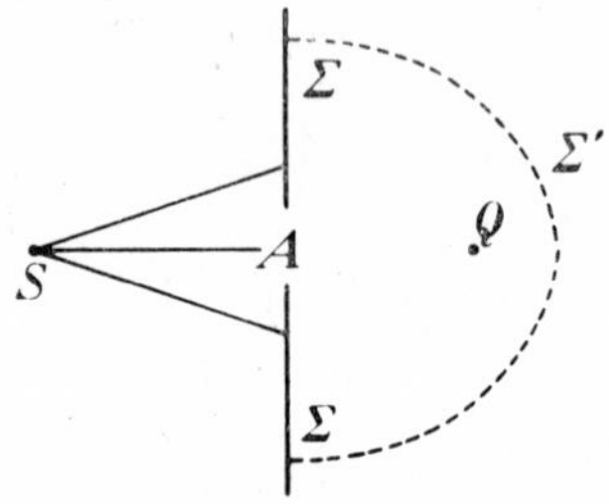

Fig. 40

bounded screen with an aperture A. We want to evaluate the illumination at a point Q beyond the screen. To this end it is customary to supplement Σ by an ideal surface Σ' to obtain a closed surface. The ideal surface is then removed to infinity. It seems natural to assume, and may be demonstrated with rigor under very general conditions which are always realized in practice, that the contributions of all elementary surfaces distributed over Σ' tend to vanish. We are left then with the contributions of elementary sources distributed over Σ and A.

To apply (10-2) one should know beforehand the value of f as well as of its normal derivative over Σ and A. This would amount to the same as having already solved the problem or at least the most difficult part of it. However one may apply an approximate procedure which is known as the *Kirchhoff method*. This consists of the assumption that both f and its normal derivative vanish over the entire opaque part of Σ and have over A the same values as in free propagation or as in the absence of the screen.

The above assumption is by no means rigorous. First of all both f and its normal derivative have over Σ and A different values from those fixed arbitrarily. In the second place these arbitrary values are generally incosistent with one another since f must obey the wave equation. Finally, if (10-2) is applied to each component of the electromagnetic field, the resultant field does not generally speaking satisfy Maxwell's equations.

Notwithstanding these drawbacks, the Kirchhoff method has been generally applied in optics with results which are often in excellent agreement with experience. This is due to the fact that in optics the wavelength is very small, nearly always of a much smaller order of magnitude than the size of the aperture. In this case most of the aperture is at a distance from its boundary which is very large when measured in wavelengths. It is natural to expect then that the boundary will affect the field inside the aperture very little.

Furthermore the apertures which are dealt with in optics are as a rule very far from the sources, so the incident waves are plane or nearly plane at the aperture. As a consequence one makes only a negligible error in assuming that $\boldsymbol{E}$ (or $\boldsymbol{H}$) has the same (possibly complex) direction everywhere on the aperture. The field can then be specified by giving only the component of $\boldsymbol{E}$ in this direction, that is a scalar quantity f to which (10-2) can be applied. As to the other components and their derivatives they will vanish both over Σ and over A and consequently will also vanish beyond Σ, still by virtue of (10-2). Diffraction is thus reduced to a scalar problem.

This explains why in elementary wave optics the field is ordinarily specified by means of a single scalar quantity f. The preceding discussion justifies this procedure but at the same time sets the limits of its validity.

We have presented first the Helmholtz formula because of its historical importance. However today, even when Kirchhoff's method is applied, there is a tendency to utilize more complete expressions for the elementary waves, satisfying at least Maxwell's equations.

Electromagnetic Diffraction at a Plane Screen

§ 4. It was shown at 4-§9 that the function

$$f(Q,t) = -\frac{1}{4\pi}\iiint_V \frac{h(P',t_r)}{r}\,\mathrm{d}V_{P'} \tag{10-3}$$

represents a solution of the inhomogeneous d'Alembert equation

$$\nabla_Q^2 f - \frac{1}{v^2}\frac{\partial^2 f}{\partial t^2} = h(Q,t), \tag{10-4}$$

provided that t_r indicates the retarded time $t - r/v$ $(r = |Q - P'|)$. Now that we are concerned with complex amplitudes we must replace $f(Q,t)$ and $h(Q,t)$ by $f(Q)\exp(i\omega t)$ and $h(Q)\exp(i\omega t)$ respectively. With this (10-4) becomes the *wave equation*

$$\nabla_Q^2 f + k^2 f = h(Q), \tag{10-5}$$

and the solution (10-3) transforms into

$$f(Q) = -\iiint_V \frac{\exp(-ikr)}{4\pi r} h(P')\,\mathrm{d}V_{P'} = -\iiint_V G(P',Q)h(P')\,\mathrm{d}V_{P'},$$

where $G(P',Q)$ represents the Green function. If we put $h(Q) = \delta(Q-P)$ and represent by P a fixed point, we obviously get $f(Q) = -G(P,Q)$. Upon substitution of this expression of f and h into (10-5) we obtain

$$\nabla_Q^2 G(P,Q) + k^2 G(P,Q) = -\delta(Q-P). \tag{10-6}$$

This is the characteristic differential equation satisfied by the function G. It is clear that P and Q may be interchanged.

§ 5. We shall give for diffraction a discussion analogous to that made in the case of reflection and refraction. To begin with, the diffracting screen will be assumed to be plane, as it really is in a number of important cases. The surface Σ will be considered closed by means of an auxiliary ideal surface Σ' which will later be removed to infinity (Fig. 41). Let the sources be located in the left half-space and the screen Σ be opaque everywhere apart from one or more finite regions. We want to evaluate the field at a point Q in the right half-space.

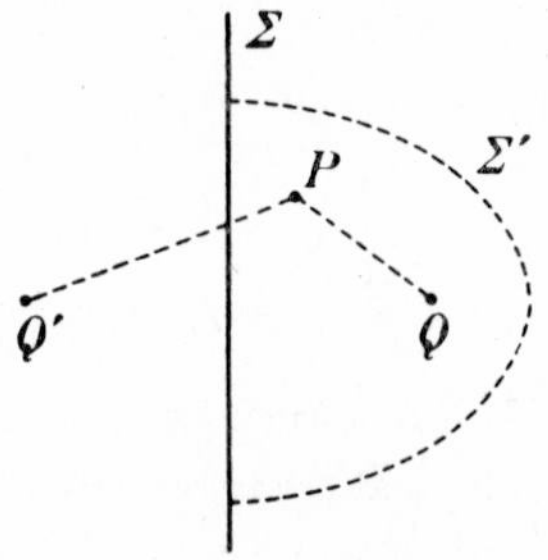

Fig. 41

Let us consider point Q' which is the mirror image of Q relative to Σ and construct the two functions

$$(10\text{-}7)\qquad \begin{cases} G_1(P, Q) = G(P, Q) - G(P, Q'), \\ G_2(P, Q) = G(P, Q) + G(P, Q'), \end{cases}$$

It will be readily noted that, when P is on Σ, G_1 vanishes and $G_2 = 2G$ while $\text{grad}_P\, G_1$ is normal and $\text{grad}_P\, G_2$ is parallel to Σ.

By (10-6) the characteristic differential equations of G_1 and G_2 will be

$$(10\text{-}8)\qquad \begin{cases} \nabla_P^2 G_1(P, Q) + k^2 G_1(P, Q) = -\,\delta(P - Q) + \delta(P - Q'), \\ \nabla_P^2 G_2(P, Q) + k^2 G_2(P, Q) = -\,\delta(P - Q) - \delta(P - Q'). \end{cases}$$

Consider now an arbitrary constant vector $\boldsymbol{c}$ and indicate by $\boldsymbol{c}_1$ and $\boldsymbol{c}_2$ respectively its components parallel and perpendicular to Σ. Next construct the vector function

$$\boldsymbol{\Gamma}(P, Q) = \boldsymbol{c}_1 G_1(P, Q) + \boldsymbol{c}_2 G_2(P, Q),$$

having by virtue of (10-8) the characteristic equation

$$(10\text{-}9)\qquad \nabla_P^2 \boldsymbol{\Gamma}(P, Q) + k^2 \boldsymbol{\Gamma}(P, Q) = \\ = -\,(\boldsymbol{c}_1 + \boldsymbol{c}_2)\delta(P - Q) + (\boldsymbol{c}_1 - \boldsymbol{c}_2)\delta(P - Q').$$

From (M1-27) we have

$$\text{(10-10)} \qquad \operatorname{div}_P \mathbf{\Gamma} = \boldsymbol{c}_1 \cdot \operatorname{grad}_P G_1 + \boldsymbol{c}_2 \cdot \operatorname{grad}_P G_2,$$

from (M1-29)

$$\text{(10-11)} \qquad \operatorname{curl}_P \mathbf{\Gamma} = \operatorname{grad}_P G_1 \wedge \boldsymbol{c}_1 + \operatorname{grad}_P G_2 \wedge \boldsymbol{c}_2,$$

and from (M1-30) and (10-9)

$$\text{(10-12)} \quad \operatorname{curl}_P \operatorname{curl}_P \mathbf{\Gamma} = \operatorname{grad}_P \operatorname{div}_P \mathbf{\Gamma} - \nabla_P^2 \mathbf{\Gamma} = \\ = \operatorname{grad}_P \operatorname{div}_P \mathbf{\Gamma} + k^2 \mathbf{\Gamma} + \boldsymbol{c}\delta(P-Q) - (\boldsymbol{c}_1 - \boldsymbol{c}_2)\delta(P-Q').$$

If P is on Σ, it is readily seen from the preceding equations that $\mathbf{\Gamma}$ is perpendicular to Σ, $\operatorname{div}_P \mathbf{\Gamma}$ vanishes and $\operatorname{curl}_P \mathbf{\Gamma}$ coincides with the component of $\operatorname{grad}_P(G_1 + G_2) \wedge (\boldsymbol{c}_1 + \boldsymbol{c}_2) = 2\operatorname{grad}_P G \wedge \boldsymbol{c}$ which is parallel to Σ.

Finally we note that in a homogeneous and non-absorbing medium it follows from the Maxwell equations (7-18, 19) that

$$\text{(10-13)} \qquad \operatorname{curl} \operatorname{curl} \boldsymbol{E} = -\eta_m \operatorname{curl} \boldsymbol{H} = -\eta_m \eta_e \boldsymbol{E} = k^2 \boldsymbol{E},$$

as well as $\operatorname{div} \boldsymbol{E} = 0$.

§ 6. The reader shall bear in mind all the results of the preceding section. Representing by V the volume bounded by Σ and Σ' (the last surface will be removed to infinity and will give a vanishing contribution) one readily gets (We shall simply write $\boldsymbol{E}$ in place of $\boldsymbol{E}(P)$)

$$\text{(10-14)} \quad \begin{aligned} &\iiint_V (\mathbf{\Gamma} \cdot \operatorname{curl}_P \operatorname{curl}_P \boldsymbol{E} - \boldsymbol{E} \cdot \operatorname{curl}_P \operatorname{curl}_P \mathbf{\Gamma}) dV_P = \\ &= \iiint_V [-\boldsymbol{E} \cdot \operatorname{grad}_P \operatorname{div}_P \mathbf{\Gamma} - \boldsymbol{E} \cdot \boldsymbol{c}\delta(P-Q) + \\ &\qquad + \boldsymbol{E} \cdot (\boldsymbol{c}_1 - \boldsymbol{c}_2)\delta(P-Q')] dV_P = \\ &= -\iiint_V \operatorname{div}_P (\boldsymbol{E} \operatorname{div}_P \mathbf{\Gamma}) dV_P - \boldsymbol{c} \cdot \boldsymbol{E}(Q) = \\ &= \iint_\Sigma (\operatorname{div}_P \mathbf{\Gamma})(\boldsymbol{E} \cdot \boldsymbol{k}) d\Sigma_P - \boldsymbol{c} \cdot \boldsymbol{E}(Q) = -\boldsymbol{c} \cdot \boldsymbol{E}(Q), \end{aligned}$$

where $\boldsymbol{k}$ represents the normal to Σ directed to the right. Next we apply the successive transformations

$$\begin{aligned}
&\iint_\Sigma (\boldsymbol{E}\wedge \operatorname{curl}_P \boldsymbol{\Gamma} - \boldsymbol{\Gamma}\wedge \operatorname{curl}_P \boldsymbol{E})\cdot \boldsymbol{k}\mathrm{d}\Sigma_P = \iint_\Sigma \boldsymbol{E}\cdot \operatorname{curl}_P \boldsymbol{\Gamma}\wedge \boldsymbol{k}\mathrm{d}\Sigma_P = \\
&\quad = 2\iint_\Sigma \boldsymbol{E}\cdot(\operatorname{grad}_P G \wedge \boldsymbol{c}) \wedge \boldsymbol{k}\mathrm{d}\Sigma_P = \\
(10\text{-}15)\quad &\quad = 2\iint_\Sigma [-(\boldsymbol{E}\cdot \operatorname{grad}_P G)(\boldsymbol{c}\cdot\boldsymbol{k}) + (\boldsymbol{E}\cdot\boldsymbol{c})(\operatorname{grad}_P G\cdot\boldsymbol{k})]\mathrm{d}\Sigma_P = \\
&\quad = 2\iint_\Sigma \boldsymbol{c}\cdot(\boldsymbol{k}\wedge\boldsymbol{E})\wedge \operatorname{grad}_P G\,\mathrm{d}\Sigma_P.
\end{aligned}$$

On the other hand, the left sides of (10-14, 15) on account of (M1-37) are equal with opposite signs (because $\boldsymbol{k}$ represents now the inside normal). Hence taking into account that $\boldsymbol{c}$ is an arbitrary vector we have

$$(10\text{-}16)\qquad \boldsymbol{E}(Q) = 2\iint_\Sigma [\boldsymbol{k}\wedge \boldsymbol{E}(P)] \wedge \operatorname{grad}_P G(P, Q)\mathrm{d}\Sigma_P.$$

This interesting formula allows the electric field to be evaluated in the right-hand half-space when its tangential component is known over Σ.

§ 7. Replacing grad_P with $-\operatorname{grad}_Q$ in (10-16) and recalling (M1-29), one may write

$$(10\text{-}17)\qquad \boldsymbol{E}(Q) = 2\iint_\Sigma \operatorname{curl}_Q [G\boldsymbol{k}\wedge \boldsymbol{E}(P)]\mathrm{d}\Sigma_P.$$

A comparison with the second equation (8-12) shows that each element of Σ behaves like a magnetic dipole having the moment

$$(10\text{-}18)\qquad \mathrm{d}\boldsymbol{N} = \frac{2}{i\omega}\boldsymbol{E}\wedge\boldsymbol{k}\mathrm{d}\Sigma.$$

The magnetic field strength $\boldsymbol{H}$ may be then evaluated by means of the first equation (8-12) or by applying the operator curl_Q to both sides of (10-17) and having recourse to the second Maxwell equation. In this way it is obtained

$$H(Q) = \frac{2}{i\omega\mu} \iint_{\Sigma} \operatorname{curl}_Q \operatorname{curl}_Q [G\boldsymbol{E}(P) \wedge \boldsymbol{k}] \, \mathrm{d}\Sigma_P . \tag{10-19}$$

Thus we have found a form which may be assumed by Huygens' principle for the electromagnetic field. However this form is not the only one possible. To see this one has only to note that if we had utulized the magnetic instead of the electric field strength we would have found instead of (10-17)

$$\boldsymbol{H}(Q) = 2 \iint_{\Sigma} \operatorname{curl}_Q [G\boldsymbol{k} \wedge \boldsymbol{H}(P)] \, \mathrm{d}\Sigma_P . \tag{10-20}$$

By compaiing with the first equation (8-3) one may conclude that each element of Σ is equivalent to an electric dipole having the moment

$$\mathrm{d}\boldsymbol{L} = \frac{2}{i\omega} \boldsymbol{k} \wedge \boldsymbol{H} \, \mathrm{d}\Sigma. \tag{10-21}$$

The electric field strength would then be represented by

$$\boldsymbol{E}(Q) = \frac{2}{i\omega\varepsilon} \iint_{\Sigma} \operatorname{curl}_Q \operatorname{curl}_Q [G\boldsymbol{k} \wedge \boldsymbol{H}(P)] \, \mathrm{d}\Sigma_P . \tag{10-22}$$

It is clear that one could also utilize at the same time both a distribution of magnetic dipoles and a distribution of electric dipoles in an arbitrary ratio, obtaining in this way an entire series of admissible expressions for the Huygens principle. All these expressions are perfectly equivalent from a mathematical standpoint provided that $\boldsymbol{H}(P)$ and $\boldsymbol{E}(P)$ are given the values of the magnetic and electric fields really existing over Σ. When one applies instead the simplified Kirchhoff method, some differences arise. However, these differences are often very small; in optics they are nearly always negligible.

A more profound mathematical discussion would also show that the solutions found for the half-space on the right of Σ are unique provided that the radiation condition is assumed to be satisfied. This amounts to the same as requiring that the electromagnetic field is radiated from the apertures of Σ, as is physically necessary.

Inverse Interference Principle

§ **8.** The discussion of the foregoing sections shows that to evaluate the electromagnetic field in the half-space beyond Σ it is sufficient to know the tangential projection of the electric (or magnetic) force over Σ. Actually it was shown that it is sufficient to know $\boldsymbol{k} \wedge \boldsymbol{E}(P)$.

Let us assume that $\boldsymbol{k} \wedge \boldsymbol{E}(P)$ is known over the whole surface Σ and let us express it by a Fourier integral according to (M3-14, 15). We obtain

$$\text{(10-23)} \quad \boldsymbol{k} \wedge \boldsymbol{E}(P) = \int_{-\infty}^{+\infty} \int_{-\infty}^{+\infty} \boldsymbol{A}(\boldsymbol{v}) \exp\,(i\boldsymbol{v} \cdot (P - O)] \,\mathrm{d}v_x \mathrm{d}v_y\,,$$

with

$$\text{(10-24)} \quad \boldsymbol{A}(v) = \frac{1}{4\pi^2} \iint_{\Sigma} [\boldsymbol{k} \wedge \boldsymbol{E}(P')] \exp\,[-i\boldsymbol{v} \cdot (P' - O)]\,\mathrm{d}\Sigma_{P'}\,.$$

Forget for a moment the existence of the material screen Σ and consider a plane wave in the direction $\boldsymbol{s}$ from the left to the right half-spaces bounded by Σ (this requires $s_z > 0$). The electric field strength of the wave will have the expression $\boldsymbol{E} \exp\,[-ik\boldsymbol{s} \cdot (Q - O)]$ with $\boldsymbol{E}$ perpendicular to $\boldsymbol{s}$.

If instead of a single wave we consider a number of waves of the same type corresponding to different directions $\boldsymbol{s}$, theii fields will add. We shall introduce a continuous double infinity of such plane waves. The resultant electric field strength will have the expression

$$\text{(10-25)} \qquad \boldsymbol{E}(Q) = \iint \boldsymbol{E}(\boldsymbol{s}) \exp\,[-ik\boldsymbol{s} \cdot (Q - O)]\,\mathrm{d}\Omega,$$

where $\boldsymbol{E}(\boldsymbol{s})$ designates the complex amplitude per unit solid angle Ω for the wave traveling in the direction $\boldsymbol{s}$.

If P represents a point of Σ, we obtain

$$\boldsymbol{k} \wedge \boldsymbol{E}(P) = \iint [\boldsymbol{k} \wedge \boldsymbol{E}(\boldsymbol{s})] \exp [-ik\boldsymbol{s} \cdot (P - O)] \frac{\mathrm{d}s_x \mathrm{d}s_y}{s_z},$$

having replaced $\mathrm{d}\Omega$ by its value $\mathrm{d}s_x\mathrm{d}s_y/s_z$ in terms of the direction cosines of $\boldsymbol{s}$ (†).

By comparing this equation with (10-23) we see that the tangential projection of $\boldsymbol{E}(P)$ will equal that really existing over Σ provided that we put $-k\boldsymbol{s} = \boldsymbol{v}$ and $\boldsymbol{k} \wedge \boldsymbol{E}(\boldsymbol{s})\, \mathrm{d}s_x \mathrm{d}s_y/s_z = \boldsymbol{A}(\boldsymbol{v})\, \mathrm{d}v_x \mathrm{d}v_y$ (whence $\boldsymbol{k} \wedge \boldsymbol{E}(\boldsymbol{s}) = k^2 \boldsymbol{A}(\boldsymbol{v}) s_z$) and that both s_x and s_y are made to vary between $-\infty$ and $+\infty$ like v_x and v_y. By (10-24) we shall then put (with $k^2 = 4\pi^2/\lambda^2$)

$$\boldsymbol{k} \wedge \boldsymbol{E}(\boldsymbol{s}) = \frac{s_z}{\lambda^2} \iint_{\Sigma} [\boldsymbol{k} \wedge \boldsymbol{E}(P')] \exp [ik\boldsymbol{s} \cdot (P' - O)]\, \mathrm{d}\Sigma_{P'} .$$

Making the vector product on the right with $\boldsymbol{s}$ (which is perpendicular to $\boldsymbol{E}(\boldsymbol{s})$) we obtain

$$\text{(10-26)} \quad \boldsymbol{E}(\boldsymbol{s}) = \frac{1}{\lambda^2} \iint_{\Sigma} [\boldsymbol{k} \wedge \boldsymbol{E}(P')] \wedge \boldsymbol{s} \exp [ik\boldsymbol{s} \cdot (P' - O)]\, \mathrm{d}\Sigma_{P'} .$$

We can conclude that a set of plane waves with the amplitudes given in terms of $\boldsymbol{s}$ by (10-26) when superimposed (or when interfering) give rise over Σ to the actual physical distribution of the tangential electric field. And, since the tangential electric field over Σ is sufficient to determine the field on the right of Σ, we conclude that the field is constituted by that set of plane waves.

Thus we have found for the case of a plane screen a mathematical formulation of the *principle of inverse interference*. This principle in its most general form states that, if a given set of waves when interfering over a surface Σ gives rise to a certain distribution of the electromagnetic field, conversely by artificially

(†) Consider a sphere of unit radius having its center on Σ. Its surface will be the locus of the end points of $\boldsymbol{s}$ when the starting point is assumed fixed at the center of the sphere. A surface element of the sphere corresponding to the direction $\boldsymbol{s}$ when projected on Σ has the area $\mathrm{d}\Omega s_z$. On the other hand a surface element of Σ is represented by $\mathrm{d}s_x\mathrm{d}s_y$, whence the required relation.

producing the same distribution over Σ one will obtain the same set of waves (*diffracted waves*). This principle like Huygens' principle is capable of being formulated in many different mathematical ways and lends itself in a simple manner to an approximate treatment of diffraction problems.

Going back to the particular case of a plane screen Σ we note that the radiation condition which guarantees the uniqueness of the solution is represented by $s_z > 0$.

Finally we call attention to the fact that s_x and s_y represent direction cosines so that it might appear absurd to allow them to vary between $-\infty$ and $+\infty$ as was demonstrated to be necessary. However one has only to recall what was said in 7-§19 to see that the waves corresponding to s_x, $s_y > 1$ are nothing but evanescent waves. In conclusion we may say that generally speaking the diffracted waves are represented by a set of plane waves in conjunction with a set of evanescent waves.

The Fresnel and Fraunhofer Phenomena

§ 9. The diffraction phenomena which are observed at an infinite distance from the diffracting surface Σ are called the *Fraunhofer phenomena*. They may be easily observed by placing behind Σ an optical system of sufficiently wide aperture (Fig. 42).

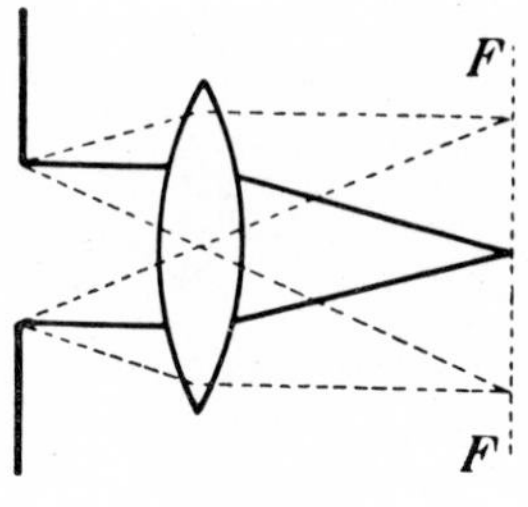

Fig. 42

The plane at infinity is then imaged onto the focal plane FF so that on this plane there will be projected the Fraunhofer diffraction pattern.

Each beam of parallel rays emanating from Σ will be concentrated into a point of the focal plane. To predict the aspect of the Fraunhofer pattern one needs only to divide the diffracted radiation into many parallel beams or what amounts to the same into many plane waves. It is evident that (10-26) solves this problem. One may derive from it the amplitude of the plane wave diffracted in the direction $\mathbf{s}$.

The diffraction phenomena which are observed at a finite distance from the Σ screen are known as *Fresnel phenomena*. They result from the interference of all the plane waves diffracted. After evaluating the complex amplitudes of these waves at the origin by means of (10-26) one can evaluate their interference by adding all their complex amplitudes at the considered point Q by means of (10-25). Alternatively one may utilize (10-16). In both cases one arrives as a rule at some very difficult integrations which can be carried out only by approximation. We will not enter here into the details of these calculations which may be seen in wave optics text-books.

We shall show instead how the finite distance pattern evolves into the infinite distance pattern making use of (10-16). Let Q be a point at a great distance from the apertures of Σ or more precisely at a distance which is great in comparison with the size of the apertures. Let O represent a point of reference on Σ and put $Q = O + R\mathbf{s}$. We shall then have

$$r = |Q-P| = |R\mathbf{s}-(P-O)| = \sqrt{R^2-2R\mathbf{s}\cdot(P-O)+(P-O)^2} =$$

$$= R\sqrt{1-2\mathbf{s}\cdot(P-O)/R+(P-O)^2/R^2}.$$

Since R is very great in comparison with $|P-O|$, the square root may be expanded in series. We shall neglect all terms of higher order than the first in $(P-O)/R$ writing

$$r = R - \mathbf{s}\cdot(P-O),$$

whence with a good approximation

$$G(P, Q) = \frac{\exp(-ikr)}{4\pi r} = \frac{\exp(-ikR)}{4\pi R}\exp[ik\mathbf{s}\cdot(P-O)].$$

By recalling (M1-26) and (M2-28, 38) which give grad $[\boldsymbol{s}\cdot(P-O)] = \boldsymbol{s}\cdot\text{grad}\,(P-O) = \boldsymbol{s}\cdot\boldsymbol{U} = \boldsymbol{s}$, there follows

$$\text{grad}_P\, G(P, Q) = \frac{\exp\,(-\,ikR)}{4\pi R}\, ik\boldsymbol{s}\exp\,[ik\boldsymbol{s}\cdot(P-O)].$$

Substituting into (6-16) we finally get

$$\boldsymbol{E}(Q) = \frac{\exp\,(-\,ikR)}{R}\,\frac{i}{\lambda}\iint_{\Sigma}[\boldsymbol{k}\wedge\boldsymbol{E}(P)]\wedge\boldsymbol{s}\exp\,[ik\boldsymbol{s}\cdot(P-O)]\,\mathrm{d}\Sigma_P,$$

and upon comparison with (10-26)

$$\text{(10-27)}\qquad \boldsymbol{E}(Q) = i\lambda\boldsymbol{E}(\boldsymbol{s})\,\frac{\exp\,(-\,ikR)}{R}.$$

The last factor shows that at a great distance from Σ the diffracted radiation appears like a spherical wave emanating from O. The amplitude is not constant throughout the wave surface, being instead proportional (with the coefficient of proportionality $i\lambda$) to the amplitude $\boldsymbol{E}(\boldsymbol{s})$ of the plane wave diffracted in the direction considered. For a spherical wave of large radius we have $Z\boldsymbol{H} = \boldsymbol{s}\wedge\boldsymbol{E}$ so that the density of the energy flow will be

$$\text{(10-28)}\qquad \overline{\boldsymbol{S}} = \frac{1}{2}\mathscr{Re}\,\boldsymbol{E}(Q)\wedge\boldsymbol{H}^*(Q) =$$

$$= \frac{1}{2Z}\boldsymbol{E}(Q)\cdot\boldsymbol{E}^*(Q)\boldsymbol{s} = \frac{1}{2Z}\left(\frac{\lambda}{R}\right)^2\boldsymbol{E}(\boldsymbol{s})\cdot\boldsymbol{E}^*(\boldsymbol{s})\boldsymbol{s},$$

having assumed Z to be real. Equation (10-28) shows how a Fresnel pattern evolves into a Fraunhofer pattern when observed at an ever growing distance from Σ: at a great distance the diffraction pattern is specified by the distribution $\boldsymbol{E}(\boldsymbol{s})$ of the complex amplitudes of the diffracted waves.

Images Formed by Coherent Light

§ 10. In 9-§14 we briefly outlined how an optical instrument may form the image of a light point. It is not difficult to understand the formation of the image of an extended object when all its points may be considered as separate and independent sources of electromagnetic waves.

However, sometimes one has to deal with objects illuminated with coherent light; all the different points of the object show then a fixed phase relation with respect to one another. As an example we may mention the case of a microscope when the condenser is stopped down to a very small aperture. In this case one is confronted with a diffraction problem. To understand how the image is formed it is expedient to utilize the inverse interference principle. Let the partially transparent object Σ (Fig. 43) be illuminated by

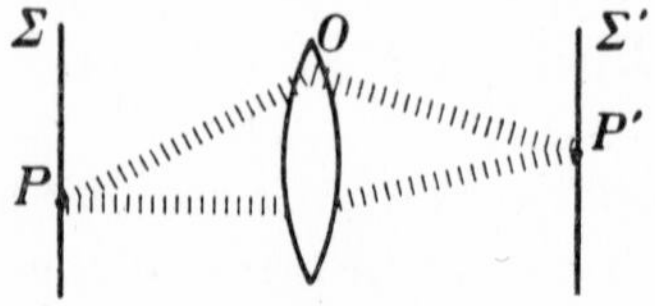

Fig. 43

coherent light (for instance, by a plane wave). The object will, by inverse interference give rise, to a set of both plane and evanescent waves. Consider a point P of Σ and on each diffracted wave a small surface element about P. This element will travel in the direction of its normal and then will be deflected by the lens O toward point P' of the image plane Σ'. Hence P' will receive all the diffracted waves coming from P and, since all optical paths from P to P' are equal, the phase differences between different waves will be the same as in P. It is then readily seen why the image of Σ is formed on Σ'; the image is generated by direct interference on Σ' of the waves diffracted at Σ by inverse interference.

For the image to be an exact reproduction of the object it would be necessary that all the waves produced by inverse interference could arrive at Σ' and interfere on it. However it is clear that neither the evenescent waves nor the waves which are diffracted at an angle exceeding the lens aperture on the object side will arrive at the image plane. For this reason the image will never reproduce the object with all its details; the finest details will be absent since they are responsible for the production of evanescent waves.

Babinet's Principle

§ 11. Let us now apply the Kirchhoff approximation to the diffraction at two complementary screens placed at different times in the path of the same incident wave.

Both cases are illustrated in Fig. 44. The incident wave is re-

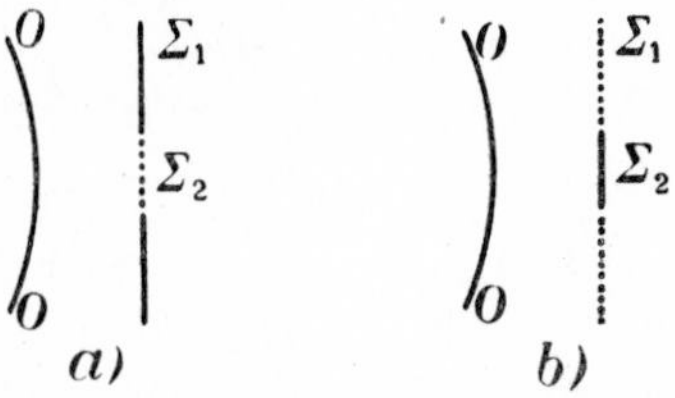

Fig. 44

presented by OO. In case (a) the surface Σ consists of an opaque screen Σ_1 and an aperture Σ_2; in case (b) Σ_2 is opaque while Σ_1 is free.

In Kirchhoff's approximation the diffracted field for case (a) will be evaluated by assuming that the electromagnetic field vanishes over Σ_1 and equals the field of a free wave over Σ_2. We may apply (10-16).

In case (b) we shall have recourse to an artifice. We shall consider the field over Σ as consisting of two parts: the first part equals the field of the free wave over the whole of Σ, while the second part vanishes everywhere except over Σ_2 where it is equal to the field of the free wave with reversed sign or opposite phase. It is clear that the resultant field over Σ_2 will vanish as is required by Kirchhoff's approximation.

As a consequence in case (b) we shall get on the right of Σ the free wave OO plus the field diffracted by the aperture of case (a) but with the sign reversed. Hence at all points which are not illuminated by the direct wave OO the field in the two complementary cases is equal but with opposite phase. The illumination (namely, the density of energy flow) is equal.

This is the *Babinet principle* which is often utilized in the problems of wave optics.

Diffraction Gratings

§ 12. Let us now consider a plane screen Σ having a transparency which is a periodic function of a single Cartesian coordinate, say x. In particular the screen might consist of many equal and opaque strips all parallel to the y axis and equispaced. This is the most simple example of a *diffraction grating*, a device which is extensively dealt with in wave optics.

If a represents the spacing of the grating and the incident wave is plane and parallel to Σ, on the other side of the grating the distribution of the quantity $\boldsymbol{k} \wedge \boldsymbol{E}(P)$ will be a periodic function of x with period a and will be independent of y.

With a natural generalization we shall consider a *cross-grating* where the transparency is a periodic function both with respect to x (period a) and with respect to y (period b). Some examples are represented by a net, a sieve or a tissue. The ordinary grating is obtained as a particular case ($b = \infty$). If a plane wave parallel to Σ is incident on a cross-grating the function $\boldsymbol{k} \wedge \boldsymbol{E}(P)$ on the other side will be a periodic function having the same periods a and b. If instead the direction of incidence $\boldsymbol{s}^i$ is different from $\boldsymbol{k}$, the complex amplitude on Σ will contain the factor $\exp[-ik\boldsymbol{s}^i \cdot (P-O)]$ and, since in Kirchhoff's approximation the complex amplitude on the output side of Σ is proportional to the incident complex amplitude, the quantity $\boldsymbol{k} \wedge \boldsymbol{E}(P)$ on the output side will be a cross periodical function multiplied by $\exp[-ik\boldsymbol{s}^i \cdot (P-O)]$ (†). Hence $\boldsymbol{k} \wedge \boldsymbol{E}(P) \exp[ik\boldsymbol{s}^i \cdot (P-O)]$ is again a cross periodical function and may be expanded in a Fourier series. Setting

$$(10\text{-}29) \qquad k\boldsymbol{v}_{nm} = \frac{2n\pi}{a}\boldsymbol{i} + \frac{2m\pi}{b}\boldsymbol{j},$$

and recalling (M3-7, 8) we have

$$(10\text{-}30) \quad \boldsymbol{k} \wedge \boldsymbol{E}(P) \exp[ik\boldsymbol{s}^i \cdot (P-O)] = \sum_{-\infty}^{+\infty} \boldsymbol{A}_{nm} \exp[ik\boldsymbol{v}_{nm} \cdot (P-O)],$$

(†) It could be shown that this conclusion is not only valid in Kirchhoff's approximation but is also rigorous.

with

$$(10\text{-}31) \quad \boldsymbol{A}_{nm} = \frac{1}{ab} \iint\limits_{\Sigma_p} \boldsymbol{k} \wedge \boldsymbol{E}(P') \exp\,[ik\boldsymbol{s}^i \cdot (P' - O)] \exp\,[-ik\boldsymbol{v}_{nm} \cdot (P' - O)]\, \mathrm{d}\Sigma_{P'},$$

where Σ_p represents the period rectangle. Equation (10-30) may also be written in the form

$$(10\text{-}32) \quad \boldsymbol{k} \wedge \boldsymbol{E}(P) = \sum_{-\infty}^{+\infty}{}_{n,m} \boldsymbol{A}_{nm} \exp\,[-ik(\boldsymbol{s}^i - \boldsymbol{v}_{nm}) \cdot (P - O)].$$

Applying the inverse interference principle, we shall attempt to reproduce the distribution $\boldsymbol{k} \wedge \boldsymbol{E}(P)$ by means of a set of diffracted waves. We shall naturally have recourse to a discrete set of plane waves (and possibly of evanescent waves), each one being specified by its direction of propagation $\boldsymbol{s}_{nm}$. For the electric field strength at a general point Q we obtain

$$\boldsymbol{E}(Q) = \sum_{-\infty}^{+\infty} \boldsymbol{E}_{nm} \exp\,[-ik\boldsymbol{s}_{nm} \cdot (Q - O)].$$

If P is on Σ we may write

$$\boldsymbol{k} \wedge \boldsymbol{E}(P) = \sum_{-\infty}^{+\infty}{}_{n,m} \boldsymbol{k} \wedge \boldsymbol{E}_{nm} \exp\,[-ik\boldsymbol{s}_{nm} \cdot (P - O)].$$

By comparing with (10-32) one derives

$$(10\text{-}33) \qquad \boldsymbol{s}_{nm} = \boldsymbol{s}^i - \boldsymbol{v}_{nm} + g\boldsymbol{k}$$

where g represents a scalar and $\boldsymbol{k} \wedge \boldsymbol{E}_{nm} = \boldsymbol{A}_{nm}$ or by (10-31) upon vector multiplication on the right by $\boldsymbol{s}_{nm}$

$$(10\text{-}34) \quad \boldsymbol{E}_{nm} = \frac{1}{ab\boldsymbol{k} \cdot \boldsymbol{s}_{nm}} \iint\limits_{\Sigma_p} [\boldsymbol{k} \wedge \boldsymbol{E}(P')] \wedge \boldsymbol{s}_{nm} \exp\,[ik(\boldsymbol{s}^i - \boldsymbol{v}_{nm}) \cdot (P' - O)]\, \mathrm{d}\Sigma_{P'}.$$

Thus we have found the directions as well as the amplitudes of the diffracted waves.

In the language of theoretical physics, (10-33) is said to determine the *eigenvalues* (vector eigenvalues) and (10-34) the coefficients of the *eigenfunctions* of the problem.

From (10-33) we may derive through use of (10-29)

$$(10\text{-}35) \qquad \boldsymbol{s}_{nm} = \boldsymbol{s}^i - n\frac{\lambda}{a}\boldsymbol{i} - m\frac{\lambda}{b}\boldsymbol{j} + g\boldsymbol{k},$$

For $b \to \infty$ we obtain in this way a well-known formula of ordinary gratings which give rise to a simple infinity of diffracted waves.

It is clear that the above reasoning would still be valid if in place of the grating we considered a general non-periodic screen Σ. Fourier series would then transform into Fourier integrals and the diffracted waves as well as the vectors $\boldsymbol{v}_{nm}$ would form a continuous double infinity. However, (10-33) would still give the correct law of variation for the direction of a given diffracted wave in terms of the direction of the incident wave. If in the following we refer solely to gratings and to discrete eigenvalues we shall do so only for the sake of simplicity.

Generalized Gratings

§ 13. We shall further generalize the definition of a grating by considering a plane or curved screen Σ having a transparency which is a periodic function of two curvilinear and rectangular coordinates u, v chosen on its surface. Let the periods be respectively a and b. The grating will show the appearance represented in Fig. 45. The lines of the grating will have the equations $u =$ *constant* and $v =$ *constant* respectively.

In a sufficiently small region of Σ the grating will appear as an ordinary plane grating with straight rulings like that introduced in the preceding section. The unit vectors $\boldsymbol{i}$ and $\boldsymbol{j}$ will be represented now by (†) $\text{grad}_\Sigma u/|\text{grad}_\Sigma u|$ and $\text{grad}_\Sigma v/|\text{grad}_\Sigma v|$; the periods or the lengths along $\boldsymbol{i}$ and $\boldsymbol{j}$ corresponding to an increase of u by a and of v by b respectively will equal $a/|\text{grad}_\Sigma u|$ and $b/|\text{grad}_\Sigma v|$. Substituting into (10-35) we get

(†) By grad_Σ is meant the *surface gradient* or the gradient in two-dimensional space represented by Σ. Apart from the reduction of the number of dimensions, this definition is identical with that given in M1-§3 for three-dimensional space. It is clear that grad_Σ is tangent to Σ.

$$(10\text{-}36)\qquad \boldsymbol{s}_{nm} = \boldsymbol{s}^i - n\frac{\lambda}{a}\,\mathrm{grad}_\Sigma\, u - m\frac{\lambda}{b}\,\mathrm{grad}_\Sigma\, v + g\boldsymbol{N},$$

where $\boldsymbol{N}$ indicates a unit vector normal to Σ. A small element of a plane wave incident on Σ in the direction $\boldsymbol{s}$ will be diffracted according to (10-36). With a procedure similar to that followed in 9-§10 for the introduction of geometrical optics, we shall consider any wave of general shape incident on Σ as being divided into many plane elements which will be diffracted according to (10-36). As in the case of geometrical optics, one may ask whether it is possible to join all the diffracted elements corresponding to a given pair of indices so as to form a single diffracted wave. This question will be answered positively in the next section by a theorem which is a generalization of that of Malus-Dupin.

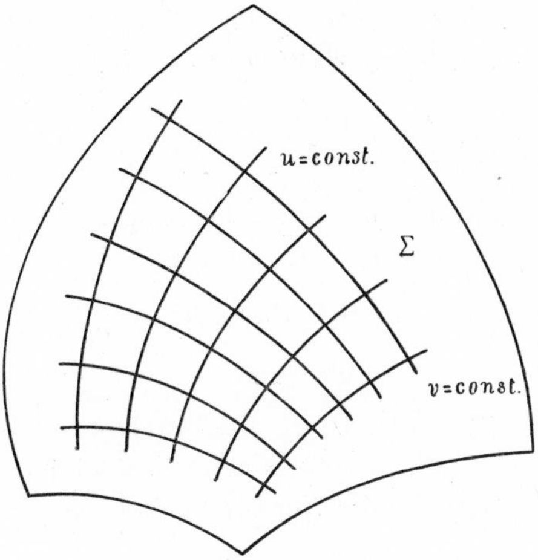

Fig. 45

For the time being we conclude that when a wave of general shape is incident on the grating Σ there will take rise a double infinity of diffracted waves, each being characterized by a pair of indices m, n. Naturally also in this generalization b may be infinite (simple grating) giving then rise to only a simple infinity of diffracted waves. The last case is represented for example by the spherical grating and by the zonal grating which are treated in nearly all advanced text-books of physics.

Parageometrical Optics

§ **14.** Let the normal set of rays corresponding to the incident wave be specified by the unit vectors $\boldsymbol{s}$ and the diffracted set corresponding to a fixed pair of indices m, n by the unit vectors $\boldsymbol{s}'$. Equation (10-36) may be simply written as

$$\boldsymbol{s}' = \boldsymbol{s} + \text{grad}_\Sigma f + g\boldsymbol{N}, \tag{10-37}$$

where $f(Q)$ represents a scalar function of the position Q on Σ. We shall now make the convention that the application of the operators d or δ means a derivation with respect to the first or the second curvilinear coordinate of a general system fixed on Σ and a multiplication by the corresponding differential of the coordinate. By differentiating (10-37) with d and multiplying scalarly by δQ we obtain

$$\mathrm{d}\boldsymbol{s}' \cdot \delta Q = \mathrm{d}\boldsymbol{s} \cdot \delta Q + \mathrm{d}(\text{grad}_\Sigma f) \cdot \delta Q + g\mathrm{d}\boldsymbol{N} \cdot \delta Q.$$

By interchanging d and δ and subtracting the equation thus obtained from the preceding one we find

$$\mathrm{d}\boldsymbol{s}' \cdot \delta Q - \delta\boldsymbol{s}' \cdot \mathrm{d}Q = \mathrm{d}\boldsymbol{s} \cdot \delta Q - \delta\boldsymbol{s} \cdot \mathrm{d}Q + \mathrm{d}(\text{grad}_\Sigma f) \cdot \delta Q - \\ - \delta(\text{grad}_\Sigma f) \cdot \mathrm{d}Q + g(\mathrm{d}\boldsymbol{N} \cdot \delta Q - \delta\boldsymbol{N} \cdot \mathrm{d}Q).$$

As the incident set is normal, the first two terms in the right-hand side cancel by (9-21). The last term vanishes for the same reason. The other two terms of the right-hand side may be transformed into

$$\mathrm{d}(\text{grad}_\Sigma f \cdot \delta Q) - \text{grad}_\Sigma f \cdot \mathrm{d}\delta Q - \delta(\text{grad}_\Sigma f \cdot \mathrm{d}Q) + \text{grad}_\Sigma f \cdot \delta\mathrm{d}Q = \\ = \mathrm{d}\delta f - \delta\mathrm{d}f - \text{grad}_\Sigma f \cdot (\mathrm{d}\delta Q - \delta\mathrm{d}Q),$$

and give a null result due to the permutability of second derivatives. In conclusion we arrive at the relation

$$\mathrm{d}\boldsymbol{s}' \cdot \delta Q - \delta\boldsymbol{s}' \cdot \mathrm{d}Q = 0,$$

which shows that the diffracted set is again normal.

This theorem generalizes that of Malus-Dupin and permits us to say that all the diffracted elements considered really fit into a single wave. This shows that in the Kirchhoff approximation diffraction retains one of the essential properties of geometrical optics. For this reason we shall say that such approximation leads to *parageometrical optics.*

In the field of validity of parageometrical optics one may deal with rays as in geometrical optics. The only difference is that now a single incident set gives rise to several normal sets on the output side.

Also the Fermat principle is generalized in parageometrical optics. We shall recall what was said in 9-§13 and refer again to Fig. 45. The optical path from P to P' is now represented by

$$l = r + r'.$$

We give to Q a displacement $\mathrm{d}Q$ tangent to Σ along the line $f =$ *constant*; recalling (M2-36) and (10-37) we have

$$\mathrm{d}l = \mathrm{grad}_Q\, l \cdot \mathrm{d}Q = (\mathrm{grad}_Q\, r + \mathrm{grad}_Q\, r') \cdot \mathrm{d}Q = \\ = (\mathbf{s} - \mathbf{s}') \cdot \mathrm{d}Q = \mathrm{d}f = 0.$$

Thus the optical path from P to P' is stationary subject to the constraint $f(Q) =$ *constant*. This is the form assumed by the Fermat principle in parageometrical optics.

Kirchhoff's Approximation and Geometrical Optics

§ 15. The treatment of geometrical optics presented in the preceding chapters did not include the case when a beam of rays is limited by a diaphragm. We shall now deal briefly with this case.

Let a wave sent out by a source S (Fig. 46) be limited by an opaque screen DD with an aperture a. Let Q be a point on the other side of the screen where we want to evaluate the field. We shall assume that both the distances of S and of Q from DD as well as the dimensions of the aperture are very large compared with the wavelength. In this situation Kirchhoff's approximation may be applied. The surface Σ will be placed on the plane of the screen. Each point of Σ may be considered as an elementary electric dipole of moment $\mathrm{d}L$ given by (10-21); the electric field produced at Q will be given by (8-9)

$$\mathrm{d}\boldsymbol{E}(Q) = -\,\omega k Z \frac{\exp(-ikr)}{4\pi r} \boldsymbol{s} \wedge (\boldsymbol{s} \wedge \mathrm{d}\boldsymbol{L}).$$

By adding the contributions of all elementary dipoles of Σ we get

$$(10\text{-}38) \quad \boldsymbol{E}(Q) = -\frac{\omega k Z}{4\pi} \iint_a \frac{1}{r} \exp(-ikr)\boldsymbol{s} \wedge (\boldsymbol{s} \wedge \mathrm{d}\boldsymbol{L}).$$

Let OMM_0O represent a wave surface. On this surface the field will have a constant phase that without loss of generality will be assumed to be zero. At point P the phase will equal the length

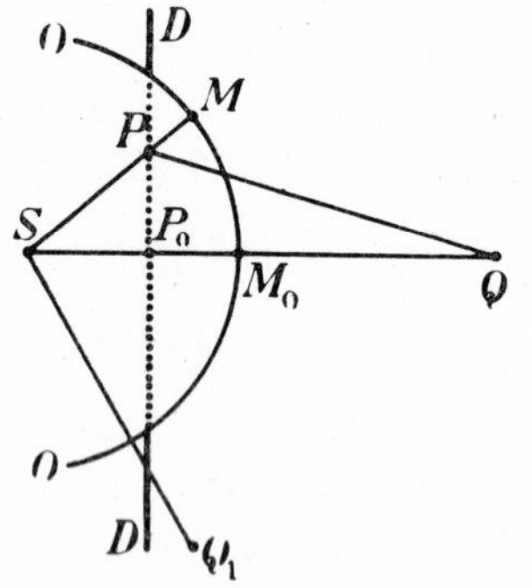

Fig. 46

PM times ik. Representing by $r'(P)$ the length PM we may say that the field at P (and consequently the moment of the elementary dipole) will contain as a factor the expression $\exp(ikr')$ so that (10-38) will take the form

$$(10\text{-}39) \qquad \boldsymbol{E}(Q) = \iint_a \boldsymbol{v}(P) \exp[-ik(r - r')]\mathrm{d}\Sigma,$$

where $r = |\,Q - P\,|$ and $\boldsymbol{v}$ is a vector function of P which is unnecessary to specify further.

We now take into account the assumption that the wavelength is very small or that k is very large. We are confronted with an integral of the type (M4-7) and may then apply the principle of stationary phase. We have to find the point P_0 where $r - r'$ is stationary or has a vanishing gradient. An easy geometrical consideration shows that for such point the ray P_0Q is perpendicular to the wave surface and consequently passes also through S. A small displacement from that position would cause equal increments of r and r', thus leaving the optical path stationary.

We may apply (M4-11) (changing i into $-i$) with the result

$$\text{(10-40)} \qquad \boldsymbol{E}(Q) = \boldsymbol{v}(P_0) \frac{-2i\pi}{k\sqrt{\det \operatorname{grad} \operatorname{grad} (r - r')}} \exp(-ikr_0),$$

where $r = | Q - M_0 |$.

We conclude that the point really important for the determination of the field $\boldsymbol{E}(Q)$ is the *pole* M_0 of the wave with respect to Q or the point that also in the case of free propagation would send a ray to Q. If M_0 does not exist being screened out by the diaphragm (as is the case for point Q_1) we get a practically vanishing illumination that is *shade.*

These are the well-known elementary laws of geometrical optics in the presence of opaque obstacles.

History of the Wave Theory

§ 16. The first electromagnetic waves to attract attention and to be investigated by scientists were naturally light waves. For this reason the problem of their nature was for a long time identified with the problem of the nature of light.

The classical and the middle ages often confused *light* and *vision* and scientists found themselves as it were in a complicate labyrinth.

A rational way to attack the problem could not be found until Kepler (1604) published a theory of the formation of the image on the retina by the rays, which is substantially the same as that utilized today. This gave rise to the question of the nature of these rays considered as external entities of the physical world, independent of the eye of the observer.

The theory which appeared to be more obvious was the *emission* theory. According to it light was to be considered as a fluid or a shower of particles thrown out with a very great velocity by luminous bodies; the rays were nothing but the paths of these particles. This theory of which the greatest follower was Newton (*Philosophiae Naturalis Principia Mathematica,* 1685; *Opticks,* 1704) was able to explain rectilinear propagation, reflection and refraction (provided the assumption was made that a particle was more strongly attracted by the more refractive body so as to acquire a greater velocity in it), but could not explain diffraction and interference or why two beams of rays could meet without disturbing one another.

Diffraction had already been discovered and given its present name by Grimaldi (*De Lumine,* 1665) who had performed a series of very interesting experiments. For example, he had observed that light not only penetrated into the shadow of an obstacle but in so doing traveled along a curved path; a phenomenon which was irreconcilable with the emission theory.

Newton himself had discovered a case of interference (*Newton rings*) which also could not be accounted for in a very convincing way by emission. However, Newton did not abandon the emission theory simply because there did not appear to exist a better one. Naturally the theory lived for a long time after him because it had been followed by such a genius.

The *wave* theory was suggested long before Newton. According to it, light was nothing but a wave propagation, like sound. It may appear strange that this hypothesis was not stated immediately at the expense of its direct rival. But this did not happen for a very good reason. At that time there was still no clear understanding of the mechanism by which waves are propagated, and the appropriate mathematical instruments had not yet been developed.

A very important step in this direction is due to Huygens (*Traité de la Lumière,* 1690) who stated the principle of elementary waves which bears his name. By means of this principle Huygens was able to explain all the phenomena of geometrical optics as well as those of double refraction. But he could not explain diffraction because he did not have an exact idea of how elementary waves interfere with one another. He limited himself to finding a new wave front as the envelope of all elementary waves emitted by an original wave front; this is equivalent to geometrical optics.

More than a century elapsed before the wave theory took another decisive step. In 1802 Young produced the most simple and unambiguous phenomenon of interference and discovered the rule that, when light goes from a source to the eye following two different paths, the illumination is a maximum if the path difference is a multiple of a well-determined length and is a minimum in intermediate cases. Thus the wavelength had been discovered.

The final victory of wave theory is due to Fresnel, who in a series of papers submitted to the French Academy from 1815 to 1819 gave a clear and exact explanation of all diffraction phenomena. The instrument which enabled him to reach this success was the principle of the elementary waves, modified in such a way as to take into account the relative phases of the waves and consequently their interference (*Huygens-Fresnel principle*).

Later, in order to explain the polarization of light, Fresnel made the hypothesis that light waves are transverse and in this way obtained very good results. For example, he was able to derive the formulas of reflection and refraction which bear his name.

But, with the assumption that light vibrations are transverse, there arises a very serious problem concerning the medium in which the vibrations take place. How this difficulty was overcome by passing from the elastic theory to the electromagnetic theory has been outlined in 3-§11.

The last great proof of the validity of the wave theory was represented by the direct measurement of the velocity of light in water which was made by Foucault in 1850. This velocity proved to be less than that in air, contrary to what had been assumed by the emission theory but in agreement with the prediction of the wave theory.

CHAPTER 11

Guided Propagation

Parallel Plate Guide

§ 1. Consider a plane wave linearly polarized in a perfect and homogeneous dielectric. Let the direction of propagation be that of the z-axis, the electric force being in the direction of the x-axis. We shall have

$$(11\text{-}1) \qquad \boldsymbol{E} = A\boldsymbol{i} \exp(-ikz), \qquad \boldsymbol{H} = YA\boldsymbol{j} \exp(-ikz),$$

where Y represents the intrinsic admittance of the medium.

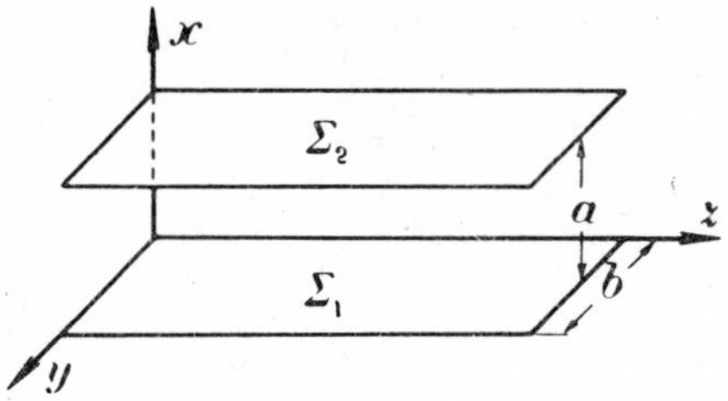

Fig. 47

Let us now limit the portion of dielectric considered (Fig. 47) by means of two plane metal plates Σ_1, Σ_2 which are to be considered unbounded and infinitely thin. Let Σ_1 coincide with the xy-plane and Σ_2 be parallel to it at the height $x = a$. The metal of the plates will be assumed to be a perfect conductor.

We shall inquire whether the field (11-1) can exist between the two plates, the outside field being zero. In this situation the normal component of the electric force and the tangential projection of the magnetic force are both discontinuous across Σ_1 and Σ_2. An application of (3-1, 2, 3, 4) shows immediately that the lower plate Σ_1 will carry a surface current of density $\boldsymbol{\iota}_1$ given by

$$(11\text{-}2) \qquad \boldsymbol{\iota}_1 = \boldsymbol{i} \wedge \boldsymbol{H} = YA\boldsymbol{k} \exp(-ikz),$$

together with a surface charge having the density σ_1 equal to

$$\sigma_1 = \boldsymbol{i} \cdot \boldsymbol{D} = \varepsilon A \exp(-ikz). \tag{11-3}$$

It is readily verified that this current and this charge obey the equation of continuity $\operatorname{div}_\Sigma \boldsymbol{\iota}_1 + i\omega\sigma_1 = 0$, where $\operatorname{div}_\Sigma$ represents the divergence in the two-dimensional space constituted by Σ. The currents and charges arising on Σ_2 will be equal and have opposite sign (because the corresponding discontinuities are reversed); thus $\boldsymbol{\iota}_2 = -\boldsymbol{\iota}_1$ and $\sigma_2 = -\sigma_1$.

Imagine now (†) that two corresponding strips (Fig. 47) parallel to the z axis and of width b are cut out of the plates. These strips form something very similar to the transmission line considered in 6-§13 (Fig. 20). The only difference is that in that case the two conductors were wires while they are now metal strips; however this difference is not essential.

The current carried by the line (in opposite directions in the lower and upper conductors) is given by $I = \boldsymbol{\iota} \cdot \boldsymbol{k} b$; whence by (11-2)

$$I = YAb \exp(-ikz). \tag{11-4}$$

The voltage V between the conductors is readily found from equation (11-1):

$$V = Aa \exp(-ikz). \tag{11-5}$$

We can as usual define the characteristic impedance of the line $Z_l = V/I$ with the result

$$Z_l = Z\frac{a}{b}. \tag{11-6}$$

If both strips are one *meter* wide and placed one *meter* apart from one another, there results $Z_l = Z$. We saw that the wave in the portion of dielectric considered has absolutely the same form whether the plates exist or not (free space, unbounded dielectric).

(†) This operation must be purely mental. In reality both plates must remain unbounded in all directions. Otherwise there would arise some boundary effects which would alter the field.

This justifies the introduction of the intrinsic impedance of an unbounded and homogeneous medium. Such medium, as far as plane waves are concerned, is perfectly equivalent to a transmission line having the characteristic impedance Z per unit height and width.

From (11-4, 5) one readily derives

$$\text{(11-7)} \qquad \frac{\mathrm{d}V}{\mathrm{d}z} = -\, i\omega\mu \frac{a}{b} I, \qquad \frac{\mathrm{d}I}{\mathrm{d}z} = -\, i\omega\varepsilon \frac{b}{a} V,$$

which are equivalent to (6-37, 38). There follows

$$\text{(11-8)} \qquad \begin{cases} \mathscr{Z} = \mathscr{R} + i\omega\,\mathscr{L} = i\omega\mu\,\dfrac{a}{b}, \\[2ex] \mathscr{Y} = \mathscr{G} + i\omega\,\mathscr{C} = i\omega\varepsilon\,\dfrac{b}{a}, \end{cases}$$

or $\mathscr{R} = 0$, $\mathscr{G} = 0$, $\mathscr{L} = \mu a/b$, $\mathscr{C} = \varepsilon b/a$. In particular for $a = b = 1$, μ turns out equal to the inductance per unit length and ε to the capacitance per unit length. Once again we find that we are justified in measuring μ and ε respectively in *henrys/meter* and in *farads/meter.*

The complex power W carried by the line is, by (6-52), $VI^*/2$ or, utilizing (11-4, 5),

$$W = \frac{1}{2} YAA^*ab.$$

This is equal to the power carried by the electromagnetic field, as is readily seen by constructing the complex Poynting vector by means of (11-1) and integrating its flux over the rectangle ab. It is therefore a matter of indifference whether we picture the transmission as occurring through the current in the conductors or through the electromagnetic field in the dielectric.

It is evident that besides the progressive waves one could consider regressive waves by changing k into $-\,k$ and Z into $-\,Z$.

§ **2.** The parallel plates investigated above represent the simplest example of a *wave guide.* The electromagnetic wave is guided as it were by Σ_1 and Σ_2 without entering the outside space.

The case just considered is that of a *TEM* wave. But this is not the only possible case. There are also other modes of propagation naturally all subject to the conditions that the tangential projection of $\boldsymbol{E}$ and the normal component of $\boldsymbol{H}$ both vanish on the walls.

We already know from 8-§11 that in an unbounded dielectric *TE* or *TM* waves can also exist when two plane waves interfere. Let us consider for example the *TM* waves specified by (8-41); removing the useless multiplier 2 and putting $k \cos \theta = k_g$ we shall write

$$\text{(11-9)} \quad TM \begin{cases} \boldsymbol{E} = A[\boldsymbol{i} \cos \theta \cos (kx \sin \theta) + \\ \qquad\qquad + i\boldsymbol{k} \sin \theta \sin (kx \sin \theta)] \exp (-ik_g z), \\ \boldsymbol{H} = AY\boldsymbol{j} \cos (kx \sin \theta) \exp (-ik_g z). \end{cases}$$

The tangential component of $\boldsymbol{E}$ is that parallel to $\boldsymbol{k}$ and vanishes at the lower plate ($x = 0$). But for this component to be zero at the upper plate also ($x = a$) one must set the condition $ka \sin \theta = m\pi$ or

$$\text{(11-10)} \qquad \sin \theta = m \frac{\lambda}{2a},$$

m being an integer and λ the wavelength corresponding to an unbounded dielectric.

Equation (11-10) gives the eigenvalues of the problem and (11-9) the corresponding eigenfunctions. Each mode is specified by the progressive number of its eigenvalue. We have presented the TM_m modes.

For each of these modes the surfaces of constant phase or the wave surfaces are the planes $z =$ *constant.* The velocity of propagation v_g of these planes is readily found from (11-9) to be

$$\text{(11-11)} \qquad v_g = \frac{\omega}{k_g} = \frac{v}{\cos \theta},$$

where v represents the velocity of light in the unlimited dielectric. Equation (11-11) represents a velocity always exceeding v. Also the wavelength λ_g or the spacing between two consecutive planes of constant phase is increased in the same ratio as compared to λ.

We shall give the name of *wave impedance* to the ratio Z_g of E_x and H_y for the mode considered. From (11-9) we derive

$$Z_g = Z \cos \theta. \tag{11-12}$$

The reciprocal value $Y_g = 1/Z_g$ is named *wave admittance.*

Note now that (11-10) yields a real value for θ only if $m\lambda/2a \leqq 1$. In the contrary case $|\sin \theta|$ is greater than unity and both interfering waves are evanescent as those discussed in 7-§§19, 20. In this case $\cos \theta$ is imaginary and the field is attenuated in the direction of z. No power travels along the wave guide. This results also by considering that by (11-2) the wave impedance is imaginary or a pure reactance; then the z component of the complex Poynting vector is purely imaginary.

Thus the TM modes which really travel in the wave guide are a finite number; all the others are evanescent modes. A mode of a given number m will present propagation only if the wavelength λ is smaller than the *critical wavelength* or *cut-off wavelength* λ_c, for which $\sin \theta$ becomes equal to 1. From (11-10) we have

$$\lambda_c = \frac{2a}{m}. \tag{11-13}$$

The corresponding frequency $\nu_c = v/\lambda_c$ is called *cut-off frequency* and represents the lower limit of the frequencies which are propagated in the mode TM_m.

§ 3. In the foregoing cases the transverse component of $\boldsymbol{E}$ is parallel to x. It is evident that such component cannot be parallel to y in a TEM mode which is equal to a free plane wave, because in that case the tangential component of $\boldsymbol{E}$ could not vanish on Σ_1 and Σ_2. However this is not impossible for the TE modes represented by (8-40). We shall write

$$TE \begin{cases} \boldsymbol{E} = A\boldsymbol{j} \sin (kx \sin \theta) \exp (-ik_g z), \\ \boldsymbol{H} = AY[-\boldsymbol{i} \cos \theta \sin (kx \sin \theta) + \\ \qquad + \boldsymbol{i}\boldsymbol{k} \sin \theta \cos (kx \sin \theta)] \exp (-ik_g z). \end{cases} \tag{11-14}$$

where the interchange of the sines with the cosines is obtained by a simple shift of the origin of x.

The condition for the tangential component of $\boldsymbol{E}$ to vanish on the walls is still represented by (11-10); hence we obtain a discrete set of eigenvalues and eigenfunctions. The mode of number m will be indicated by TE_m. The velocity of propagation of the planes of constant phase is still (11-11).

The wave impedance or the ratio of E_y and $-H_x$ is found from (11—14) to be

$$Z_g = \frac{Z}{\cos\theta}. \tag{11-15}$$

For the evanescent modes this impedance is purely imaginary or a reactance. The cut-off wavelength is still represented by (11-13).

Note that, if we want the evanescent modes to be attenuated in the positive direction of the z-axis, $\cos\theta$ must be chosen equal to $-i\sqrt{\sin^2\theta - 1}$. As a result the wave reactance in the TM case is capacitive, and in the TE case inductive.

Metal Lenses

§ 4. The curious property that between two metal plates the phase velocity can exceed the phase velocity in the free dielectric

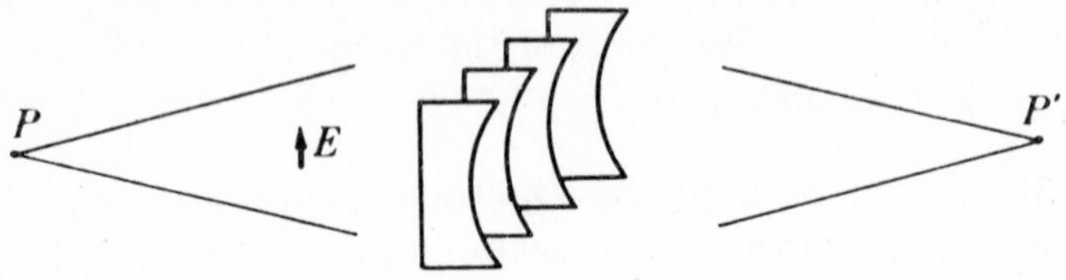

Fig. 48

has found an interesting application in *metal lenses*. Such lenses consist of a set of parallel and equispaced plates having the shape represented in Fig. 48. One utilizes the mode TE_1 arising within each pair of plates when the electric field of a incident wave is parallel to the plates. One proceeds in such a way that all other TE modes are evanescent; one needs only to choose a value of λ

exceeding the critical wavelengths (11-13) for all $m > 1$ (and naturally not exceeding the critical wavelength of $m = 1$).

Since the velocity between the plates is greater than v, the system is equivalent to a lens having a refractive index less than 1. As a consequence the lens represented in the figure is positive contrary to what one might believe at first sight.

Obviously these considerations cannot claim a great rigor; both at the input and at the output of the lens there arise diffraction effects which we have not taken into account. Nevertheless metal lenses give in practice excellent results and are employed with success in the field of microwaves.

Rectangular Wave Guide

§ 5. We shall now consider a metal wave guide having a rectangular cross section with the sides a, b parallel to x, y respectively (Fig. 49). The procedure for finding the modes traveling in the wave guide will be similar to that followed in the preceding case.

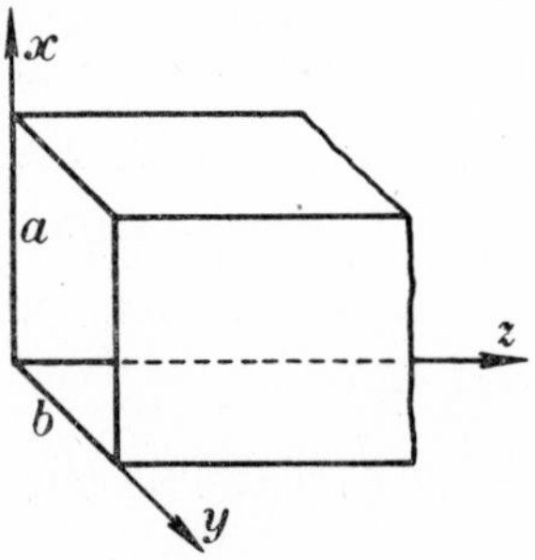

Fig. 49

In the two plate guide the modes result from the interference of two plane waves, each being the mirror image of the other with respect to both plates. Also from the physical standpoint it would be correct to think of a single plane wave reflected an infinite number of times by both walls.

It is a natural guess that in the case of a rectangular wave guide one must have recourse to four plane waves representing the mirror images of an initial plane wave with respect to the four walls. The directions of propagation $\boldsymbol{s}_1$, $\boldsymbol{s}_2$, $\boldsymbol{s}_3$, $\boldsymbol{s}_4$ will be represented respectively by

$$\text{(11-16)}\quad \begin{cases} \boldsymbol{s}_1 = \quad s_x\boldsymbol{i} + s_y\boldsymbol{j} + s_z\boldsymbol{k}, \\ \boldsymbol{s}_2 = -\, s_x\boldsymbol{i} + s_y\boldsymbol{j} + s_z\boldsymbol{k}, \\ \boldsymbol{s}_3 = \quad s_x\boldsymbol{i} - s_y\boldsymbol{j} + s_z\boldsymbol{k}, \\ \boldsymbol{s}_4 = -\, s_x\boldsymbol{i} - s_y\boldsymbol{j} + s_z\boldsymbol{k}. \end{cases}$$

One may convince oneself that these expressions are correct by considering that s_y has its sign reversed by reflection at a surface parallel to xz while s_x has its sign reversed by reflection at a surface parallel to yz.

Let us consider a TE plane wave or a plane wave having its electric vector in the plane xy. If $\boldsymbol{s}$ designates a unit vector in the direction of propagation the electric field will be perpendicular to both $\boldsymbol{s}$ and $\boldsymbol{k}$ and may be represented by the expression $A\boldsymbol{s} \wedge \boldsymbol{k} = A(s_y\boldsymbol{i} - s_x\boldsymbol{j})$. Taking into account (11-16) we shall get the four waves

$$\text{(11-17)}\quad \begin{cases} \boldsymbol{E}_1 = A(s_y\boldsymbol{i} - s_x\boldsymbol{j}) \exp\left[-\,ik(s_x x + s_y y + s_z z)\right], \\ \boldsymbol{E}_2 = A(s_y\boldsymbol{i} + s_x\boldsymbol{j}) \exp\left[-\,ik(-\,s_x x + s_y y + s_z z)\right]. \\ \boldsymbol{E}_3 = A(-\,s_y\boldsymbol{i} - s_x\boldsymbol{j}) \exp\left[-\,ik(s_x x - s_y y + s_z z)\right], \\ \boldsymbol{E}_4 = A(-\,s_y\boldsymbol{i} + s_x\boldsymbol{j}) \exp\left[-\,ik(-\,s_x x - s_y y + s_z z)\right]. \end{cases}$$

By adding these equations and removing a useless multiplier $-\,4i$ one arrives at the expression

$$\text{(11-18)}\quad TE \quad \boldsymbol{E} = A[s_y\boldsymbol{i}\cos(ks_x x)\sin(ks_y y) - \\ -\, s_x\boldsymbol{j}\sin(ks_x x)\cos(ks_y y)]\exp(-\,ik_g z),$$

where $k_g = ks_z$.

As to the magnetic field, we note that for a wave of the type considered $\boldsymbol{H} = Y\boldsymbol{s} \wedge \boldsymbol{E} = Y\boldsymbol{s}_T \wedge \boldsymbol{E} + Ys_z\boldsymbol{k} \wedge \boldsymbol{E}$ if by $\boldsymbol{s}_T$ we understand the transverse component of $\boldsymbol{s}$. The multiplier $Ys_z\boldsymbol{k}$ in the second vector product is identical for the four waves so that upon addition the transverse component of $\boldsymbol{H}$ will turn out to be simply $Ys_z\boldsymbol{k} \wedge (\boldsymbol{E}_1 + \boldsymbol{E}_2 + \boldsymbol{E}_3 + \boldsymbol{E}_4)$; hence

$$\text{(11-19)}\quad TE \quad \boldsymbol{H}_T = Ys_z\boldsymbol{k} \wedge \boldsymbol{E},$$

$\boldsymbol{E}$ being given by (11-18). There remain the four terms of the type $Y\boldsymbol{s}_T \wedge \boldsymbol{E}$ or, apart from the exponentials, of the type $Y\boldsymbol{s}_T \wedge (A\boldsymbol{s} \wedge \boldsymbol{k}) = -YAs_T^2\boldsymbol{k}$, which are equal for the four waves. In this situation one has simply to add the four exponentials of (11-17) to obtain

$$\text{(11-20)} \quad TE \quad H_z = -iYAs_T^2 \cos(ks_x x) \cos(ks_y y) \exp(-ikz_g),$$

where a factor $-4i$ has been removed as in (11-19). From (11-18, 19) we obtain also

$$\text{(11-21)} \quad TE \quad \boldsymbol{H}_T = Ys_z A[s_x \boldsymbol{i} \sin(ks_x x) \cos(ks_y y) + \\ + s_y \boldsymbol{j} \cos(ks_x x) \sin(ks_y y)] \exp(-ik_g z).$$

Let us now determine the eigenvalues. By requiring that the tangential component of $\boldsymbol{E}$ vanish on the walls we derive from (11-18) $ks_x a = m\pi$ and $ks_y b = n\pi$, whence

$$\text{(11-22)} \qquad s_x = m\frac{\lambda}{2a}, \qquad s_y = n\frac{\lambda}{2b}.$$

Recalling the relation $s_x^2 + s_y^2 + s_z^2 = 1$ we have

$$\text{(11-23)} \qquad s_z = \sqrt{1 - m^2\frac{\lambda^2}{4a^2} - n^2\frac{\lambda^2}{4b^2}}.$$

Thus we get a double infinity of eigenvalues for $\boldsymbol{s}$, each being specified by a pair of integers m, n. Upon substitution into (11-18, 19, 20) the corresponding eigenfunctions or the modes TE_{mn} are obtained.

The planes of constant phase travel in the direction of the z-axis with the velocity

$$\text{(11-24)} \qquad v_g = \frac{v}{s_z},$$

which is always greater than v. The cut-off wavelength for the mode considered is that for which s_z vanishes or by (11-23)

$$\text{(11-25)} \qquad \lambda_c = \frac{1}{\sqrt{\dfrac{m^2}{4a^2} + \dfrac{n^2}{4b^2}}}.$$

For a shorter wavelength the mode mn is evanescent.

According to (11-19) the wave admittance will be equal to Ys_z hence the wave impedance will be

$$\text{(11-26)} \qquad TE \qquad Z_g = \frac{Z}{s_z}.$$

For a non-attenuated mode this is a pure resistance while for an evanescent mode it is a pure inductive reactance. The wave admittance will be denoted by Y_g and (11-19) will read

$$\text{(11-27)} \qquad \boldsymbol{H}_T = Y_g \boldsymbol{k} \wedge \boldsymbol{E}.$$

To evaluate the power carried by the wave one has to construct the longitudinal component $\boldsymbol{S}_z$ of the complex Poynting vector which is $\boldsymbol{S}_z = \boldsymbol{E} \wedge \boldsymbol{H}_T^*/2$ or by (11-27)

$$\text{(11-28)} \qquad S_z = \frac{1}{2} Y_g^* \boldsymbol{E} \cdot \boldsymbol{E}^*.$$

The total power transmitted is found by taking the real part of S_z and integrating over the cross section Σ of the wave guide. We thus find

$$\text{(11-29)} \qquad \overline{W} = \frac{1}{2} \mathscr{Re}\, Y_g^* \iint_\Sigma \boldsymbol{E} \cdot \boldsymbol{E}^* \, \mathrm{d}\Sigma.$$

It is readily seen that an evanescent mode does not carry any energy along the guide, because its Y_g is a purely imaginary quantity.

Let us consider a non-evanescent mode having a real wave admittance Ys_z. We have

$$\text{(11-30)} \qquad \overline{W} = \frac{1}{2} Ys_z \iint_\Sigma \boldsymbol{E} \cdot \boldsymbol{E}^* \, \mathrm{d}\Sigma.$$

By substituting into this equation the expression (11-18) for $\boldsymbol{E}$, we write

$$\overline{W} = \frac{1}{2} Ys_z AA^* \iint_\Sigma [s_y^2 \cos^2 (ks_x x) \sin^2 (ks_y y) + \\ + s_x^2 \sin^2 (ks_x x) \cos^2 (ks_y y)] \, \mathrm{d}x \, \mathrm{d}y,$$

and, carrying out the integration,

$$\overline{W} = \frac{1}{8} Y s_z s_T^2 A A^* ab, \tag{11-31}$$

where, as usual, $s_T^2 = s_x^2 + s_y^2 = 1 - s_z^2$.

§ 6. The transverse magnetic modes TM_{mn} are derived from the TE_{mn} modes by the well-known procedure (see 7-§11) of interchanging $\boldsymbol{E}$ with $Z\boldsymbol{H}$ and $Z\boldsymbol{H}$ with $-\boldsymbol{E}$. It is convenient also for our purpose to interchange the sines with the cosines in (11-18, 19, 20) which amounts to the same as a change of origin and to put $-A$ in place of A. Thus from (11-18) we have

$$TM \qquad Z\boldsymbol{H} = -A[s_y \boldsymbol{i} \sin(ks_x x)\cos(ks_y y) - s_x \boldsymbol{j}\cos(ks_x x)\sin(ks_y y)]\exp(-ik_g z), \tag{11-32}$$

and from (11-19)

$$\boldsymbol{E}_T = s_z Z\boldsymbol{H} \wedge \boldsymbol{k}. \tag{11-33}$$

Upon substitution of the previous expression of $Z\boldsymbol{H}$ into the last equation we get

$$TM \qquad \boldsymbol{E}_T = A s_z [s_x \boldsymbol{i}\cos(ks_x x)\sin(ks_y y) + s_y \boldsymbol{j}\sin(ks_x x)\cos(ks_y y)]\exp(-ik_g z), \tag{11-34}$$

while (11-20) by said interchanges yields

$$TM \qquad E_z = -iAs_T^2 \sin(ks_x x)\sin(ks_y y)\exp(-ik_g z). \tag{11-35}$$

Thus we have obtained a complete expression for the electric force of a typical TM mode. To find the eigenvalues one must require that the tangential component of E vanish on each wall (and this time one must also take into account E_z). It is readily verified that the corresponding conditions are the same as in the TE case; as a consequence we still have the eigenvalues (11-22), the phase velocity (11-24) and the cut-off wavelength (11-25).

As to the wave impedance, we find from (11-33)

$$TM \qquad Z_g = Zs_z, \tag{11-36}$$

which is a value different from (11-26). Taking the vector product of (11-33) and $\boldsymbol{k}$, we may also write

(11-37) $\quad TM \qquad \boldsymbol{H}_T = Y_g \boldsymbol{k} \wedge \boldsymbol{E}_T.$

To evaluate the transmitted power we must start again from the expression (11-28) for S_z replacing $\boldsymbol{E}_T$ by $\boldsymbol{E}$. An evanescent mode does not carry any energy because Y_{mn} is a pure imaginary. For a non-evanescent mode putting $Y_{mn} = Y/s_z$ we have as in (11-30)

$$\overline{W} = \frac{1}{2s_z} Y \iint_{\Sigma} \boldsymbol{E}_T \cdot \boldsymbol{E}_T^* \mathrm{d}\Sigma.$$

By introducing the expression (11-33) of $\boldsymbol{E}_T$ we shall write

$$\overline{W} = \frac{1}{2} Y s_z A A^* \int_0^a \int_0^b [s_x^2 \cos^2(ks_x x) \sin^2(ks_y y) + s_y^2 \sin^2(ks_x x) \cos^2(ks_y y)]\, \mathrm{d}x\, \mathrm{d}y,$$

whence

(11-38) $$\overline{W} = \frac{1}{8} Y s_z s_T^2 A A^* ab,$$

as in the TE case.

§ 7. Let us examine a little closer the TE and TM modes which have been found.

First of all let us investigate whether or not a TEM mode can exist as in the case of the two plate guide. From (11-20) it is seen that for H_z to vanish in a TE mode the condition $\boldsymbol{s}_T = 0$ or $s_x = s_y = 0$ must be verified. But in this case $\boldsymbol{E}$ and $\boldsymbol{H}$ will be identically zero on account of (11-18, 19). Conversely let us see whether E_z can vanish in a TM mode. Equation (11-35) shows that this requires only that either s_x or s_y be zero. However it is seen from (11-34, 37) that in either case both $\boldsymbol{E}$ and $\boldsymbol{H}$ would identically vanish. Hence in a rectangular wave guide we cannot have a TEM mode or a *principal mode.*

The foregoing shows that we cannot select the value zero for both m and n. If the mode is TM it is not even possible for one of them to be zero.

On the contrary the TE_{0n} and TE_{m0} modes can very well exist as is seen from (11-18, 19, 20). A particular importance attaches to the TE_{01} and TE_{10} modes because their cut-off wavelengths have the largest possible values in the wave guide, as is shown by (11-25). For TE_{01} we have $\lambda_c = 2b$ and for TE_{10}, $\lambda_c = 2a$. Which of the two

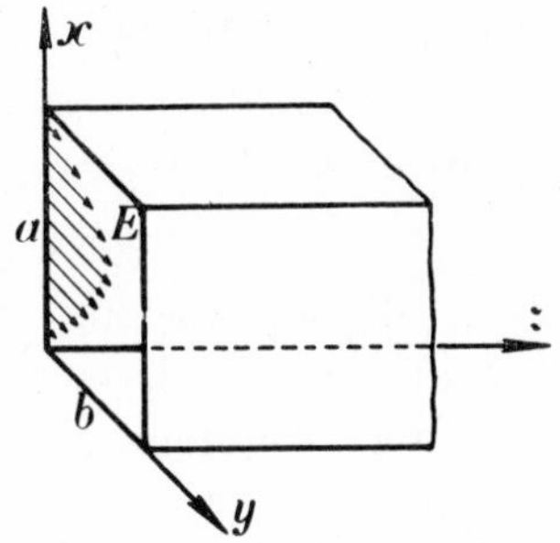

Fig. 50

wavelengths is larger depends on the shape of the wave guide or on which side is called a and which b. Ordinarily one sets $a > b$ so the larger cut-off wavelength is that of the TE_{10} mode. It is clear that, if the wavelength employed is between $2a$ and $2b$, only the TE_{10} mode will be capable of traveling in the guide. This condition is often realized purposely to have the simplest type of propagation. The TE_{10} mode is termed the *dominant mode.* In Fig. 50 the mode is represented by means of lines proportional to the electric field.

Attenuation in a Rectangular Wave Guide

§ 8. So far we have assumed that the wave guide is filled by a perfect dielectric and that the metal walls are perfect conductors. The first assumption is nearly always very close to reality; but the second one is in many cases usefully replaced by a better approximation.

The finite conductivity of the walls will give rise to a power absorption at the expense of the power $\overline{W}$ carried by the guide. Let us denote by $\overline{W}_p$ the power absorbed by the walls per unit length of the guide. In a length $\mathrm{d}z$ the carried power will diminish by the amount $\overline{W}_p \mathrm{d}z$. Dividing by $\overline{W}$ we write

$$\frac{\mathrm{d}\overline{W}}{\overline{W}} = -\frac{\overline{W}_p}{\overline{W}}\mathrm{d}z. \tag{11-39}$$

We shall see later that the quotient

$$\frac{\overline{W}_p}{\overline{W}} = 2\alpha, \tag{11-40}$$

is constant so that upon integration of (11-39) we get

$$\overline{W} = \overline{W}_0 \exp(-2\alpha z).$$

The power is attenuated while traveling along the guide, the attenuation constant being 2α. We have now to evaluate $\overline{W}_p$.

Since the propagation in a wave guide has been dealt with as a series of reflections of a plane wave at the walls, it is natural to apply the same procedure which in 9-§8 was employed for the evaluation of the reflection coefficient of a metal. In other words, we shall assume the intrinsic impedance Z_p of the walls to be so small as not to alter appreciably the value of $\boldsymbol{H}$ holding in the case of perfect conductivity. If $\boldsymbol{H}_t$ denotes the tangential component of $\boldsymbol{H}$ on the wall, the tangential component of $\boldsymbol{E}$ will be $\boldsymbol{E}_t = Z_p \boldsymbol{H}_t \wedge \boldsymbol{n}$, where by $\boldsymbol{n}$ we understand the unit normal of the wall directed toward the metal.

The energy flow $\overline{\boldsymbol{S}}$ across a unit surface of the wall will then be given by $\overline{\boldsymbol{S}} = (1/2)\,\mathcal{R}e\,\boldsymbol{E}_t \wedge \boldsymbol{H}_t^* = (1/2)\,\mathcal{R}e\,Z_p(\boldsymbol{H}_t \wedge \boldsymbol{n}) \wedge \boldsymbol{H}_t^* = (1/2)\,\mathcal{R}e\,Z_p(\boldsymbol{H}_t \cdot \boldsymbol{H}_t^*)\boldsymbol{n}$. Hence, taking into account that $\boldsymbol{H}$ is always parallel to the wall, we have

$$\overline{S} = \frac{1}{2}\mathcal{R}e\,Z_p \boldsymbol{H}\cdot\boldsymbol{H}^* = \frac{1}{2}R_p \boldsymbol{H}\cdot\boldsymbol{H}^*,$$

where $R_p = \sqrt{\omega\mu/2\gamma}$ represents the intrinsic resistance of the metal of the walls. The walls will absorb per unit length of the wave guide a power $\overline{W}_p$ given by

$$\overline{W}_p = \frac{1}{2}R_p \oint \boldsymbol{H}\cdot\boldsymbol{H}^*\mathrm{d}l, \tag{11-41}$$

the integration being over the boundary of a normal cross section of the guide.

By separating the contributions of each of the four walls we have

$$(11\text{-}42)\quad \overline{W}_p = \frac{1}{2} R_p \int_0^a [H_x H_x^* + H_z H_z^*]_{y=0}\, dx +$$

$$+\frac{1}{2} R_p \int_0^a [H_x H_x^* + H_z H_z^*]_{y=b}\, dx + \frac{1}{2} R_p \int_0^b [H_y H_y^* + H_z H_z^*]_{x=0}\, dy +$$

$$+\frac{1}{2} R_p \int_0^b [H_y H_y^* + H_z H_z^*]_{x=a}\, dy.$$

Consider now a TE mode. The components of $\boldsymbol{H}$ will be derived from (11-20, 21). By substituting into (11-42) and carrying out the integration we find

$$\overline{W}_p = \frac{1}{2} R_p Y^2 AA^* [(a + b) s_T^4 + (as_x^2 + bs_y^2) s_z^2].$$

Dividing by the value of $\overline{W}$ as given by (11-31) and recalling (11-40), we obtain the value of the attenuation constant:

$$(11\text{-}43)\qquad TE \qquad \alpha = 2R_p Y \frac{(a + b)s_T^4 + (as_x^2 + bs_y^2) s_z^2}{abs_z s_T^2},$$

where of course the values of the components of $\boldsymbol{s}$ are given by (11-22, 23).

In a TM case the components of $\boldsymbol{H}$ are found from (11-32). Substituting into (11-42) and carrying out the integrations

$$\overline{W} = \frac{1}{2} R_p Y^2 AA^* (as_y^2 + bs_x^2),$$

whence by (11-38)

$$(11\text{-}44)\qquad TM \qquad \alpha = 2R_p Y \frac{as_y^2 + bs_x^2}{abs_z s_T^2},$$

the components of $\boldsymbol{s}$ being still given by (11-22, 23).

Coaxial Line

§ **9.** It is of interest in many applications to consider a wave guide consisting of two coaxial cylinders having the radii r_1, r_2 (Fig. 51) and separated by a dielectric. This kind of wave guide admits of many modes of propagation. However, we shall restrict ourselves to investigating whether or not there exists a principal

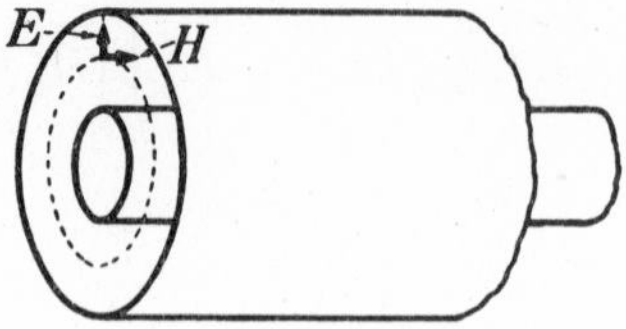

Fig. 51

mode or a mode where both $\boldsymbol{E}$ and $\boldsymbol{H}$ are perpendicular to the direction of propagation. This direction will be assumed as the z-axis. Symmetry considerations and boundary conditions ($\boldsymbol{E}$ perpendicular and $\boldsymbol{H}$ parallel to the walls) suggest that $\boldsymbol{E}$ be directed along the radius and $\boldsymbol{H}$ along a circle coaxial with the cylinders.

It is natural to refer to cylindrical coordinates r, φ, z and to set $\boldsymbol{E} = E\boldsymbol{i}_r$ and $\boldsymbol{H} = H\boldsymbol{i}_\varphi$. Maxwell's equations (7-18, 19) in conjunction with the second equation (M1-24) yield immediately

$$-\frac{\partial H}{\partial z}\boldsymbol{i}_r + \frac{1}{r}\frac{\partial (rH)}{\partial r}\boldsymbol{k} = i\omega\varepsilon E\boldsymbol{i}_r,$$

$$\frac{\partial E}{\partial z}\boldsymbol{i}_\varphi - \frac{1}{r}\frac{\partial E}{\partial \varphi}\boldsymbol{k} = -i\omega\mu H\boldsymbol{i}_\varphi.$$

Hence we see that E does not depend on φ; in addition,

$$\frac{\partial (rH)}{\partial r} = 0, \tag{11-45}$$

and finally

$$\begin{cases} \dfrac{\partial E}{\partial z} = -i\omega\mu H, \\[2ex] \dfrac{\partial H}{\partial z} = -i\omega\varepsilon E. \end{cases} \tag{11-46}$$

Equations (11-46) are of a well-known type; they have the same form as (7-27) or (6-37, 38) and represent the equations of a transmission line with $\mathscr{Z} = i\omega\mu$ and $\mathscr{Y} = i\omega\varepsilon$. We immediately conclude that the considered mode travels along the guide with a velocity $v = 1/\sqrt{\varepsilon\mu}$ and a wave impedance $E/H = \sqrt{\mu/\varepsilon} = Z$ which are identical with those of free propagation.

Since E is independent of φ the same must be true for H. Let us return to (11-45) which states that H is inversely proportional to r. This may also be proved in another way: taking into account that $\boldsymbol{E}$ is parallel to the radius and applying the first Maxwell equation (2-19) to a complete circle one finds

(11-47) $$H = \frac{I}{2\pi r},$$

where I represents the current flowing along the inner cylinder. This is nothing but the Biot and Savart law (1-9) which for a direct current is unconditionally valid while here depends on the assumption $E_z = 0$.

By virtue of (11-47) I will be a function of z in the same way as H, i.e., through the factor $\exp(-ikz)$ with $k = \omega\sqrt{\varepsilon\mu}$.

To find the current flowing in the outer cylinder one has only to apply (9-15); it is readily seen that the surface density of the current equals $-H$. By integrating around the whole circle we obtain from (11-47) a total current equal to $-I$. Hence the two cylinders behave like the two conductors of the balanced line discussed in Chap. 6.

The characteristic impedance $Z_l = V/I$ of the line does not equal the wave impedance $E/H = Z$. To be convinced one has only to evaluate V by

$$V = \int_{r_1}^{r_2} E \,\mathrm{d}r = Z \int_{r_1}^{r_2} H \,\mathrm{d}r = \frac{ZI}{2\pi} \int_{r_1}^{r_2} \frac{\mathrm{d}r}{r} = \frac{ZI}{2\pi} \log \frac{r_2}{r_1},$$

with the result

(11-48) $$Z_l = \frac{Z}{2\pi} \log \frac{r_2}{r_1}.$$

The power carried by the line is

$$\overline{W} = \frac{1}{2} \mathscr{Re}\, VI^* = \frac{Z}{4\pi} II^* \log \frac{r_2}{r_1}, \tag{11-49}$$

and it might be readily verified that this expression is identical with that arrived at by means of the Poynting vector.

The power absorbed by the walls can be evaluated by means of (11-41)

$$\overline{W}_p = \frac{1}{4\pi} R_p II^* \left(\frac{1}{r_1} + \frac{1}{r_2}\right),$$

and by (11-40, 49) there follows the value of the attenuation constant

$$\alpha = \frac{1}{2} R_p Y \frac{1/r_1 + 1/r_2}{\log (r_2/r_1)}. \tag{11-50}$$

The attenuation is very great when r_1 is very small.

General Theory of Cylindrical Wave Guides with Metal Walls

§ 10. After the particular cases discussed in the preceding sections we shall outline a general theory of cylindrical wave guides of general cross section and metal walls. The analogy with the preceding particular cases will serve as an orientation.

Let the z-axis be parallel to the generating lines of the cylindrical walls. We shall look for a solution of the type

$$\begin{cases} \boldsymbol{E} = (\boldsymbol{e}_T + e_z \boldsymbol{k}) \exp(-ik_g z), \\ \boldsymbol{H} = (\boldsymbol{h}_T + h_z \boldsymbol{k}) \exp(-ik_g z), \end{cases} \tag{11-51}$$

where both the transverse components $\boldsymbol{e}_T$, $\boldsymbol{h}_T$, and the longitudinal components e_z, h_z depend only on x and y and k_g is a special wave number of the wave guide which is to be determined.

With the assumption that the dielectric is perfect ($\alpha = 0$) Maxwell's equations (7-36) may be written in the form

$$\begin{cases} \text{curl}\, Z\boldsymbol{H} = ik\boldsymbol{E}, \\ \text{curl}\, \boldsymbol{E} \quad = -ikZ\boldsymbol{H}, \end{cases} \tag{11-52}$$

where $Z = \sqrt{\mu/\varepsilon}$ and $k = \omega\sqrt{\varepsilon\mu}$. Substituting (11-51) into (11-52) and recalling (M1-29) we shall have

$$(11\text{-}53)\quad \begin{cases} \operatorname{curl} Z\boldsymbol{h}_T + \operatorname{grad}(Zh_z)\wedge\boldsymbol{k} - ik_g\boldsymbol{k}\wedge Z\boldsymbol{h}_T = ik\boldsymbol{e}_T + ike_z\boldsymbol{k}, \\ \operatorname{curl}\boldsymbol{e}_T + \operatorname{grad} e_z\wedge\boldsymbol{k} - ik_g\boldsymbol{k}\wedge\boldsymbol{e}_T = -ikZ\boldsymbol{h}_T - ikZh_z\boldsymbol{k}. \end{cases}$$

It is evident that the curls appearing in these equations are parallel to $\boldsymbol{k}$ while the gradients are transverse. Then making the vector product of both equations with $\boldsymbol{k}$ there results

$$(11\text{-}54)\quad \begin{cases} -\operatorname{grad} Zh_z - ik_gZ\boldsymbol{h}_T = ik\boldsymbol{e}_T\wedge\boldsymbol{k}, \\ -\operatorname{grad} e_z - ik_g\boldsymbol{e}_T = -ikZ\boldsymbol{h}_T\wedge\boldsymbol{k}. \end{cases}$$

Solving the first equation for $Z\boldsymbol{h}_T$ and substituting into the second and conversely solving the second for $\boldsymbol{e}_T$ and substituting into the first we get

$$(11\text{-}55)\quad \begin{cases} \boldsymbol{e}_T = -i\dfrac{k_g}{k_c^2}\operatorname{grad} e_z + i\dfrac{Zk}{k_c^2}\boldsymbol{k}\wedge\operatorname{grad} h_z, \\ \boldsymbol{h}_T = -i\dfrac{k_g}{k_c^2}\operatorname{grad} h_z - i\dfrac{Yk}{k_c^2}\boldsymbol{k}\wedge\operatorname{grad} e_z, \end{cases}$$

with $k_c^2 = k^2 - k_g^2$. On the other hand substituting (11-51) into the equations div $\boldsymbol{E} = 0$ and div $\boldsymbol{H} = 0$, we readily obtain div $\boldsymbol{e}_T =$ $= ik_ge_z$ and div $\boldsymbol{h}_T = ik_gh_z$. Taking into account these equations and forming the divergences of (11-54) we find by (M1-28)

$$(11\text{-}56)\quad \begin{cases} \nabla^2 h_z = k_g^2 h_z - ikY\boldsymbol{k}\cdot\operatorname{curl}\boldsymbol{e}_T, \\ \nabla^2 e_z = k_g^2 e_z + ikZ\boldsymbol{k}\cdot\operatorname{curl}\boldsymbol{h}_T. \end{cases}$$

By multiplying (11-53) scalarly by $\boldsymbol{k}$ we readily get

$$Z\boldsymbol{k}\cdot\operatorname{curl}\boldsymbol{h}_T = ike_z,$$
$$\boldsymbol{k}\cdot\operatorname{curl}\boldsymbol{e}_T = -ikZh_z,$$

whence upon substitution into (11-56) we finally obtain

$$(11\text{-}57)\quad \begin{cases} \nabla^2 e_z + k_c^2 e_z = 0, \\ \nabla^2 h_z + k_c^2 h_z = 0. \end{cases}$$

we thus have found all the equations necessary for the discussion of the problem. Equations (11-57) have the form of the wave equation (10-5) of the homogeneous kind.

§ 11. If we disregard for a moment the boundary conditions, the procedure to be applied is the following. By solving (11-57) we get the longitudinal components of the field; we substitute their expressions into (11-55) and obtain the transverse components. However, it is readily noted that from this general solution two kinds of independent solutions can be separated. We can take for the first equation (11-57) the particular solution $e_z = 0$, obtaining from (11-55)

$$\text{(11-58)} \qquad TE \qquad \begin{cases} \boldsymbol{e}_T = \dfrac{iZk}{k_c^2}\,\boldsymbol{k} \wedge \operatorname{grad} h_z\,, \\[2ex] \boldsymbol{h}_T = -\dfrac{ik_g}{k_c^2}\operatorname{grad} h_z\,. \end{cases}$$

In this way we have clearly a TE mode. Conversely, taking for the second equation (11-57) a particular solution $h_z = 0$, (11-55) yield

$$\text{(11-59)} \qquad TM \qquad \begin{cases} \boldsymbol{e}_T = -\dfrac{ik_g}{k_c^2}\operatorname{grad} e_z\,, \\[2ex] \boldsymbol{h}_T = -\dfrac{iYk}{k_c^2}\,\boldsymbol{k} \wedge \operatorname{grad} e_z\,, \end{cases}$$

which represent a TM mode. From either (11-58) or (11-59) one may write

$$\text{(11-60)} \qquad TE,\ TM \qquad Z_g \boldsymbol{h}_T = \boldsymbol{k} \wedge \boldsymbol{e}_T\,,$$

the wave impedance Z_g being given by

$$\text{(11-61)} \qquad TE \qquad Z_g = \frac{k}{k_g} Z$$

in the TE case, and by

$$\text{(11-62)} \qquad TM \qquad Z_g = Z\frac{k_g}{k}$$

in the TM case. In general, the field will be represented by a superposition of TE and TM modes.

Let us now consider the boundary conditions. They require that on the walls $\boldsymbol{E}$ be perpendicular and $\boldsymbol{H}$ parallel. Now it is readily seen from (11-58, 59) that to this end it is sufficient to require that e_z as well as the normal derivative of h_z vanish on the walls. Thus the mathematical problem reduces to finding a solution of the wave equation which either vanishes or has a vanishing normal derivative on the boundary of the wave guide cross section. In the first case the solution will be denoted by e_z and the mode will be TM, while in the second case the solution will be denoted by h_z and the mode will be TE.

In textbooks on mathematical physics it is shown that such problems, when the wave guide cross section is bounded, admit of an infinity of discrete solutions, each corresponding to a well-determined and real value of k_c. In other words, there are an infinite number of eigenvalues, each one giving rise either to a TE or to a TM mode.

It will be noted that since the eigenvalues are real, (11-57) have real coefficients. As a consequence any complex eigenfunction e_z or h_z can be considered as a combination of two real eigenfunctions (†); we are then allowed to assume that all the eigenfunctions are real. As a consequence the phase is constant over any plane $z = constant$. The wave surfaces are planes perpendicular to the z axis. The same will hold for the transverse eigenfunctions as is readily seen from (11-58, 59).

§ 12. Let us denote by k_c the eigenvalue corresponding to a given mode of the guide. By the above given definition of k_c we have

$$k^2 = k_c^2 + k_g^2, \tag{11-63}$$

a relation which enables us to evaluate the wave number k_g within the guide. Let us assume that k_g is real and consequently less than

(†) It is evident that both the real and the imaginary parts of a complex eigenfunction satisfy both the differential equation and the boundary conditions.

or equal to k. The velocity of propagation of the phase along the guide will be given by

$$v_g = \frac{\omega}{k_g} = \frac{k}{k_g} v, \tag{11-64}$$

and the wavelength by

$$\lambda_g = \frac{k}{k_g} \lambda \tag{11-65}$$

Both have values greater than or equal to those holding in a free dielectric.

Solving (11-63) for k_g,

$$k_g = \sqrt{k^2 - k_c^2}, \tag{11-66}$$

we see that k_g is real (and positive by definition) as long as k is greater than or equal to the constant k_c, which is called the *critical wave number* for the mode considered. When k is smaller than k_c, $k_g = -i\sqrt{k_c^2 - k^2}$ is imaginary (†). As a result both v_g and λ_g are also imaginary. The mode is evanescent and falls off exponentially in the direction of z without carrying any power. From (11-61, 62) we see that the wave impedance is a pure reactance, inductive in the TE case and capacitive in the TM case. The critical wavelength is naturally

$$\lambda_c = \frac{2\pi}{k_c}, \tag{11-67}$$

and the critical frequency $\nu_c = v/\lambda_c$.

In conclusion we may say that for a fixed value of k the wave guide admits of a well determined number of TE and TM modes which actually travel along its axis ($k_c < k$) and an infinite number of TE and TM modes which are attenuated ($k_c > k$) and do not carry any power. The mode having the smallest critical wave number or the longest critical wavelength is called the *dominant*

(†) As already explained the minus sign has the purpose of making the field (11-51) to vanish instead of tending to infinity when $z \to \infty$.

mode. If the wavelength employed is shorter than the critical wavelength of the dominant mode and longer than the critical wavelengths of all the remaining modes, the only mode which can travel along the guide is the dominant mode.

Suppose there exists a mode with a very small value of k_c. From (11-58, 59) it is seen that the transverse field may not be very weak even if h_z or e_z are very small. In the limit a mode having $k_c = 0$ will admit a non-vanishing transverse field even if both h_z and e_z vanish. Hence we conclude that $k_c = 0$ gives rise to a *TEM* mode. When this mode exists it is termed the *principal mode* and it represents at the same time the dominant mode. It has $k_g = k$ and consequentely the velocity of propagation (11-64), the wavelength (11-65) and the wave impedance (11-61, 62) will coincide with those in the free dielectric. The critical wavelength is infinite so that the mode travels in the guide whatever the frequency.

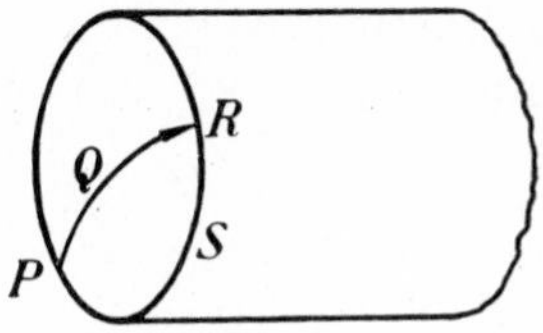

Fig. 52

However, the principal mode need not always exist. The condition for its existence is that the wave guide consist of at least two distinct conductors isolated from one another. To show this let us first assume that this condition is not satisfied. We recall that any line of electric force *PQR* (Fig. 52) starts from a point *P* and ends at a point *R* of the walls, having in both points the direction of the normal to the wall. The line integral of the electric force along *PQR* equals the electromotive force along the circuit *PQRSP*; as such an integral does not vanish, the circuit must be linked with a magnetic current. However, no longitudinal magnetic current can exist because $h_z = 0$. Hence it is impossible for the electric force line *PQR* to belong to a principal mode.

If the wall consists of two or more conductors isolated from one another the above reasoning does not hold. Actually we have already seen two examples of principal modes namely in the case of the two plate wave guide and in the case of the coaxial line. Also the two wire line discussed in Chap. 6 is clearly a wave guide admitting of a principal mode. The guide walls, however strange this may appear, are represented by the two wires; if the wires are perfect conductors the mode of propagation investigated in Chap. 6 by means of the currents and voltages is exactly the principal mode.

Orthogonality of Wave Guide Modes

§ 13. Let us write the eigenvalues in any prefixed order giving to each one a subscript (integer).

Consider two TE modes corresponding to two different eigenvalues k_{cm}, k_{cn} and denote by h_{zm}, h_{zn} respectively the longitudinal components of their magnetic forces. Since the eigenvalues, as already remarked, are always real, h_{zm} and h^*_{zn} satisfy the two wave equations

$$\text{(11-68)} \qquad \nabla^2 h_{zm} + k^2_{cm} h_{zm} = 0, \quad \nabla^2 h^*_{zn} + k^2_{cn} h^*_{zn} = 0.$$

Let us apply to these two functions the second Green formula (M1-53) carrying out the integration over a slice of wave guide having unit thickness. As h_z is independent of z the integration with respect to z is readily carried out with the result

$$\text{(11-69)} \quad \iint_{\Sigma} (h_{zm}\nabla^2 h^*_{zn} - h^*_{zn}\nabla^2 h_{zm})\,\mathrm{d}\Sigma = \iint_{\Sigma_p} \left(h_{zm}\frac{\partial h^*_{zn}}{\partial n} - h^*_{zn}\frac{\partial h_{zm}}{\partial n} \right) \mathrm{d}\Sigma_p,$$

where Σ denotes the cross section of the wave guide, Σ_p the walls of the unit slice and n their normal (†) (the bases of the slice obviously give a null contribution because over them $\partial/\partial n = \pm\partial/\partial z$). The right hand side of (11-69) is zero because the normal derivative of h vanishes on the walls. Hence, expressing the Laplacian

(†) Naturally this unit vector has nothing to do with the subscript of h_{zn}.

operators by means of (11-68) equation (11-69) yields

$$(k_{cm}^2 - k_{cn}^2) \iint_\Sigma h_{zm} h_{zn}^* \, d\Sigma = 0,$$

and since the two eigenvalues are distinct, there results

$$\iint_\Sigma h_{zm} h_{zn}^* \, d\Sigma = 0. \tag{11-70}$$

The two functions h_{zm}, h_{zn} are said to be *orthogonal* to one another (†).

Let us now apply to the same functions the first Green formula (M1-34); we obtain

$$\iint_\Sigma h_{zm} \nabla^2 h_{zn}^* \, d\Sigma = -\iint_\Sigma \operatorname{grad} h_{zm} \cdot \operatorname{grad} h_{zn}^* \, d\Sigma + \iint_{\Sigma_p} h_{zm} \frac{\partial h_{zn}^*}{\partial n} \, d\Sigma_p. \tag{11-71}$$

The last integral vanishes for the reasons already explained, while the first vanishes by virtue of (11-69, 70). We are left then with the second integral which by (11-58) readily yields

$$\iint_\Sigma \boldsymbol{e}_{Tm} \cdot \boldsymbol{e}_{Tn}^* \, d\Sigma = 0, \qquad \iint_\Sigma \boldsymbol{h}_{Tm} \cdot \boldsymbol{h}_{Tn}^* \, d\Sigma = 0. \tag{11-72}$$

With similar reasoning, taking into account that E vanishes at the walls, we can find for two TM modes

$$\iint_\Sigma e_{zm} e_{zn}^* \, d\Sigma = 0, \tag{11-73}$$

as well as the relations (11-72).

Finally let e_{zm} and h_{zn} belong to a mode TM and to a mode TE respectively. A straightforward application of the divergence theorem to the wave guide slice yields

$$\iint_\Sigma \operatorname{div} [e_{zm} \operatorname{curl} (h_{zn}^* \boldsymbol{k})] \, d\Sigma = \iint_{\Sigma_p} e_{zm} \operatorname{curl} (h_{zn}^* \boldsymbol{k}) \cdot \boldsymbol{n} \, d\Sigma_P,$$

the integration of the right-hand side being extended only over

(†) It can be shown that if two or more distinct modes have the same eigenvalue (degenerate case) the modes can always be chosen in such a way that the orthogonality relation (11-70) holds between any two of them.

the walls, since the bases give equal and opposite contributions (†). On the other hand, e_z vanishes on the walls, so the right-hand side vanishes. As for the left side, its integrand by virtue of (M1-27, 29) may be written grad $e_{zm} \cdot$ grad $h_{zm} \wedge \boldsymbol{k}$. Hence, recalling (11-58, 59), we find again the first equation (11-72); and with similar reasoning we would find again the second. We may conclude that the orthogonality relations (11-72) hold for any pair of distinct modes.

When m and n are equal, we have obviously a single mode and (11-72) cease to be valid as one may easily verify by considering that in such case the integrands are always positive. Of course the values of the integrals will depend on the value of the field, which is arbitrary. We shall choose the intensity of the field in such a way that

(11-74) $$\iint_{\Sigma} \boldsymbol{e}_{Tm} \cdot \boldsymbol{e}_{Tm}^{*} \, d\Sigma = |Z_{gm}|.$$

This is called the condition of *normalization*. From the dimensional standpoint it may appear absurd. However we can accept (11-74) for the following reason. The eigenfunction $\boldsymbol{e}_{Tm}$ serves only the purpose of fixing the relative distribution of the transverse electric field, and in practice it must be multiplied by a coefficient (amplitude) determining the intensity of the mode in each real case. Hence we may as well assume that $\boldsymbol{e}_{Tm}$ is the square root of an impedance divided by a length and is measured in *ohm*$^{\frac{1}{2}}$ · *meters*$^{-1}$ as is required by (11-74); we shall then ascribe to the amplitude the necessary dimension for the product to be an electric field (*volt/meter*). It is readily seen that the amplitude will be measured in *watts*$^{\frac{1}{2}}$.

Taking into account (11-60), we find from (11-74) the normalization condition for $\boldsymbol{h}_{Tm}$:

(11-75) $$\iint_{\Sigma} \boldsymbol{h}_{Tm} \cdot \boldsymbol{h}_{Tm}^{*} \, d\Sigma = |Y_{gm}|.$$

(†) Actually both contributions are zero because the curl has a vanishing longitudinal component.

Finally we note that for the traveling modes the wave impedance is real and it is unnecessary to indicate the absolute values in (11-74, 75).

Representation of the Field by a Sum of Orthogonal Modes

§ 14. It has already been mentioned that the most general field existing in the wave guide results from a superposition of all the possible modes in arbitrary proportions. Naturally, if the field is propagated in the direction of the z axis (as for instance when the generator is placed at a smaller abscissa than that considered) the component modes will also be progressive in the positive direction of z; they will be the modes discussed in the preceding sections.

Having accepted these assumptions as intuitive let us investigate how a given electromagnetic field is distributed among the different modes. Denoting by $\boldsymbol{E}_T(x, y, z)$ the transverse electric field we write by (11-51)

$$\boldsymbol{E}_T(x, y, z) = \sum_{0}^{\infty}{}_m A_m \boldsymbol{e}_{Tm} \exp(-ik_{gm}z). \tag{11-76}$$

We have to determine the coefficients A_m of this expansion, i.e., the amplitudes. We may follow the classical procedure applied in M3 to the Fourier series. We multiply both sides scalarly by $\boldsymbol{e}_{Tn}^*$ and integrate over the guide cross section. From the conditions of orthogonality and normalization we readily find

$$A_n = |Y_{gn}| \exp(ik_{gn}z) \iint_{\Sigma} \boldsymbol{E}_T(x, y, z) \cdot \boldsymbol{e}_{Tn}^* \, d\Sigma,$$

or in a simpler form setting $z = 0$ and taking into account that A_n is independent of z

$$A_n = |Y_{gn}| \iint_{\Sigma} \boldsymbol{E}_T(x, y, 0) \cdot \boldsymbol{e}_{Tn}^* \, d\Sigma. \tag{11-77}$$

We thus find that in order to evaluate the different proportions of the modes in the resultant field we need only know the transverse electric field at $z = 0$ (which is an arbitrary cross section of the guide). Naturally the same holds for the magnetic field.

In order to evaluate A_m from a knowledge of $\boldsymbol{E}_T(x, y, z)$ it was necessary to assume that the field contained only progressive modes; this is the radiation condition in the form holding for a wave guide. But the most general field will consist of a set of progressive modes plus a set of regressive modes. The regressive modes may be derived from the progressive ones simply by reversing the sign of k_g. We shall denote by the subscript $-m$ the regressive mode corresponding to the progressive mode of subscript m. Setting $\boldsymbol{e}_{T,-m} = \boldsymbol{e}_{Tm}$, $k_{g,-m} = -k_{gm}$ and consequentely by (11-61, 62) $Y_{g,-m} = -Y_{gm}$, we shall be able to complete (11-76) and express the most general field within the guide in the following way

$$\text{(11-78)} \qquad \boldsymbol{E}_T(x, y, z) = \sum_{-\infty}^{+\infty}{}_m A_m \boldsymbol{e}_{Tm} \exp(-ik_{gm}z),$$

where it has been assumed that m takes both the value $+0$ and the value -0. The coefficient A_m is called the (complex) amplitude of mode m; as already stated it is measured in *watts*$^{\frac{1}{2}}$.

From (11-78) the magnetic field is found by (11-60) to be

$$\text{(11-79)} \quad \boldsymbol{H}_T(x, y, z) = \sum_{-\infty}^{+\infty}{}_m A_m Y_{gm} \boldsymbol{k} \wedge \boldsymbol{e}_{Tm} \exp(-ik_{gm}z).$$

Electromagnetic Energy in the Guide

§ 15. To evaluate the complex power carried by the field along the guide we shall consider for simplicity the cross section $z = 0$ obtaining

$$W = \frac{1}{2}\boldsymbol{k} \cdot \iint_\Sigma [\boldsymbol{E}_T \wedge \boldsymbol{H}_T^*]_{z=0} \mathrm{d}\Sigma =$$
$$= \frac{1}{2}\boldsymbol{k} \cdot \iint_\Sigma \left\{ \sum_{-\infty}^{+\infty}{}_{m,n} A_m A_n^* Y_{gn}^* [\boldsymbol{e}_{Tm} \wedge (\boldsymbol{k} \wedge \boldsymbol{e}_{Tn}^*)] \right\} \mathrm{d}\Sigma.$$

By interchanging the integrations and the sums and expanding the double vector product we find by virtue of the orthogonality and normalization conditions

$$W = \sum_0^\infty{}_m W_m + \sum_0^\infty{}_m W'_m,$$

having set

$$(11\text{-}80)\quad \begin{cases} W_m = \dfrac{1}{2}\dfrac{Y^*_{gm}}{|Y_{gm}|}(A_m A^*_m - A_{-m}A^*_{-m}) \quad \textit{watts}, \\[2ex] W'_m = \dfrac{1}{2}\dfrac{Y^*_{gm}}{|Y_{gm}|}(A^*_m A_{-m} - A_m A^*_{-m}) \quad \textit{watts}. \end{cases}$$

If the mode m is a traveling mode, Y_{gm} is real and positive; therefore equations (11-80) become

$$(11\text{-}81)\quad \begin{cases} W_m = \dfrac{1}{2}(A_m A^*_m - A_{-m}A^*_{-m}), \\[2ex] W'_m = \dfrac{1}{2}(A^*_m A_{-m} - A_m A^*_{-m}). \end{cases}$$

In this case W_m is real and represents the real power carried by the progressive mode minus the power carried by the regressive mode. On the contrary, W' is purely imaginary, being the difference of two complex conjugate quantities; therefore W' does not give any contribution to the real power. Hence we may derive the remarkable conclusion that each progressive or regressive mode of the traveling type carries its own power, no matter whether it is isolated or accompanied by other modes. Such modes may be superimposed without any mutual disturbance or interaction.

The situation is different when the mode m is evanescent; Y_{gm} is pure imaginary so (11-80) become

$$(11\text{-}82)\quad \begin{cases} W_m = \pm\dfrac{i}{2}(A_m A^*_m - A_{-m}A^*_{-m}), \\[2ex] W'_m = \pm\dfrac{i}{2}(A^*_m A_{-m} - A_m A^*_{-m}). \end{cases}$$

In this case W_m is imaginary and does not contribute to the real power. However it is interesting to note that W'_m is real and consequently gives rise to an actual energy flow. But we call attention to the fact that this occurs only when both the $+m$ and the $-m$ modes are present at the same time. In many cases only the evanescent modes of the progressive set or those of the regressive set are present, so that W'_m vanishes. The presence of both sets of modes is of importance when the guide contains two successive obstacles located rather close to one another.

§ 16. Let us now deal with the energy stored in a unit length of the guide. For simplicity we shall restrict the investigation to a single traveling mode. The electric and magnetic energies will be found from (11-51, 78, 79) to be

$$(11\text{-}83)\quad \begin{cases} \overline{U}_e = \dfrac{1}{4}\varepsilon \displaystyle\iiint_V \boldsymbol{E}\cdot\boldsymbol{E}^* \mathrm{d}V = \dfrac{1}{4}\varepsilon A A^* \iint_\Sigma (\boldsymbol{e}_T\cdot\boldsymbol{e}_T^* + e_z e_z^*)\,\mathrm{d}\Sigma, \\ \overline{U}_m = \dfrac{1}{4}\mu \displaystyle\iiint_V \boldsymbol{H}\cdot\boldsymbol{H}^* \mathrm{d}V = \dfrac{1}{4}\mu A A^* \iint_\Sigma (\boldsymbol{h}_T\cdot\boldsymbol{h}_T^* + h_z h_z^*)\,\mathrm{d}\Sigma, \end{cases}$$

the volume of a unit length of wave guide having been denoted by V and the surface of the cross section by Σ. Let the mode considered be TE. Then by (11-58) the preceding equations become

$$(11\text{-}84)\quad \begin{cases} \overline{U}_e = \dfrac{1}{4}\varepsilon Z^2 \dfrac{k^2}{k_c^4} A A^* \displaystyle\iint_\Sigma \operatorname{grad} h_z \cdot \operatorname{grad} h_z^*\,\mathrm{d}\Sigma, \\ \overline{U}_m = \dfrac{1}{4}\mu \dfrac{k_g^2}{k_c^4} A A^* \displaystyle\iint_\Sigma \operatorname{grad} h_z \cdot \operatorname{grad} h_z^*\,\mathrm{d}\Sigma + \dfrac{1}{4}\mu A A^* \iint_\Sigma h_z h_z^*\,\mathrm{d}\Sigma. \end{cases}$$

By means of (11-71) and of the first equation (11-68), and taking into account the boundary conditions, we get

$$\iint_\Sigma \operatorname{grad} h_z \cdot \operatorname{grad} h_z^*\,\mathrm{d}\Sigma = \iint_{\Sigma_p} h_z \frac{\partial h_z^*}{\partial n}\,\mathrm{d}\Sigma_p - \iint_\Sigma h_z \nabla^2 h_z^*\,\mathrm{d}\Sigma = k_c^2 \iint_\Sigma h_z h_z^*\,\mathrm{d}\Sigma.$$

Substituting into (11-84) and recalling (11-63), the following is readily obtained:

$$(11\text{-}85)\qquad TE\quad \overline{U}_e = \overline{U}_m = \frac{1}{4}\mu \frac{k^2}{k_c^2} A A^* \iint_\Sigma h_z h_z^*\,\mathrm{d}\Sigma \qquad \textit{joules/meter}.$$

Thus the electric and magnetic energies stored in the guide are equal.

In a similar way we derive for a *TM* mode

$$\text{(11-86)} \qquad TM \quad \overline{U}_e = \overline{U}_m = \frac{1}{4}\varepsilon\frac{k^2}{k_c^2}AA^*\iint\limits_{\Sigma} e_z e_z^* \, d\Sigma \qquad \textit{joules/meter},$$

and again $\overline{U}_e$ and $\overline{U}_m$ are equal.

For the evanescent modes the situation is different because k_g is imaginary. The exponentials of (11-51) have real exponents and do not cancel in the product of the two complex conjugate quantities. Besides, $k_c^2 + k_g k_g^*$ is greater than $k^2 = k_c^2 + k_g^2$. Taking into account these facts we may repeat the previous calculation. The most interesting result arrived at in this way is that $\overline{U}_e$ does not equal $\overline{U}_m$. We have instead

$$\text{(11-87)} \qquad TE \qquad \frac{\overline{U}_e}{\overline{U}_m} = \frac{k_c^2 - |k_g|^2}{k_c^2 + |k_g|^2},$$

for the *TE* case and

$$\text{(11-88)} \qquad TM \qquad \frac{\overline{U}_e}{\overline{U}_m} = \frac{k_c^2 + |k_g|^2}{k_c^2 - |k_g|^2},$$

for the *TM* case. Hence in the *TE* case the magnetic energy is greater than the electric energy and vice versa.

Velocity of Energy

§ 17. Consider a progressive mode traveling along the guide. As by (11-85, 86) the electric and magnetic energies are equal, the total energy $\overline{U}$ stored in the unit length of the guide will be

$$\overline{U} = 2\overline{U}_e = 2\overline{U}_m.$$

Let the mode be *TE*. Then from the first equation (11-83) we have

$$\overline{U} = \frac{1}{2}\varepsilon AA^*\iint\limits_{\Sigma} \mathbf{e}_T \cdot \mathbf{e}_T^* \, d\Sigma,$$

and by (11-74) taking into account that Z_g is real and positive

$$\text{(11-89)} \qquad TE \qquad \overline{U} = \frac{1}{2}\varepsilon Z_g AA^*.$$

in an analogous way for a TM mode we shall utilize the second equation (11-83) obtaining

$$\overline{U} = \frac{1}{2}\mu AA^* \iint_{\Sigma} \boldsymbol{h}_T \cdot \boldsymbol{h}_T^* \,\mathrm{d}\Sigma,$$

and by (11-75)

$$\text{(11-90)} \qquad TM \qquad \overline{U} = \frac{1}{2}\mu Y_g AA^*.$$

However taking into account (11-61, 62) we see that (11-89, 90) yield the same value for $\overline{U}$, namely,

$$\text{(11-91)} \quad TE, TM \quad \overline{U} = \frac{1}{2}\frac{k}{k_g}\sqrt{\varepsilon\mu}\,AA^* = \frac{1}{2}\frac{k}{k_g}\frac{1}{v}AA^* \quad \textit{joules/meter}.$$

Let us now assume that this energy travels in the guide with the velocity v_e. The energy flow or the power crossing a given section of the guide will be represented by

$$\text{(11-92)} \qquad \overline{W} = \overline{U}v_e = \frac{1}{2}\frac{k}{k_g}\frac{v_e}{v}AA^*.$$

Now we know that the power actually carried by the guide is $AA^*/2$; whence

$$\text{(11-93)} \qquad v_e = \frac{k_g}{k}v,$$

or by (11-66)

$$\text{(11-94)} \qquad v_e = \frac{\sqrt{k^2 - k_c^2}}{k^2}v.$$

Hence we see that the velocity of the energy is always smaller than v.

A comparison of (11-93) and (11-64) shows that

(11-95) $$v_g v_e = v^2.$$

Hence the phase velocity in the unbounded dielectric is the geometric mean of the phase velocity and the energy velocity within the guide.

Attenuation in a Wave Guide

§ 18. Sometimes one must take into account that the metallic walls have only a finite conductivity and that the dielectric is not perfect. Both facts give rise to a dissipation of energy and consequently to an attenuation.

The power dissipated peı unit length in the walls may be evaluated by the same formula (11-41) which was derived for the rectangular guide. It will be represented by

$$\overline{W}_p = \frac{1}{2} R_p \oint \boldsymbol{H} \cdot \boldsymbol{H}^* \mathrm{d}l,$$

where R_p denotes the intrinsic resistance of the walls and the integral is extended around the boundary of a normal cross section of the guide. In our case we may also write

(11-96) $$\overline{W}_p = \frac{1}{2} R_p A A^* \oint (\boldsymbol{h}_T \cdot \boldsymbol{h}_T^* + h_z h_z^*)\, \mathrm{d}l.$$

As usual, we shall define Q_p in such a way that ω/Q_p be equal to the ratio of the absorbed power and the stored energy. Hence by (11-91) we find

(11-97) $$\frac{1}{Q_p} = R_p \frac{k_g}{k^2} \oint (\boldsymbol{h}_T \cdot \boldsymbol{h}_T^* + h_z h_z^*)\, \mathrm{d}l.$$

The power dissipated per unit length in the dielectric will be given by

(11-98) $$\overline{W}_d = \frac{1}{2} \gamma \iiint_V \boldsymbol{E} \cdot \boldsymbol{E}^* \mathrm{d}V,$$

where V indicates the volume of a unit length of the guide. The right-hand side is similar to that of the first equation (11-83) except for the change of $\varepsilon/4$ into $\gamma/2$. If we bear in mind the arguments developed when passing from (11-83) to (11-89), we conclude that from (11-98) we may pass to

$$\overline{W}_d = \frac{1}{2}\gamma Z \frac{k}{k_g} AA^*. \tag{11-99}$$

We may now define Q_d in such manner as to have $\omega/Q_d = \overline{W}_d/\overline{U}$; from (11-91, 99) it is then found

$$Q_d = \frac{\omega}{v\gamma Z} = \frac{\omega\varepsilon}{\gamma}, \tag{11-100}$$

which simply represents the Q of the unbounded dielectric as given by (7-47).

It is evident that defining an overall Q by $\omega/Q = (\overline{W}_p + \overline{W}_d)/\overline{U}$ we obtain

$$\frac{1}{Q} = \frac{1}{Q_p} + \frac{1}{Q_d}. \tag{11-101}$$

This formula is similar to (6-70), which holds for a transmission line.

§ 19. The dissipation of energy gives rise, as already stated, to an attenuation in the wave guide. To evaluate this attenuation we shall consider an infinitesimal slice of the wave guide having the thickness $\mathrm{d}z$. The power entering the slice will be represented by $\overline{W}(z)$ and the power leaving it by $\overline{W}(z + \mathrm{d}z)$. The difference represents the power dissipated $(\overline{W}_p + \overline{W}_d)\mathrm{d}z$; hence we have

$$\overline{W}(z) - \overline{W}(z + \mathrm{d}z) = (\overline{W}_p + \overline{W}_d)\,\mathrm{d}z.$$

However $\overline{W}_p + \overline{W}_d$ may be replaced by $\overline{U}\omega/Q$ whence

$$\frac{\mathrm{d}\overline{W}}{\mathrm{d}z} = -\frac{\omega}{Q}\overline{U}.$$

By recalling (11-92) we may write also

$$\frac{\mathrm{d}\overline{W}}{\mathrm{d}z} = -\frac{\omega}{Qv_e}\overline{W},$$

Upon integration of this differential equation we get

$$\overline{W}(z) = \overline{W}(0) \exp\left(-\frac{\omega}{Qv_e} z\right).$$

This equation governs the power attenuation in the guide. The attenuation constant α_g of the electric or magnetic field is obviously half that of the power. Consequently we have

$$\alpha_g = \frac{1}{2} \frac{\omega}{Qv_e}, \tag{11-102}$$

a formula which is perfectly similar to (7-48) holding in the case of free propagation.

In conclusion we may say that the propagation constant in the guide is

$$h_g = \alpha_g + ik_g, \tag{11-103}$$

instead of $h_g = ik_g$ as in the case of a lossless wave guide.

CHAPTER 12

Wave Guides as Transmission Lines

Voltage and Current in a Wave Guide

§ 1. It has already been seen that a two plate wave guide or a coaxial guide when operating with a *TEM* mode may be pictured as transmission lines. This means that, instead of considering the electromagnetic field inside the guide, one may consider the voltage V and the current I. The two interpretations are absolutely equivalent; however, as a rule the first is more convenient because V and I depend only on z (in the well-known exponential way) while $\boldsymbol{E}$ and $\boldsymbol{H}$ depend also in a more or less complicated manner on x and y. It is natural to ask whether or not it is always possible to replace a wave guide carrying any given mode m by an equivalent transmission line.

Now it is readily seen, for instance, referring to a rectangular guide that it is not always obvious how to determine in a unique way the values of V and I; the value of V depends on the choice of the two points of a cross section between which the voltage is measured and for a *TE* mode also on the path followed; the current I may also present a transverse component. However this partial arbitrariness in the choice of V and I is not a drawback and may be utilized to set up a simple and elegant representation of propagation in a wave guide.

Suppose the wave guide carries only a non-evanescent mode m (progressive or regressive). Naturally we must proceed in such a way that the real power evaluated by means of V and I be equal to that actually flowing in the guide. However we shall take advantage of the above mentioned arbitrariness by setting a more stringent condition; we shall require that the complex power $VI^*/2$ be identical with the complex power $W_m + W'_m$ evaluated by means of the field vectors. By (11-81) we have at $z = 0$

$$VI^* = A_m A_m^* - A_{-m} A_{-m}^* + A_m^* A_{-m} - A_m A_{-m}^* .$$

It is readily verified that we may set

$$\text{(12-1)} \qquad \begin{cases} V = A_m + A_{-m}, \\ I = A_m - A_{-m}. \end{cases}$$

These relations are absurd from a dimensional standpoint. By convention A_m is measured in *watts*$^{\frac{1}{2}}$ while V and I are measured in *volts* and in *amperes* respectively. However it will be understood that (12-1) hold in a purely numerical sense. For instance the number of *volts* which measures V is equal to the number of *watts*$^{\frac{1}{2}}$ which measures $A_m + A_{-m}$. As a consequence relations (12-1) would change if the units were changed.

The above conditions amount to the same as setting equal to unity the characteristic impedance of the line; this is easily derived from (12-1) in the case when no regressive wave is present ($A_{-m} = 0$).

One might suppose that the introduction of V and I as in a transmission line would allow us to treat in as simple a way the reflection in a wave guide. Unfortunately the situation in a wave guide is somewhat more complicated than in a transmission line because ordinarily it is not sufficient to consider an incident wave, a reflected wave and a transmitted wave. One of the very few cases where this is possible is represented by a wave guide of uniform cross section with a sudden change at $z = 0$ of the inner dielectric; in this case reflection takes place in the same way as for a free plane wave. In practice such a situation does not present much interest.

Let us consider instead the junction of two wave guides of different cross section. The transverse components of the field must change with continuity from the first to the second guide. Now it happens that in general this continuity cannot be obtained by simply considering one incident mode, one reflected mode and one transmitted mode; there arises instead an entire set of reflected as well as transmitted modes. Therefore the junction of two different wave guides is equivalent to the junction of several transmission lines and requires a new treatment. The same assertion is valid for the case when a diaphragm, a wire or an obstacle of any kind is introduced in a wave guide of constant cross section; the obstacle gives rise to an entire set of progressive and of regressive modes, and hence is equivalent to the junction of several lines.

Tensor Impedance

§ **2.** We shall now consider the junction of n wave guides. It will be represented (Fig. 53) by a metal box fed by the guides. The wave guides will have different cross sections; however, they will all be assumed lossless. A dissipation will possibly take place within the box.

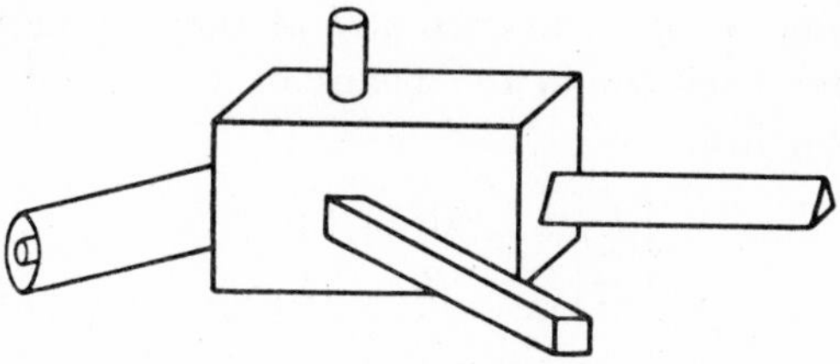

Fig. 53

Let a single progressive mode and its corresponding regressive mode travel in each guide. This condition might be realized by taking the cross section so small as to admit only the dominant mode, as is nearly always done in practice. However, it is not necessary that such a condition be realized in physical reality (†). If a wave guide is capable of carrying more than one traveling mode, we shall picture it as a combination of several guides superimposed on one another, each carrying a single mode; this is possible, as already noted, on account of the mutual independence of both the amplitudes and the powers of different modes.

For each guide we shall choose a z axis directed toward the junction box and a reference plane $z = 0$ which will be called the *terminal* of the wave guide. The terminal will be assumed sufficiently removed from the junction so as to authorize us to dis-

(†) In some cases this is even impossible because the wave guide admits more than one dominant mode (degenerate case), as it happens for instance in a rectangular wave guide.

regard all the evanescent modes arising at the junction. In conclusion in each guide at $z = 0$ we shall have to consider a wave of amplitude A^i traveling toward the junction and a wave of amplitude A^r coming from the junction; the subscript m is now useless and will be omitted. The transverse components of the electric and magnetic forces will be found from (11-78, 79) to be represented by

$$\text{(12-2)} \qquad \begin{cases} \boldsymbol{E}_T(x, y, 0) = (A^i + A^r)\,\boldsymbol{e}_T, \\ \boldsymbol{H}_T(x, y, 0) = Y_g(A^i - A^r)\,\boldsymbol{k} \wedge \boldsymbol{e}_T, \end{cases}$$

$\boldsymbol{e}_T$, being the transverse eigenfunction of the mode traveling in the guide and Y_g the corresponding wave admittance.

If the voltage V and the current I at the terminal ($z = 0$) are introduced for each guide by means of (12-1), equation (12-2) will transform into

$$\text{(12-3)} \qquad \begin{cases} \boldsymbol{E}_T(x, y, 0) = V\boldsymbol{e}_T, \\ \boldsymbol{H}_T(x, y, 0) = I\boldsymbol{h}_T. \end{cases}$$

We already know that $\mathscr{R}e VI^*/2$ represents the difference of the progressive and regressive powers or the overall power carried into the box by the wave guide considered.

We shall denote each wave guide as well as all the physical quantities referring to it by an integral subscript (ranging from 1 to n). Let us interpret $V_1, V_2, \ldots V_n$ and $I_1, I_2, \ldots I_n$ as the rectangular components of two vectors $\boldsymbol{V}$ and $\boldsymbol{I}$ respectively in an n-dimensional space. The complex power W entering the junction box will be represented by the very simple expression

$$\text{(12-4)} \qquad W = \frac{1}{2}\,\boldsymbol{V} \cdot \boldsymbol{I}^*,$$

which is readily verified.

§ 3. We shall now derive an important uniqueness theorem: The knowledge of the transverse components of either the electric or the magnetic field over all the guide terminals is sufficient to completely determine the electromagnetic field inside the box.

First of all let us recall (7-25) and integrate both sides over a volume enclosed by a surface Σ which coincides with the junction box and intersects each guide at the corresponding terminal. By the divergence theorem we shall obtain

$$\frac{1}{2}\iint_{\Sigma} \boldsymbol{E} \wedge \boldsymbol{H}^* \cdot \boldsymbol{k} \mathrm{d}\Sigma = \iiint_{V} [\overline{W}_m + \overline{W}_e + 2i\omega(\overline{U}_m - \overline{U}_e)] \, \mathrm{d}V. \tag{12-5}$$

having taken into account that $\boldsymbol{k}$ represents the inner normal. The surface integral of the left side is extended only over the guide terminals since everywhere else over Σ the integrand vanishes. We recall that $\overline{W}_m$ and $\overline{W}_e$ represent the powers dissipated per unit volume on account of the magnetic and electric Joule effects while $\overline{U}_m$ and $\overline{U}_e$ represent the densities of the magnetic and electric energies stored in the medium.

Let us now assume for a moment that there exist two different solutions $\boldsymbol{E}$, $\boldsymbol{H}$ and $\boldsymbol{E}'$, $\boldsymbol{H}'$ of Maxwell's equations having on the terminals the same transverse components either of the electric or of the magnetic field. The difference of these two solutions will in turn represent a solution of Maxwell's equations to which we may apply (12-5), assuming that the medium filling the box is a dispersionless dielectric presenting a very small conductivity γ. We shall thus obtain

$$\frac{1}{2}\iint_{\Sigma} (\boldsymbol{E} - \boldsymbol{E}') \wedge (\boldsymbol{H}^* - \boldsymbol{H}'^*) \cdot \boldsymbol{k} \mathrm{d}\Sigma = \iiint_{V} \left\{ \frac{1}{2}\gamma(\boldsymbol{E} - \boldsymbol{E}') \cdot (\boldsymbol{E}^* - \boldsymbol{E}'^*) + \right.$$

$$\left. + \frac{1}{2} i\omega\mu(\boldsymbol{H} - \boldsymbol{H}') \cdot (\boldsymbol{H}^* - \boldsymbol{H}'^*) - \frac{1}{2} i\omega\varepsilon (\boldsymbol{E} - \boldsymbol{E}') \cdot (\boldsymbol{E}^* - \boldsymbol{E}^{*\prime}) \right\} \mathrm{d}V.$$

The left side vanishes if $\boldsymbol{E} = \boldsymbol{E}'$ or if $\boldsymbol{H} = \boldsymbol{H}'$ over Σ (indeed the equality of the transverse components would be sufficient); both the real and imaginary parts of the right-hand side must vanish, so we may conclude that $\boldsymbol{E} = \boldsymbol{E}'$ and $\boldsymbol{H} = \boldsymbol{H}'$ everywhere.

To demonstrate this uniqueness theorem, we had to assume $\gamma \neq 0$. However, since a very small value or even an infinitesimal value of γ is sufficient for the demonstration, the theorem will apply in the limit also to the case of a good dielectric.

An obvious consequence of the uniqueness theorem is that the knowledge of the transverse value of $\boldsymbol{H}$ on all the terminals is sufficient to determine also the transverse component of $\boldsymbol{E}$ on the terminals. This by (12-3) is equivalent to the assertion that the knowledge of $\boldsymbol{I}$ is sufficient for determining $\boldsymbol{V}$. On the other hand, owing to the linearity of Maxwell's equations, the dependency of V on I cannot be but linear; in other words, the components of $\boldsymbol{V}$ must be linear combinations of those of $\boldsymbol{I}$. Hence there must exist a tensor of the second order $\boldsymbol{Z}$ in n-dimensional space such that

$$V = \boldsymbol{Z} \cdot \boldsymbol{I}. \tag{12-6}$$

It is natural to call $\boldsymbol{Z}$ the *tensor impedance* (†) or simply the impedance.

In terms of the tensor impedance the complex power (12-4) may be written, recalling (M2-16),

$$W = \frac{1}{2} \boldsymbol{Z} : \boldsymbol{I}\boldsymbol{I}^*. \tag{12-7}$$

It will be remarked now that, in the same way as it was shown that the knowledge of $\boldsymbol{I}$ is sufficient to determine $\boldsymbol{V}$, it could have been shown that the knowledge of $\boldsymbol{V}$ is sufficient to determine $\boldsymbol{I}$. As a consequence there shall exist a tensor of the second order $\boldsymbol{Y}$ such that

$$\boldsymbol{I} = \boldsymbol{Y} \cdot \boldsymbol{V}. \tag{12-8}$$

Naturally $\boldsymbol{Y}$ will be termed the *tensor admittance*. Comparison of (12-6, 8) shows that (see M2-§8)

$$\boldsymbol{Y} = \boldsymbol{Z}^{-1}, \tag{12-9}$$

or, in words, the tensor admittance is the reciprocal of the tensor impedance. As a consequence we must always have det $\boldsymbol{Z} \neq 0$.

(†) As a matter of fact, in the case of $\boldsymbol{Z}$ we shall not make use of the fundamental property of tensors, i.e., their characteristic variance under an orthogonal transformation. Therefore $\boldsymbol{Z}$ represents only a set of n^2 numbers or a *matrix*. However we shall still speak of a tensor in order to utilize without any change the notations and the properties established in M2. The same will be understood in the similar cases which will be encountered in the following.

Reciprocity Theorem

§ **4.** Equations (12-3) enable us to write the transverse electromagnetic field existing in a given wave guide at $z = 0$ in the form

$$(12\text{-}10)\qquad \begin{cases} \boldsymbol{E}_T(x, y, 0) = V\boldsymbol{e}_T, \\ \boldsymbol{H}_T(x, y, 0) = Y_g I\boldsymbol{k} \wedge \boldsymbol{e}_T. \end{cases}$$

It will be expedient to choose a real value for the eigenfunction $\boldsymbol{e}_T$.

Let us denote by $\boldsymbol{E}$, $\boldsymbol{H}$ and $\boldsymbol{E}'$, $\boldsymbol{H}'$ two possible fields existing in the guide, and by V, I and V', I' the corresponding voltages and currents. Equations (12-10) in conjunction with the normalization condition (11-75) enable us to find

$$(12\text{-}11)\qquad \iint_\Sigma (\boldsymbol{E} \wedge \boldsymbol{H}') \cdot \boldsymbol{k}\, \mathrm{d}\Sigma = Y_g VI' \iint_\Sigma [\boldsymbol{e}_T \wedge (\boldsymbol{k} \wedge \boldsymbol{e}_T)] \cdot \boldsymbol{k}\, \mathrm{d}\Sigma = VI',$$

where the integrations are extended over the cross section $z = 0$. If now we consider the whole set of guides arriving at the junction and assume $\boldsymbol{V}$, $\boldsymbol{I}$ and $\boldsymbol{V}'$, $\boldsymbol{I}'$ to be two possible determinations of the voltages and currents we need only understand by Σ the above-mentioned surface consisting of the box and all the terminals to obtain from (12-11)

$$\iint_\Sigma (\boldsymbol{E} \wedge \boldsymbol{H}') \cdot \boldsymbol{k}\mathrm{d}\Sigma = \boldsymbol{V} \cdot \boldsymbol{I}'$$

where $\boldsymbol{k}$ naturally represents the direction of the z axis of each guide. By an interchange of primes and a subtraction we obtain

$$\iint_\Sigma (\boldsymbol{E} \wedge \boldsymbol{H}' - \boldsymbol{E}' \wedge \boldsymbol{H}) \cdot \boldsymbol{k}\mathrm{d}\Sigma = \boldsymbol{V} \cdot \boldsymbol{I}' - \boldsymbol{V}' \cdot \boldsymbol{I}.$$

By applying the divergence theorem to the left side ($\boldsymbol{k}$ is the inner normal to Σ) and recalling (M1-28) as well as Maxwell's equations (7-18, 19) we may obtain in turn

$$\boldsymbol{V} \cdot \boldsymbol{I}' - \boldsymbol{V}' \cdot \boldsymbol{I} = - \iiint_V \mathrm{div}\, (\boldsymbol{E} \wedge \boldsymbol{H}' - \boldsymbol{E}' \wedge \boldsymbol{H})\, \mathrm{d}V =$$

$$= \iiint_V (\boldsymbol{E} \cdot \mathrm{curl}\, \boldsymbol{H}' - \boldsymbol{H}' \cdot \mathrm{curl}\, \boldsymbol{E} - \boldsymbol{E}' \cdot \mathrm{curl}\, \boldsymbol{H} + \boldsymbol{H} \cdot \mathrm{curl}\, \boldsymbol{E}')\mathrm{d}V =$$

$$= \iiint_V (\eta_e \boldsymbol{E} \cdot \boldsymbol{E}' + \eta_m \boldsymbol{H} \cdot \boldsymbol{H}' - \eta_e \boldsymbol{E} \cdot \boldsymbol{E}' - \eta_m \boldsymbol{H} \cdot \boldsymbol{H}')\, \mathrm{d}V = 0.$$

Hence, expressing $\boldsymbol{V}$ and $\boldsymbol{V}'$ by (12-6),

$$\boldsymbol{Z} : (\boldsymbol{I}\boldsymbol{I}' - \boldsymbol{I}'\boldsymbol{I}) = 0.$$

This equation of the kind (M2-17) shows that $\boldsymbol{Z}$ is a symmetrical tensor. The same property is easily shown for $\boldsymbol{Y}$.

Hence we derive the *reciprocity theorem*, which may be worded as follows: Let voltage V be maintained in guide 1 and a vanishing voltage in all the other guides, and let I represent the current resulting in guide 2; if the voltage V is applied to guide 2 and a vanishing voltage to all the other guides, a current I will result in guide 1.

Diffraction Tensor

§ 5. Some times one is more interested in knowing the amplitudes A^i and A^r than the voltages V and the currents I. Hence it is expedient to consider a vector $\boldsymbol{A}^i$ and a vector $\boldsymbol{A}^r$ in n-dimensional space, having their components represented by the A^i and the A^r of the different guides. With this position (12-1) may be written as

$$\begin{cases} \boldsymbol{V} = \boldsymbol{A}^i + \boldsymbol{A}^r, \\ \boldsymbol{I} = \boldsymbol{A}^i - \boldsymbol{A}^r. \end{cases} \tag{12-12}$$

Upon substitution of these expressions into (12-6) it is obtained

$$\boldsymbol{A}^i + \boldsymbol{A}^r = \boldsymbol{Z} \cdot (\boldsymbol{A}^i - \boldsymbol{A}^r),$$

or

$$(\boldsymbol{Z} + \boldsymbol{U}) \cdot \boldsymbol{A}^r = (\boldsymbol{Z} - \boldsymbol{U}) \cdot \boldsymbol{A}^i,$$

$\boldsymbol{U}$ representing the fundamental tensor. Solving for $\boldsymbol{A}^r$ we obtain

$$\boldsymbol{A}^r = \boldsymbol{S} \cdot \boldsymbol{A}^i, \tag{12-13}$$

with

$$\boldsymbol{S} = (\boldsymbol{Z} + \boldsymbol{U})^{-1} \cdot (\boldsymbol{Z} - \boldsymbol{U}). \tag{12-14}$$

We shall name $\boldsymbol{S}$ the *diffraction tensor* (†); indeed by (12-13) this tensor enables us to pass from any set of waves incident at the junction to the set of waves which rebounds back from the junction. This is a generalization of the definition of diffraction; we shall see in a moment that the traditional definition represents only a particular case.

We note now that both $\boldsymbol{Z} + \boldsymbol{U}$ and $\boldsymbol{Z} - \boldsymbol{U}$ are symmetric tensors; also $(\boldsymbol{Z} + \boldsymbol{U})^{-1}$ will represent a symmetric tensor. Further it is evident that

$$(\boldsymbol{Z} + \boldsymbol{U}) \cdot (\boldsymbol{Z} - \boldsymbol{U}) = (\boldsymbol{Z} - \boldsymbol{U}) \cdot (\boldsymbol{Z} + \boldsymbol{U}).$$

Hence multiplying (12-14) scalarly first on the left and then on the right by $\boldsymbol{Z} + \boldsymbol{U}$ we may write

$$(\boldsymbol{Z} + \boldsymbol{U}) \cdot \boldsymbol{S} \cdot (\boldsymbol{Z} + \boldsymbol{U}) = (\boldsymbol{Z} + \boldsymbol{U}) \cdot (\boldsymbol{Z} - \boldsymbol{U}),$$

and multiplying this equation first on the left and then on the right by $(\boldsymbol{Z} + \boldsymbol{U})^{-1}$ we have

$$\boldsymbol{S} = (\boldsymbol{Z} - \boldsymbol{U}) \cdot (\boldsymbol{Z} + \boldsymbol{U})^{-1}.$$

This equation is identical with (12-14) except for the interchange of both factors in the right hand side. It would not be difficult to prove (by writing the scalar products in rectangular components) that when the product of two symmetrical tensors has the commutative property it represents a symmetrical tensor. We derive therefore the remarkable conclusion that the diffraction tensor is symmetrical.

In this way we have derived a new theorem of reciprocity. It says that, if an incident wave A^i in guide 1 gives rise to a wave A^r in guide 2, conversely an incident wave A^i in guide 2 will give rise to a wave A^r in guide 1.

This assertion enables us to rewrite (12-13) in the alternative form

$$\boldsymbol{A}^r = \boldsymbol{A}^i \cdot \boldsymbol{S}.$$

(†) In theoretical physics it is often named the *scattering matrix*. It should not be confused with the Poynting vector which is denoted by the same symbol.

Hence and from (12-13) there results

$$\frac{1}{2}\boldsymbol{A}^r \cdot \boldsymbol{A}^{r*} = \frac{1}{2}\boldsymbol{A}^i \cdot \boldsymbol{S} \cdot \boldsymbol{S}^* \cdot \boldsymbol{A}^{i*}.$$

The left side represents the power carried by the waves traveling away from the junction; if the box does not cause any loss this power must equal the incident power $\boldsymbol{A}^i \cdot \boldsymbol{A}^{i*}/2$. As a result we have in this case

$$\boldsymbol{S} \cdot \boldsymbol{S}^* = \boldsymbol{U}, \tag{12-15}$$

which is ordinarily expressed by saying that $\boldsymbol{S}$ *is a unit tensor.*

§ 6. Let us now justify the name diffraction tensor which was given to $\boldsymbol{S}$. To this end consider first one of the simplest cases of ordinary diffraction, namely, that arising at a plane grating AB (Fig. 54) with straight, parallel and equispaced rulings. Let us

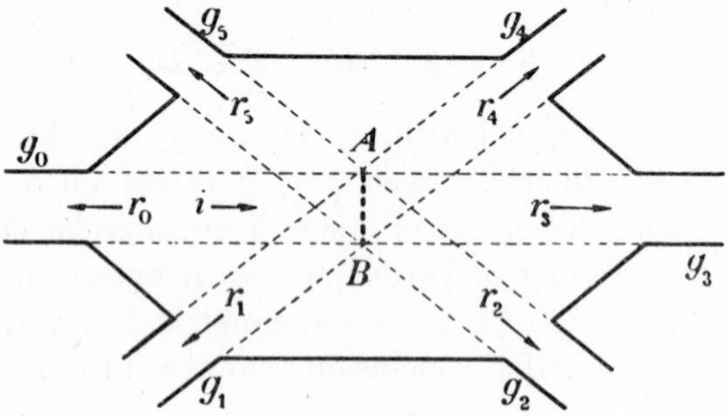

Fig. 54

assume that the incident wave is linearly polarized and denote by $r_0, r_1, r_2, r_3, r_4, r_5$ the waves diffracted both forward and backward. For our purpose the grating should be unbounded; in practice it will be sufficient to assume its dimensions to be extremely large in comparison with the wavelength. Then both the incident and the diffracted waves outside the region of superposition will be governed by the laws of geometrical optics; the two plate wave guides $g_0, g_1, g_2, g_3, g_4, g_5$ with the walls perpendicular to the electric force will not disturb the waves in any way. Nor will the waves be disturbed if we enclose the entire system by a sufficiently large box, as indicated in the Figure. It is clear that in this way we have obtained a junction box like that discussed in the preceding section. There will be a diffraction tensoı $\boldsymbol{S}$, and the reciprocity theorem will be valid.

The number of diffracted waves may be made to increase more and more, provided both the size of the box and the number of wave guides is also made to grow. In the limit we shall arrive at the case of a diffracting screen of unrestricted type giving rise to a continuous set of diffracted waves.

Thus diffraction as defined and discussed in Chap. 10 becomes a particular case of the phenomena arising at the junction of several wave guides.

Reflections in Wave Guides

§ 7. For dealing with reflection problems in the field of wave guides it will be expedient to consider the particular case where the only guide feeding the junction box is the guide considered. One can easily reduce to this case in the following manner.

Let guide 1 be the one we are interested in and carrying the incident wave. We shall choose the terminals of the remaining guides 2, 3, . . ., n very far away from the junction box, introducing before these terminals (on the box side) an absorbing material which absorbs all the power without giving rise to reflected waves. We may imagine for instance that the dielectric contained in the guides 2, 3, . . ., n presents a conductivity which is zero right at the box and then gradually grows in going toward the terminals; before arriving at the terminals the power coming from the box will be completely absorbed without giving rise to reflected waves. All this of course does not affect guide 1 where everything happens as though guides 2, 3, . . ., n were free and unbounded. However, if we consider the surface Σ containing all the terminals, we must say that the only terminal where the field does not vanish is terminal 1. Hence the system is equivalent to a junction box with a single wave guide.

By this procedure we can restrict our considerations to a single voltage V and a single current I, namely, those of the first guide; (12-6) will simply reduce to (†)

$$V = ZI, \tag{12-16}$$

and (12-12) will reduce to

$$\begin{cases} V = A^i + A^r, \\ I = A^i - A^r. \end{cases} \tag{12-17}$$

From these three equations the reflection coefficient is readily derived:

$$r = \frac{A^r}{A^i} = \frac{Z-1}{Z+1}. \tag{12-18}$$

Recalling (6-56), we see that we have obtained the reflection coefficient of a transmission line of characteristic impedance 1, closed by an impedance Z. Hence, as far as guide 1 is concerned, the junction is simply equivalent to an impedance Z terminating the line.

It is of interest to compare (12-18) with (12-14); it is seen that the diffraction tensor $\boldsymbol{S}$ represents only a generalization of the reflection coefficient. Indeed it enables us to derive from the different A^i the values of the A^r while the reflection coefficient relates a single A^i to a single A^r.

§ 8. It is of interest to evaluate the impedance Z appearing in (12-16). To this end we have recourse to (12-5), assuming that the guides $2, 3, \ldots, n$ contain the above-mentioned absorbers. The integration surface Σ might as well reduce to the terminal of guide 1 since everywhere else $\boldsymbol{E} \wedge \boldsymbol{k}$ vanishes. By taking into account (12-10) and the condition of normalization (11-74), the left-hand side of (12-5) may be transformed in the following way:

(†) It is clear that Z does not indicate the intrinsic impedance of the dielectric but that component of $\boldsymbol{Z}$ which should be more exactly denoted by Z_{11}.

$$(12\text{-}19)\quad \frac{1}{2}\iint_{\Sigma} \boldsymbol{E}\wedge\boldsymbol{H}^*\cdot\boldsymbol{k}\,\mathrm{d}\Sigma = \frac{1}{2}\,Y_g^* VI^* \iint_{\Sigma} \boldsymbol{e}_T\wedge(\boldsymbol{k}\wedge\boldsymbol{e}_T^*)\cdot\boldsymbol{k}\,\mathrm{d}\Sigma =$$

$$= \frac{1}{2}\,VI^* = \frac{1}{2}\,ZII^* = \frac{1}{2}\,Y^*VV^*,$$

the useless subscript 1 being omitted. Let us denote by $\overline{W}$ the total power (instead of its density) dissipated inside the box and in the absorbers, and by $\overline{U}_m$ and $\overline{U}_e$ the magnetic and electric energies stored. From (12-5, 19) we may deduce

$$(12\text{-}20)\qquad Z = \frac{2\overline{W} + 4i\omega(\overline{U}_m - \overline{U}_e)}{II^*}.$$

This represents an interesting expression of Z. It immediately shows the division into resistance and reactance. The power absorbed is responsible for the resistance, while the difference of the magnetic and electric energies stored is responsible for the reactance.

In a similar manner, by utilizing (12-5, 19) again, the admittance Y of the junction is found to be

$$(12\text{-}21)\qquad Y = \frac{2\overline{W} - 4i\omega(\overline{U}_m - \overline{U}_e)}{VV^*},$$

where the conductance and the susceptance appear explicitly.

If the junction box, as is the case in practice, does not appreciably dissipate energy, $\overline{W}$ simply represents the power which would be swallowed by the absorbers. On the contrary the term $\overline{U}_m - \overline{U}_e$ takes rise only at the junction since the electric and magnetic energies are equal for each traveling mode in the guides. As a consequence we may choose the terminals of the guides 2, 3, . . ., n at any distance, however large, from the junction without altering the results (12-20, 21). Hence the conclusion is derived that $\overline{W}$ simply represents the power which is transmitted to the guides 2, 3, . . ., n when these guides are infinite and free from the absorbers which were introduced only for convenience.

Impedance Matching

§ 9. Guide 1 is said to be matched to the junction if an incident wave does not give rise to a reflected wave. In this case the whole power goes into the guides 2, 3, . . ., n. From (12-17), by setting $A^r = 0$ we may derive that the incident power is represented by $A^i A^{i*}/2 = VV^*/2 = II^*/2$. On the other hand, if no reflection is present we must necessarily have $Z = 1$. Hence by (12-20) we must also have $\overline{U}_m = \overline{U}_e$. Thus a necessary condition for matching the guide to the junction is that the magnetic and electric energies stored should be equal.

A particularly important case of junction is that of two guides which admit each a single traveling mode or the fundamental mode. As was already mentioned, in order to obtain field continuity all of the higher order modes are generally necessary. At the junction there arise also evanescent modes and we know that the electric and magnetic energies of such modes are not equal. In a TM mode the electric energy is greater while in a TE mode the magnetic energy is greater. When attempting to match two guides one must so proceed as to obtain properly balanced TE and TM modes. It is not at all easy to solve this problem; however with the aid of some reflection and experience one can anticipate which evanescent modes will take rise at the junction and in what direction the junction must be deformed to give rise to some new evanescent modes which may balance the first ones.

In particular both guides may be identical. Thus one can deal with the frequent case where an obstacle, as for instance a bearing for the inner coaxial cylinder, is placed in the guide. Any portion of the guide containing the obstacle may be considered as being the junction box. Hence we derive the conclusion that, generally speaking, an obstacle placed within a wave guide gives rise to a reflection. To eliminate the reflection one may have recourse to a variety of methods. For instance another identical obstacle may be placed at a distance $\lambda/4$ apart from the first one with a procedure similar to that seen in the case of the anti-reflection coatings (see 9-§9).

CHAPTER 13

Resonant Cavities

Stationary Waves in a Wave Guide

§ 1. In the preceding chapter we discussed the phenomena arising at the junction of several wave guides, but it was not necessary to investigate in detail the field inside the junction box. We shall now be concerned with what happens inside a metal cavity into which one or more wave guides are carrying energy.

We shall begin by a very simple case similar to that considered in 6-§19, 20, 21 which lends itself to illustrate in a clear way the fundamental properties of a resonant cavity.

Consider a cylindrical wave guide with perfectly conducting walls closed by a metal plane perpendicular to the axis. In this case the guide is said to be short-circuited. On the metal plane ($z = 0$) we shall have $\boldsymbol{E}_T = 0$. Suppose the guide is carrying a progressive mode; the wave arriving at the metal plane shall undergo reflection. By recalling the first equation (12-2) we see at once that in this case $A^i = -A^r = A$. Next noting that the regressive wave will have $\boldsymbol{k}$ changed into $-\boldsymbol{k}$, we find the overall electric field strength

$$(13\text{-}1)\quad \boldsymbol{E} = A(\boldsymbol{e}_T + e_z\boldsymbol{k}) \exp(-ik_g z) - A(\boldsymbol{e}_T - e_z\boldsymbol{k}) \exp(ik_g z) = \\ = -2iA\boldsymbol{e}_T \sin k_g z + 2Ae_z\boldsymbol{k} \cos k_g z.$$

In the same way the magnetic field is found to be

$$(13\text{-}2)\quad \boldsymbol{H} = A(\boldsymbol{h}_T + h_z\boldsymbol{k}) \exp(-ik_g z) + A(\boldsymbol{h}_T - h_z\boldsymbol{k}) \exp(ik_g z) = \\ = 2A\boldsymbol{h}_T \cos k_g z - 2iAh_z\boldsymbol{k} \sin k_g z.$$

Of course if the mode is TE the longitudinal electric component e_z will vanish, while if the mode is TM the longitudinal magnetic component h_z will vanish. The phase of every component of $\boldsymbol{E}$

and $\boldsymbol{H}$ is constant along the whole guide. Hence no propagation of the phase will take place; the waves will be stationary. We shall get a set of equispaced nodes and antinodes of $\boldsymbol{E}_T$ which coincide with as many antinodes and nodes respectively of $\boldsymbol{H}_T$. The spacing between two consecutive nodes or antinodes is $\pi/k_g = \lambda_g/2$, that is, a half wavelength.

It can be shown also that the energy remains stationary instead of traveling as in an ordinary wave. As far as the propagation in the direction of the z-axis is concerned, it is sufficient to note that both the progressive and the regressive modes have the same amplitude, so that no preferred sense of propagation may exist for the energy. However, we shall give a more general demonstration, ruling out also any transverse circulation of energy in a general cross section of the guide. To this end we shall work out the value of the complex Poynting vector utilizing (13-1, 2) as well as (11-60):

$$\boldsymbol{S} = \frac{1}{2}\boldsymbol{E} \wedge \boldsymbol{H}^* =$$

$$= 2AA^*(-i\boldsymbol{e}_T \sin k_g z + e_z\boldsymbol{k} \cos k_g z) \wedge (\boldsymbol{h}_T^* \cos k_g z + ih_z^*\boldsymbol{k} \sin k_g z) =$$

$$= 2AA^*(-i\boldsymbol{e}_T \wedge \boldsymbol{h}_T^* \sin k_g z \cos k_g z + h_z^* \boldsymbol{e}_T \wedge \boldsymbol{k} \sin^2 k_g z + e_z \boldsymbol{k} \wedge \boldsymbol{h}_T^* \cos^2 k_g z) =$$

$$= 2AA^*(-iY_g \boldsymbol{e}_T \cdot \boldsymbol{e}_T^* \boldsymbol{k} \sin k_g z \cos k_g z - Z_g h_z^* \boldsymbol{h}_T^* \sin^2 k_g z - Y_g e_z \boldsymbol{e}_T^* \cos^2 k_g z).$$

If the mode is TE, we shall omit the term containing e_z; if it is TM, we shall omit the term containing h_z. In the former case, making use of (11-58, 61) to express everything in terms of h_z, we shall, after some easy transformations, obtain

$$\text{(13-3)} \quad TE \quad \boldsymbol{S} =$$

$$= -iAA^*Z\frac{k}{k_c^2}\left(\frac{k_g}{k_c^2}\operatorname{grad} h_z \cdot \operatorname{grad} h_z^* \boldsymbol{k} \sin 2k_g z - 2h_z^* \operatorname{grad} h_z \sin^2 k_g z\right).$$

In the latter case we shall make use of (11-59, 62) with the result

$$\text{(13-4)} \quad TM \quad \boldsymbol{S} =$$

$$= -iAA^*Y\frac{k}{k_c^2}\left(\frac{k_g}{k_c^2}\operatorname{grad} e_z \cdot \operatorname{grad} e_z^* \boldsymbol{k} \sin 2k_g z + 2e_z \operatorname{grad} e_z^* \cos^2 k_g z\right).$$

We recall now that, as was seen in 11-§11, the arguments of both eigenfunctions e_z and h_z are constant over any plane $z = constant$. It follows that the right hand sides of (13-3, 4) are purely imaginary. Hence the vector $\overline{\boldsymbol{S}} = \mathscr{R}e\boldsymbol{S}$ vanishes and there is no flow of energy in any direction.

Cylindrical Cavity

§ 2. Let us revert to the consideration of the nodes and antinodes of the field quantities.

Since at a node of $\boldsymbol{E}_T$ the transverse electric field is zero we may imagine a perfectly conducting plane placed at that cross section without altering the field in any way. The wave guide now bounded by two plane conductors Σ_1, Σ_2 (Fig. 55) forms a closed cavity where the field can subsist indefinitely (in the ideal case of absence of dissipation). We have thus a *resonant cavity.*

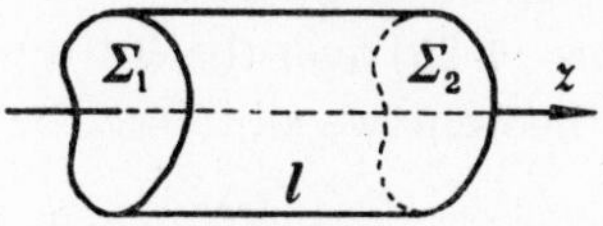

Fig. 55

If the spacing between both end bases is regularly increased, resonant conditions will be reached at regular spacings of $\lambda_g/2$ or when the length $l = -z$ of the cavity equals $n\lambda_g/2$ with n integer. We may maintain the length l of the cavity fixed and cause the frequency to vary. Taking into account that $\lambda_g = 2\pi/k_g$, the condition of resonance is written

$$l = n\frac{\pi}{k_g}, \tag{13-5}$$

and making use of (11-63) we easily find

$$k^2 = k_c^2 + \frac{n^2\pi^2}{l^2}. \tag{13-6}$$

Finally, since $k = \omega/v$, the resonance frequencies are found to be

$$\omega_n = v\sqrt{k_c^2 + \frac{n^2\pi^2}{l^2}}. \tag{13-7}$$

Each of these frequencies corresponds to a mode of the resonant cavity.

Naturally we must remember that we have started from a well determined mode of the wave guide, specified by the value of k_c. Any other mode of the guide would have given rise to a set of modes of the cavity. Hence we derive the conclusion that while the modes of the guide were a double infinity the modes of the cavity are a triple infinity.

However, the reader will bear in mind an essential difference between the modes of a wave guide and the modes of a cavity. In the case of a wave guide one can fix the frequency beforehand and then find a finite number of traveling modes plus an infinite number of attenuated modes. In the case of a cavity the different modes correspond instead to different frequencies which are perfectly determined by the shape of the cavity. And of course there are no (spatially) attenuated modes.

Let us now integrate (7-25) over the entire volume of the cavity. By the divergence theorem we obtain

$$-\oint_{\Sigma} \boldsymbol{S} \cdot \boldsymbol{n} \mathrm{d}\Sigma = 2i\omega \iiint_{V} (\overline{U}_m - \overline{U}_e) \,\mathrm{d}V, \tag{13-8}$$

where Σ denotes the walls of the cavity and $\boldsymbol{n}$ the outward normal. Making use of (13-3, 4) and taking into account the boundary conditions of h_z and e_z, we obtain

$$TE \quad AA^*Z\frac{kk_g}{k_c^4} \sin 2k_g l \iint_{\Sigma_0} \mathrm{grad}\, h_z \cdot \mathrm{grad}\, h_z^* \,\mathrm{d}\Sigma = = 2\omega \iiint_{V} (\overline{U}_m - \overline{U}_e) \,\mathrm{d}V. \tag{13-9}$$

$$TM \quad AA^*Y\frac{kk_g}{k_c^4} \sin 2k_g l \iint_{\Sigma_0} \mathrm{grad}\, e_z \cdot \mathrm{grad}\, e_z^* \,\mathrm{d}\Sigma = = 2\omega \iiint_{V} (\overline{U}_m - \overline{U}_e) \,\mathrm{d}V, \tag{13-10}$$

respectively, having denoted by Σ_0 the normal cross section of the cylindrical cavity. However, by taking into account (13-5), we see that the left-hand sides vanish. As a consequence the electric and magnetic energies inside the cavity are equal.

Rectangular Cavity

§ 3. We shall now apply the above considerations to the case of a rectangular cavity specified by its three dimensions a, b, c. We shall take as a starting point the rectangular wave guide discussed in 11-§§5, 6 setting up the stationary waves considered in the previous section. Thus from (11-18, 20, 21) by recalling that $k_g = ks_z$ and removing the useless factor 2 we derive

$$(13\text{-}11)\quad \begin{cases} \boldsymbol{E} = -iA[s_y\boldsymbol{i}\cos(ks_xx)\sin(ks_yy)\sin(ks_zz) - \\ \qquad - s_x\boldsymbol{j}\sin(ks_xx)\cos(ks_yy)\sin(ks_zz)], \\ \boldsymbol{H} = YA[s_xs_z\boldsymbol{i}\sin(ks_xx)\cos(ks_yy)\cos(ks_zz) + \\ \qquad + s_ys_z\boldsymbol{j}\cos(ks_xx)\sin(ks_yy)\cos(ks_zz) - \\ \qquad - (s_x^2 + s_y^2)\boldsymbol{k}\cos(ks_xx)\cos(ks_yy)\sin(ks_zz)]. \end{cases}$$

In a similar manner from (11-32, 34, 35) we obtain with a reversal of sign

$$(13\text{-}12)\quad \begin{cases} \boldsymbol{E} = iA[s_xs_z\boldsymbol{i}\cos(ks_xx)\sin(ks_yy)\sin(ks_zz) + \\ \qquad + s_ys_z\boldsymbol{j}\sin(ks_xx)\cos(ks_yy)\sin(ks_zz) + \\ \qquad + (s_x^2 + s_y^2)\boldsymbol{k}\sin(ks_xx)\cos(ks_yy)\cos(ks_zz), \\ \boldsymbol{H} = YA[s_y\boldsymbol{i}\sin(ks_xx)\cos(ks_yy)\cos(ks_zz) - \\ \qquad - s_x\boldsymbol{j}\cos(ks_xx)\sin(ks_yy)\cos(ks_zz)]. \end{cases}$$

Obviously it makes no sense to speak of TE or TM modes because there is no propagation and no preferred direction in the cavity. The fields (13-11, 12) simply represent two independent solutions of the Maxwell equations.

To satisfy the boundary conditions we must obviously set $ks_xa = m\pi$, $ks_yb = n\pi$, $ks_zc = p\pi$, with m, n, p integers or

$$(13\text{-}13)\qquad s_x = m\frac{\lambda}{2a}, \quad s_y = n\frac{\lambda}{2b}, \quad s_z = p\frac{\lambda}{2c}.$$

Naturally the first two conditions are identical with (11-22). Next, since $s_x^2 + s_y^2 + s_z^2 = 1$, we obtain

$$\lambda = \frac{1}{\sqrt{\dfrac{m^2}{4a^2} + \dfrac{n^2}{4b^2} + \dfrac{p^2}{4c^2}}}, \tag{13-14}$$

It is of interest to compare this equation with (11-25). Finally from (13-11) by taking into account that $\omega = 2\pi v/\lambda$ the resonance frequencies are readily found to be

$$\omega_{mnp} = 2\pi v \sqrt{\frac{m^2}{4a^2} + \frac{n^2}{4b^2} + \frac{p^2}{4c^2}}. \tag{13-15}$$

There are a triple infinity of these frequencies.

Dissipation and Attenuation

§ 4. A resonant cavity such as the one discussed above behaves like the combination of an infinite number of lossless resonant circuits. In reality the condition of no loss is purely ideal; some dissipation of energy will always take place in the walls as well as in the dielectric. As a consequence any resonant mode, once it is excited and left to itself is more or less rapidly attenuated.

To investigate the attenuated oscillations of a given mode specified by the subscript n we shall introduce the Q of the mode by our customary procedure. We write

$$\frac{\omega_n}{Q}\,\mathrm{d}t = \frac{\mathrm{d}\overline{U}}{\overline{U}}, \tag{13-16}$$

$\overline{U}$ representing the total energy stored in the cavity and $\mathrm{d}\overline{U}$ the energy dissipated within the time interval $\mathrm{d}t$. It is evident then that if Q_p refers to the losses in the walls and Q_d to the losses in the dielectric, equation (11-101) will still hold

$$\frac{1}{Q} = \frac{1}{Q_p} + \frac{1}{Q_d}, \tag{13-17}$$

as was found for a wave guide.

By integrating (13-16) we obtain the law of attenuation:

$$\overline{U}(t) = \overline{U}(0) \exp\left(-\frac{\omega_n}{Q} t\right), \tag{13-18}$$

which was found with (6-33) for a circuit with lumped constants. The fields will also be attenuated and, since the energy is related to them in a quadratic way, the law of attenuation for the fields will present the factor $\exp(-\omega_n t/2Q)$. If we add also the factor $\exp(i\omega t)$, any given field component at any given point will be expressed in the form

$$A \exp\left[\left(i\omega_n - \frac{\omega_n}{2Q}\right) t\right]. \tag{13-19}$$

It is of interest to show that this attenuated oscillation may be considered to result from an infinite number of steady oscillations, all with their different frequencies very close to ω_n. If we denote by $A(\omega)d\omega$ the complex amplitude of the oscillation having frequency ω we write

$$A \exp\left[\left(i\omega_n - \frac{\omega_n}{2Q}\right) t\right] = \int A(\omega) \exp(i\omega t)\, d\omega. \tag{13-20}$$

At this point it is convenient to note that the attenuated oscillation cannot be imagined as having always being given by (13-19) because for $t = -\infty$ such an expression tends to infinity. We shall instead assume that the oscillation was suddenly excited at $t = 0$ and then was left to itself. So the left side of (13-20) will be zero for $-\infty < t < 0$ and then have the expression indicated for $0 < t < \infty$. We must also specify the limits of the integral (13-20). As already stated, we shall see that $A(\omega)$ has a non-negligible value only in the vicinity of $\omega = \omega_n$. Therefore we may as well extend the integration from $-\infty$ to $+\infty$. Then we have only to recall the Fourier integral (M3-10, 11) to obtain

$$A(\omega) = \frac{A}{2\pi} \int_0^\infty \exp\left[\left(i\omega_n - \frac{\omega_n}{2Q}\right) t'\right] \exp(-i\omega t')\, dt'.$$

Carrying out the integration, we find

$$A(\omega) = -\frac{A}{2\pi} \frac{1}{i(\omega_n - \omega) - \frac{\omega_n}{2Q}}. \tag{13-21}$$

Since Q is a very great number we see that of all the values of $A(\omega)$ only those in the vicinity of $\omega = \omega_n$ need to be considered. Let us set $\omega = \omega_n(1 + \delta)$; (13-21) will then become

$$A(\omega) = A \frac{Q}{\pi\omega_n} \frac{1}{1 + 2iQ\delta}. \tag{13-22}$$

This remarkable equation is similar to (6-35). However, its significance is somewhat different. Equation (6-35) represented a resonance of the response under an excitation of variable frequency from outside. Here instead we have found that a natural oscillation of the cavity (i.e., an oscillation of the cavity left to itself) is the resultant of an entire band of frequencies about $\omega = \omega_n$. The greater the value of Q, the narrower is the bandwidth. The value of $1/Q$ will be assumed to represent the bandwidth.

Resonant Cavities as Circuits with Distributed Constants

§ 5. In order that the oscillations of a cavity not be attenuated one must apply a steady excitation from outside.

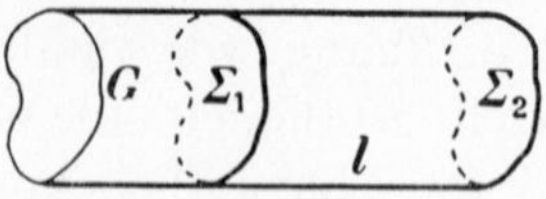

Fig. 56

For a resonant cavity of the cylindrical type discussed so far the simplest way to effect the excitation is to remove the metal base Σ_1 (Fig. 56) and to supply energy through the wave guide G of which the cavity represents a portion. We shall assume the energy to be carried by a single mode of G.

We recall now the treatment made at Chap. 12 of the wave guide as a transmission line. The basis Σ_1 will be taken as the terminal of the guide and voltage and current will be defined according to (12-3) in terms of the values of $\boldsymbol{E}_T$ and $\boldsymbol{H}_T$ at the terminal

$$(13\text{-}23) \qquad \begin{cases} \boldsymbol{E}_T = V\boldsymbol{e}_T, \\ \boldsymbol{H}_T = I\boldsymbol{h}_T. \end{cases}$$

The cavity will now represent an impedance at the end of the line. The situation is similar to that discussed in 6-§§19, 20, 21 for the particular case of a short-circuited two-wire line.

To begin with, suppose that no dissipation takes place in the cavity. From (13-1, 2), by replacing z with $-l$ we immediately have

$$\boldsymbol{E}_T = 2iA\boldsymbol{e}_T \sin k_g l,$$
$$\boldsymbol{H}_T = 2A\boldsymbol{h}_T \cos k_g l.$$

Comparing with (13-23), we obtain

$$V = 2iA \sin k_g l,$$
$$I = 2A \cos k_g l,$$

and consequently the input admittance and impedance of the cavity are

$$(13\text{-}24) \qquad Y = \frac{I}{V} = -i \cot k_g l, \qquad Z = \frac{V}{I} = i \tan k_g l.$$

These represent a pure susceptance and a pure reactance, as is natural since it was assumed that no dissipation is present. Resonance occurs every time $\cot k_g l$ becomes infinite, and anti-resonance occurs every time $\tan k_g l$ becomes infinite. Naturally we find again condition (13-5) for resonance and

$$(13\text{-}25) \qquad l = \left(n + \frac{1}{2}\right)\frac{\pi}{k_g},$$

or an intermediate condition for anti-resonance.

§ 6. To study the situation more in detail we shall assume, as always occurs in reality, that the wave guide G, and consequently the cavity also, present a certain amount of dissipation. In this case the propagation constant instead of being simply ik_g will be represented by h_g of (11-103) having the real part α_g given by (11-102). In (13-24) we shall replace k_g by $-ih_g$ obtaining

$$Y = i \cot ih_g l \qquad Z = -i \tan ih_g l,$$

By making use of the series expansions of 6-§§20, 21 we may write

$$Y = \frac{1}{h_g l} + \sum_1^\infty {}_n \frac{2h_g l}{(n\pi)^2 + (h_g l)^2}, \qquad Z = \sum_0^\infty {}_n \frac{2h_g l}{\left(\frac{2n+1}{2}\pi\right)^2 + (h_g l)^2}.$$

In place of h_g we shall put its expression $\alpha_g + ik_g$; since the attenuation is very small, we shall disregard α_g in the numerator and α_g^2 in the denominator. In this way we obtain for the nth term of each sum:

$$\text{(13-26)} \quad \begin{cases} Y_n = \dfrac{2ik_g l}{(n\pi)^2 + 2i\alpha_g k_g l^2 - k_g^2 l^2}, \\[2ex] Z_n = \dfrac{2ik_g l}{\left(\dfrac{2n+1}{2}\pi\right)^2 + 2i\alpha_g k_g l^2 - k_g^2 l^2.} \end{cases}$$

Note now that expression (11-102) for α_g may on account of (11-93) successively transform into

$$\alpha_g = \frac{1}{2}\frac{\omega}{Qv_e} = \frac{1}{2}\frac{\omega}{Qv}\frac{k}{k_g} = \frac{1}{2}\frac{\omega^2}{Qv^2}\frac{1}{k_g}.$$

Upon substitution into (13-26) we obtain

$$Y_n = \frac{2Qv^2k_g/l}{\omega^2 + iQ\left(v^2k_g^2 - \dfrac{n^2\pi^2}{l^2}v^2\right)},$$

$$Z_n = \frac{2Qv^2k_g/l}{\omega^2 + iQ\left[v^2k_g^2 - \left(n + \dfrac{1}{2}\right)^2\dfrac{\pi^2}{l^2}v^2\right]}.$$

In the denominators we shall substitute (11-66) for k_g and then ω/v for k; in this way we have

$$
(13\text{-}27)\quad \begin{cases} Y_n = \dfrac{2Qv^2k_g/l}{\omega^2 + iQ\left\{\omega^2 - v^2\left[k_c^2 + \dfrac{n^2\pi^2}{l^2}\right]\right\}}, \\[2ex] Z_n = \dfrac{2Qv^2k_g/l}{\omega^2 + iQ\left\{\omega^2 - v^2\left[k_c^2 + \left(n + \dfrac{1}{2}\right)^2 \dfrac{\pi^2}{l^2}\right]\right\}}. \end{cases}
$$

Thus we get a set of resonance and anti-resonance frequencies (which make the imaginary parts of the denominators vanish) given respectively by

$$
(13\text{-}28)\qquad \omega_n = v\sqrt{k_c^2 + \frac{\pi^2 n^2}{l^2}}, \qquad \omega_n = v\sqrt{k_c^2 + \left(n + \frac{1}{2}\right)^2 \frac{\pi^2}{l^2}}.
$$

When the value of ω is close to ω_n we may, as is customary, introduce the relative displacement δ with $\omega = (1 + \delta)\omega_n$; substituting into (13-27) and neglecting δ^2 in comparison with unity and unity in comparison with Q we arrive at

$$
(13\text{-}29)\qquad Y_n = \frac{2Qv^2k_g/\omega_n l}{1 + 2iQ\delta}, \qquad Z_n = \frac{2Qv^2k_g/\omega_n l}{1 + 2iQ\delta},
$$

which is of the well-known form (6-35) valid for the resonant and anti-resonant circuits respectively.

Thus a cavity may be considered a combination of many resonant circuits in parallel or of many anti-resonant circuits in series. The Q of each circuit is identical with the corresponding Q of the wave guide and is given by (11-97, 100, 101). Naturally, if the end base is also assumed to have finite conductivity the energy dissipated on it must be taken into account in the computation of Q_p.

Referring to what was said in 12-§3 we shall finally remark that in the present case any given mode of the wave guide gives rise only to the corresponding reflected mode. Hence all the components

Z_{ik} of the tensor impedance and Y_{ik} of the tensor admittance having $i \neq k$ vanish. If the mode excited in the guide is the mth mode the admittance and the impedance which were evaluated above are the components Y_{mm} and Z_{mm} of the corresponding tensors.

General Theory of Resonant Cavities

§ 7. The considerations developed in the preceding sections concerned particular cases of resonant cavities. We shall now give a much more general treatment which is of great interest for practical application.

We shall deal with a metal cavity of general shape fed by several cylindrical wave guides of different cross sections. In other words we refer again to the metallic junction box of Fig. 53. To simplify matters we shall only make the restriction that the walls are perfect conductors and that no loss occurs in the dielectric.

We recall that in 12-§2 a plane terminal was chosen on each guide sufficiently far away from the box for allowing the evanescent modes to be neglected. We shall consider the cavity as being formed by the box and by the portions of wave guides included between the box and the terminals.

As the dielectric is homogeneous and perfect, the electric field inside the cavity shall obey equation (10-13):

$$\text{curl curl } \boldsymbol{E} = k^2\boldsymbol{E}. \tag{13-30}$$

Our problem would now be to solve this equation for $\boldsymbol{E}(P)$ subject to the necessary boundary conditions. However, the boundary conditions are obvious only on the walls of the box (vanishing tangential component of $\boldsymbol{E}$); it is very difficult to give instead the proper conditions at the guide terminals.

We shall proceed by successive steps. First of all we shall forget the physical significance of $\boldsymbol{E}$ and look for the solutions of (13-30) which are real and have a vanishing tangential component on the entire boundary of the resonant cavity, i.e., also on the terminals of the guides. By the methods of higher mathematics it may be proved that this problem can be solved only if k has one of the values k_n of a well-determined set. These k_n (eigenvalues) are all real; to each of them there corresponds at least a solution $\boldsymbol{a}_n(P)$ (eigenfunction) of the differential equation (13-30) which satisfies the boundary condition assumed. Thus $\boldsymbol{a}_n$ obeys the equation

$$\text{curl curl } \boldsymbol{a}_n = k_n^2 \boldsymbol{a}_n\,, \tag{13-31}$$

and has a vanishing tangential component both on the walls of the box and on the terminals.

Two eigenfunctions corresponding to different eigenvalues are mutually orthogonal. This is shown by applying (M1-37) which gives

$$\iiint_V (\boldsymbol{a}_m \cdot \text{curl curl } \boldsymbol{a}_n - \boldsymbol{a}_n \cdot \text{curl curl } \boldsymbol{a}_m)\, \mathrm{d}V = \tag{13-32}$$
$$= \oint_\Sigma (\boldsymbol{a}_n \wedge \text{curl } \boldsymbol{a}_m - \boldsymbol{a}_m \wedge \text{curl } \boldsymbol{a}_n) \cdot \boldsymbol{n}\, \mathrm{d}\Sigma,$$

V representing the volume and Σ the surface of the cavity (†). The last integral vanishes because both $\boldsymbol{a}_m$ and $\boldsymbol{a}_n$ are normal to Σ. Hence substituting (13-31) in the first integral we obtain

$$(k_n^2 - k_m^2) \iiint_V \boldsymbol{a}_m \cdot \boldsymbol{a}_n \mathrm{d}V = 0,$$

whence for $k_m \neq k_n$ the required orthogonality condition holds:

$$\iiint_V \boldsymbol{a}_m \cdot \boldsymbol{a}_n \mathrm{d}V = 0. \tag{13-33}$$

If both $\boldsymbol{a}_m$ and $\boldsymbol{a}_n$ correspond to the same eigenvalue (degenerate case) it is easy to construct two linear combinations of these functions which are mutually orthogonal; and in a similar way we may proceed if more than two eigenfunctions correspond to the same eigenvalue.

We shall then require that the eigenfunctions obey the condition of normalization:

$$\iiint_V a_n^2 \mathrm{d}V = 1. \tag{13-34}$$

(†) It is clear that the normal $\boldsymbol{n}$ has nothing in common with the subscript n.

This is always possible because $\boldsymbol{a}_n$ is determined by (13-31) apart from an arbitrary factor.

Finally we shall remark that by (13-31) and (M1-9) the eigenfunctions $\boldsymbol{a}_n$ are solenoidal.

Any solenoidal vector function $\boldsymbol{v}(P)$ can be represented by a series of eigenfunctions $\boldsymbol{a}_n$ as follows

$$\boldsymbol{v}(P) = \sum_{1}^{\infty}{}_n f_n \boldsymbol{a}_n(P). \tag{13-35}$$

The coefficients f_n may be found by multiplying scalarly by $\boldsymbol{a}_n$ and integrating over the volume V; in this way it is found

$$f_n = \iiint\limits_V \boldsymbol{v} \cdot \boldsymbol{a}_n \, \mathrm{d}V, \tag{13-36}$$

having made use of (13-33, 34).

§ **8.** Consider now the vector functions $\boldsymbol{b}_n$ defined by

$$k_n \boldsymbol{b}_n = \text{curl}\, \boldsymbol{a}_n. \tag{13-37}$$

Taking the curl of both sides and recalling (13-31), we obtain

$$k_n \,\text{curl}\, \boldsymbol{b}_n = \text{curl curl}\, \boldsymbol{a}_n = k_n^2 \boldsymbol{a}_n.$$

Taking again the curl of the left and right sides, we have by (13-37)

$$\text{curl curl}\, \boldsymbol{b}_n = k_n^2 \boldsymbol{b}_n. \tag{13-38}$$

Thus the functions $\boldsymbol{b}_n$ are found to obey the same equation (13-31) as the $\boldsymbol{a}_n$. Incidentally we note the equation

$$k_n \boldsymbol{a}_n = \text{curl}\, \boldsymbol{b}_n, \tag{13-39}$$

which is symmetric to (13-37).

The eigenfunctions $\boldsymbol{a}_n$ have a vanishing tangential component on Σ. As a consequence the circulation of $\boldsymbol{a}_n$ around any closed line on Σ vanishes. Then by (13-37) and by Stokes' theorem (M1-7) the functions $\boldsymbol{b}_n$ turn out to have a vanishing normal component on Σ. As a consequence if we write (13-32) for $\boldsymbol{b}_n$ instead of $\boldsymbol{a}_n$ the integral of the right side is again zero. And in the same way as we derived (13-33) we now find

$$\iiint_V \boldsymbol{b}_m \cdot \boldsymbol{b}_n \mathrm{d}V = 0. \tag{13-40}$$

Thus also the functions $\boldsymbol{b}_n$ are orthogonal to one another.

Next we obtain from (M1-36)

$$\iiint_V [(\mathrm{curl}\, \boldsymbol{a}_n)^2 - \boldsymbol{a}_n \cdot \mathrm{curl}\,\mathrm{curl}\, \boldsymbol{a}_n] \mathrm{d}V = \oint\!\!\oint_\Sigma \boldsymbol{a}_n \wedge \mathrm{curl}\, \boldsymbol{a}_n \cdot \boldsymbol{n}\, \mathrm{d}\Sigma.$$

As before, the last integral vanishes and the first by virtue of (13-31, 37) yields

$$\iiint_V (\boldsymbol{b}_n^2 - \boldsymbol{a}_n^2)\, \mathrm{d}V = 0,$$

whence, by (13-34),

$$\iiint_V b_n^2 \,\mathrm{d}V = 1. \tag{13-41}$$

Thus the condition of normalization holds also for the $\boldsymbol{b}_n$.

A general vector function $\boldsymbol{v}(P)$ can be expanded as a series of functions $\boldsymbol{b}_n$ by means of the relations

$$\boldsymbol{v}(P) = \sum_1^\infty{}_n f_n \boldsymbol{b}_n(P), \tag{13-42}$$

$$f_n = \iiint_V \boldsymbol{v} \cdot \boldsymbol{b}_n \mathrm{d}V, \tag{13-43}$$

which are similar to (13-35, 36).

§ 9. Let now $\boldsymbol{E}(P)$, $\boldsymbol{H}(P)$ denote the electromagnetic field which actually exists in the cavity under well-determined conditions to be specified later. We shall expand $\boldsymbol{E}(P)$ and $\boldsymbol{H}(P)$ in series of $\boldsymbol{a}_n$ and $\boldsymbol{b}_n$ respectively. By (13-35, 36, 42, 43) we shall have

$$\boldsymbol{E}(P) = \sum_1^\infty{}_n E_n \boldsymbol{a}_n(P), \quad \boldsymbol{H}(P) = \sum_1^\infty{}_n H_n \boldsymbol{b}_n(P), \tag{13-44}$$

where

$$(13\text{-}45)\qquad E_n = \iiint\limits_V \boldsymbol{E}\cdot\boldsymbol{a}_n\,\mathrm{d}V,\qquad H_n = \iiint\limits_V \boldsymbol{H}\cdot\boldsymbol{b}_n\,\mathrm{d}V.$$

With a similar procedure we shall expand curl $\boldsymbol{H}$ and curl $\boldsymbol{E}$ in series of $\boldsymbol{a}_n$ and $\boldsymbol{b}_n$ respectively, writing

$$\operatorname{curl}\boldsymbol{H} = \sum_1^\infty{}_n\,\boldsymbol{a}_n \iiint\limits_V \boldsymbol{a}_n\cdot\operatorname{curl}\boldsymbol{H}\,\mathrm{d}V,\quad \operatorname{curl}\boldsymbol{E} = \sum_1^\infty{}_n\,\boldsymbol{b}_n \iiint\limits_V \boldsymbol{b}_n\cdot\operatorname{curl}\boldsymbol{E}\,\mathrm{d}V,$$

or by (13-37,39)

$$\operatorname{curl}\boldsymbol{H} = \sum_1^\infty{}_n \frac{\boldsymbol{a}_n}{k_n}\iiint\limits_V \operatorname{curl}\boldsymbol{H}\cdot\operatorname{curl}\boldsymbol{b}_n\,\mathrm{d}V,$$

$$\operatorname{curl}\boldsymbol{E} = \sum_1^\infty{}_n \frac{\boldsymbol{b}_n}{k_n}\iiint\limits_V \operatorname{curl}\boldsymbol{E}\cdot\operatorname{curl}\boldsymbol{a}_n\,\mathrm{dV}.$$

If (M1-36) is applied to these equations we get

$$\operatorname{curl}\boldsymbol{H} = \sum_1^\infty{}_n \frac{\boldsymbol{a}_n}{k_n}\left[\iiint\limits_V \boldsymbol{H}\cdot\operatorname{curl}\operatorname{curl}\boldsymbol{b}_n\,\mathrm{d}V + \oiint\limits_\Sigma \boldsymbol{H}\wedge\operatorname{curl}\boldsymbol{b}_n\cdot\boldsymbol{n}\,\mathrm{d}\Sigma\right],$$

$$\operatorname{curl}\boldsymbol{E} = \sum_1^\infty{}_n \frac{\boldsymbol{b}_n}{k_n}\left[\iiint\limits_V \boldsymbol{E}\cdot\operatorname{curl}\operatorname{curl}\boldsymbol{a}_n\,\mathrm{d}V + \oiint\limits_\Sigma \boldsymbol{E}\wedge\operatorname{curl}\boldsymbol{a}_n\cdot\boldsymbol{n}\,\mathrm{d}\Sigma\right],$$

and by (13-31, 37, 38, 39)

$$\operatorname{curl}\boldsymbol{H} = \sum_1^\infty \boldsymbol{a}_n\left[k_n\iiint\limits_V \boldsymbol{H}\cdot\boldsymbol{b}_n\,\mathrm{d}V + \oiint\limits_\Sigma \boldsymbol{H}\wedge\boldsymbol{a}_n\cdot\boldsymbol{n}\,\mathrm{d}\Sigma\right],$$

$$\operatorname{curl}\boldsymbol{E} = \sum_1^\infty \boldsymbol{b}_n\left[k_n\iiint\limits_V \boldsymbol{E}\cdot\boldsymbol{a}_n\,\mathrm{d}V + \oiint\limits_\Sigma \boldsymbol{E}\wedge\boldsymbol{b}_n\cdot\boldsymbol{n}\,\mathrm{d}\Sigma\right].$$

Finally by (13-45)

$$\text{(13-46)} \quad \begin{cases} \text{curl}\, \boldsymbol{H} = \sum_{1}^{\infty}{}_n\, \boldsymbol{a}_n \left[k_n H_n + \oiint_{\Sigma} \boldsymbol{H} \wedge \boldsymbol{a}_n \cdot \boldsymbol{n}\, \mathrm{d}\Sigma \right], \\ \text{curl}\, \boldsymbol{E} = \sum_{1}^{\infty}{}_n\, \boldsymbol{b}_n \left[k_n E_n + \oiint_{\Sigma} \boldsymbol{E} \wedge \boldsymbol{b}_n \cdot \boldsymbol{n}\, \mathrm{d}\Sigma \right]. \end{cases}$$

Note now that $\boldsymbol{a}_n$ is always perpendicular to Σ so that the first surface integral vanishes. On the other hand $\boldsymbol{E}$ is certainly normal on the walls of the box; as a consequence the only non-vanishing contribution to the second surface integral comes from the terminals, which will be denoted by Σ_0. The preceding equations will therefore be written

$$\text{(13-47)} \quad \begin{cases} \text{curl}\, \boldsymbol{H} = \sum_{1}^{\infty}{}_n\, k_n H_n \boldsymbol{a}_n, \\ \text{curl}\, \boldsymbol{E} = \sum_{1}^{\infty}{}_n \left[k_n E_n + \iint_{\Sigma_0} \boldsymbol{E} \wedge \boldsymbol{b}_n \cdot \boldsymbol{n}\, \mathrm{d}\Sigma \right] \boldsymbol{b}_n. \end{cases}$$

We now have to require that $\boldsymbol{E}$ and $\boldsymbol{H}$ obey Maxwell's equations (7-36), which in the absence of attenuation may be written in the form

$$\text{(13-48)} \quad \begin{cases} \text{curl}\, \boldsymbol{H} = ikY\boldsymbol{E}, \\ \text{curl}\, \boldsymbol{E} = -\, ikZ\boldsymbol{H}. \end{cases}$$

By substituting in these equations the expansions (13-44, 47) and equating the coefficients of $\boldsymbol{a}_n$ in both sides of the first equation and of the $\boldsymbol{b}_n$ in both sides of the second we get

$$k_n H_n = ikYE_n,$$

$$k_n E_n + \iint_{\Sigma_0} \boldsymbol{E} \wedge \boldsymbol{b}_n \cdot \boldsymbol{n}\, \mathrm{d}\Sigma = -\, ikZH_n.$$

We may solve this system for H_n with the result

$$\text{(13-49)} \quad H_n = \frac{ikY}{k^2 - k_n^2} \iint_{\Sigma_0} \boldsymbol{E} \wedge \boldsymbol{b}_n \cdot \boldsymbol{n}\, \mathrm{d}\Sigma.$$

Finally substituting into the second equation (13-44) we obtain by a circular substitution in the mixed product

$$\boldsymbol{H} = \sum_{1}^{\infty} {}_n \left[\frac{ikY}{k^2 - k_n^2} \iint_{\Sigma_0} \boldsymbol{n} \wedge \boldsymbol{E} \cdot \boldsymbol{b}_n \, \mathrm{d}\Sigma \right] \boldsymbol{b}_n. \tag{13-50}$$

This interesting equation enables us to evaluate $\boldsymbol{H}$ (and consequently $\boldsymbol{E}$ from Maxwell's equations), given the tangential component of $\boldsymbol{E}$ on every guide terminal. We already knew that this was possible from the theorem demonstrated in 12-§3.

§ 10. We shall now show how the electromagnetic field inside the cavity can be evaluated when $\boldsymbol{H}$ instead of $\boldsymbol{E}$ is given on the terminals. In this case the functions $\boldsymbol{a}_n$, $\boldsymbol{b}_n$ are no longer suitable for our purpose. We shall instead introduce a new pair of sets $\boldsymbol{c}_n$, $\boldsymbol{d}_n$ in the following manner. The function $\boldsymbol{c}_n$ is subject to the differential equation

$$\text{curl curl } \boldsymbol{c}_n = k_n^2 \boldsymbol{c}_n\,, \tag{13-51}$$

and to the conditions that its tangential component be zero on the walls of the box and that the tangential component of curl $\boldsymbol{c}_n$ be zero on the terminals. It is shown in advanced treatises on differential equations that in this case also (with mixed boundary conditions) equation (13-31) admits of an infinite set of eigenfunctions $\boldsymbol{c}_n$ corresponding to an infinite set of eigenvalues k_n (which, however, are distinct from those of the preceding case). It may be easily shown by an equation similar to (13-32) that the functions $\boldsymbol{c}_n$ form an orthogonal system. They will be normalized to unity as was done for $\boldsymbol{a}_n$ and $\boldsymbol{b}_n$.

We shall then introduce $\boldsymbol{d}_n$ with

$$k_n \boldsymbol{d}_n = \text{curl } \boldsymbol{c}_n, \tag{13-52}$$

whence it follows that

$$\text{curl curl } \boldsymbol{d}_n = k_n^2 \boldsymbol{d}_n \tag{13-53}$$

and also

$$k_n \boldsymbol{c}_n = \text{curl } \boldsymbol{d}_n. \tag{13-54}$$

The functions $\boldsymbol{d}_n$ are also orthogonal and normalized; they have vanishing normal components on the box walls and vanishing tangential components on the guide terminals. Equation (13-54) shows that the normal component of $\boldsymbol{c}_n$ is zero on the terminals.

We shall now expand $\boldsymbol{E}(P)$ as a series of $\boldsymbol{c}_n$, and $\boldsymbol{H}(P)$ as a series of $\boldsymbol{d}_n$ as follows:

$$\text{(13-55)} \qquad \boldsymbol{E}(P) = \sum_1^\infty {}_n E_n \boldsymbol{c}_n(P), \qquad \boldsymbol{H}(P) = \sum_1^\infty {}_n H_n \boldsymbol{d}_n(P),$$

with

$$\text{(13-56)} \qquad E_n = \iiint_V \boldsymbol{E} \cdot \boldsymbol{c}_n \mathrm{d}V, \qquad H_n = \iiint_V \boldsymbol{H} \cdot \boldsymbol{d}_n \mathrm{d}V.$$

Next curl $\boldsymbol{H}$ and curl $\boldsymbol{E}$ will be expanded as series of $\boldsymbol{c}_n$ and $\boldsymbol{d}_n$ respectively as follows:

$$\operatorname{curl} \boldsymbol{H} = \sum_1^\infty {}_n \boldsymbol{c}_n \iiint_V \boldsymbol{c}_n \cdot \operatorname{curl} \boldsymbol{H} \mathrm{d}V, \quad \operatorname{curl} \boldsymbol{E} = \sum_1^\infty {}_n \boldsymbol{d}_n \iiint_V \boldsymbol{d}_n \cdot \operatorname{curl} \boldsymbol{E} \mathrm{d}V.$$

By repeating the reasoning of the previous section one would arrive at the following formulas similar to (13-46):

$$\operatorname{curl} \boldsymbol{H} = \sum_1^\infty {}_n \boldsymbol{c}_n \left[k_n H_n + \oiint_\Sigma \boldsymbol{H} \wedge \boldsymbol{c}_n \cdot \boldsymbol{n} \, \mathrm{d}\Sigma \right],$$

$$\operatorname{curl} \boldsymbol{E} = \sum_1^\infty {}_n \boldsymbol{d}_n \left[k_n E_n + \oiint_\Sigma \boldsymbol{E} \wedge \boldsymbol{d}_n \cdot \boldsymbol{n} \, \mathrm{d}\Sigma \right].$$

The second surface integral vanishes because $\boldsymbol{E}$ is normal to the box walls and $\boldsymbol{d}_n$ is normal to the guide terminals. The first surface integral vanishes on the box walls because $\boldsymbol{c}_n$ is normal thereto. We are then left with

$$\operatorname{curl} \boldsymbol{H} = \sum_1^\infty {}_n \left[k_n H_n + \iint_{\Sigma_0} \boldsymbol{H} \wedge \boldsymbol{c}_n \cdot \boldsymbol{n} \, \mathrm{d}\Sigma \right] \boldsymbol{c}_n, \qquad \operatorname{curl} \boldsymbol{E} = \sum_1^\infty {}_n k_n E_n \boldsymbol{d}_n.$$

Substituting these equations and (13-55) into Maxwell's equations (13-48), we find

$$k_n H_n + \iint_{\Sigma_0} \boldsymbol{H} \wedge \boldsymbol{c}_n \cdot \boldsymbol{n} \mathrm{d}\Sigma = ikYE_n.$$

$$k_n E_n = -\, ikZH_n.$$

Solving for E_n and substituting into (13-55) we finally arrive at

$$\boldsymbol{E} = \sum_1^\infty {}_n \left[\frac{-\, ikZ}{k^2 - k_n^2} \iint_{\Sigma_0} \boldsymbol{n} \wedge \boldsymbol{H} \cdot \boldsymbol{c}_n \, \mathrm{d}\Sigma \right] \boldsymbol{c}_n. \tag{13-57}$$

We are thus in a position to evaluate the electric field (and consequently also the magnetic field by applying Maxwell's equations) given the transverse magnetic field over all of the guide terminals.

Evaluation of Tensor Admittances and Impedances

§ 11. We shall recall now the discussion of wave guides in Chapter 12 as transmission lines.

If in a given wave guide feeding the box only one mode (progressive and regressive) is traveling as in (12-3), we set

$$\boldsymbol{E}_T = V\boldsymbol{e}_T,$$
$$\boldsymbol{H}_T = I\boldsymbol{h}_T,$$

$\boldsymbol{E}_T$ and $\boldsymbol{H}_T$ denoting the transverse fields actually existing on the terminal and $\boldsymbol{e}_T$, $\boldsymbol{h}_T$ the transveise eigenfunctions of the mode considered. If there are more than one traveling mode in the guide each will separately give its contribution to $\boldsymbol{E}_T$ and $\boldsymbol{H}_T$. We shall have namely

$$\begin{cases} \boldsymbol{E}_T = V_j \boldsymbol{e}_{T_j}, \\ \boldsymbol{H}_T = I_l \boldsymbol{h}_{T_l}, \end{cases} \tag{13-58}$$

where summation is understood over repeated subscripts. These equations hold good also when $\boldsymbol{E}_T$ and $\boldsymbol{H}_T$ indicate the field on the whole set of terminals which was indicated by tne single symbol Σ_0. The sums of (13-58) must then be understood in the sense that after counting the modes of the first guide the numeration shall go on with the modes of the second, of the third and so on. Voltages and currents will be related by (12-6, 8) which will be written

$$V_j = Z_{jl} I_l, \qquad I_l = Y_{lj} V_j, \tag{13-59}$$

with Z_{jl} and Y_{lj} representing the components of the tensor impedance and admittance respectively.

It will be expedient now to express the value of $\boldsymbol{b}_n$ on the terminals as a series of eigenfunctions $\boldsymbol{h}_T$; this is possible because $\boldsymbol{b}_n$ is tangential. Thus we shall set

$$\boldsymbol{b}_n(\Sigma_0) = \beta_{nl} \boldsymbol{h}_{Tl}, \tag{13-60}$$

where a summation is understood.

Let us now express the transverse field $\boldsymbol{H}_T$ on the terminals by means of (13-50) noting that the normal $\boldsymbol{n}$ is equal to $-\boldsymbol{k}$ for each guide. We have

$$\boldsymbol{H}_T = \sum_1^\infty{}_n \left[\frac{ikY}{k_n^2 - k^2} \iint_{\Sigma_0} \boldsymbol{k} \wedge \boldsymbol{E}_T \cdot \boldsymbol{b}_n \, \mathrm{d}\Sigma \right] \boldsymbol{b}_n .$$

Let us substitute (13-58, 60) into this equation; the result will be

$$I_l \boldsymbol{h}_{Tl} = \sum_1^\infty \left[\frac{ikY}{k_n^2 - k^2} \iint_{\Sigma_0} \boldsymbol{k} \wedge V_j \boldsymbol{e}_{T_j} \cdot \beta_{nk} \boldsymbol{h}_{T_k} \, \mathrm{d}\Sigma \right] \beta_{nl} \boldsymbol{h}_{Tl} .$$

By equating the coefficients of $\boldsymbol{h}_{Tl}$ in both sides and taking into account (11-60) we get

$$I_l = \sum_1^\infty{}_n \, ikY \frac{\beta_{nk}\beta_{nl}}{k_n^2 - k^2} V_j Z_{gj} \iint_{\Sigma_0} \boldsymbol{h}_{Tj} \cdot \boldsymbol{h}_{Tk} \, \mathrm{d}\Sigma .$$

We recall now that the functions $\boldsymbol{h}_T$ are orthogonal and normalized according to (11-75) and that they can all be chosen real. The above equation then becomes

$$I_l = \sum_1^\infty{}_n \, ikY \frac{\beta_{nj}\beta_{nl}}{k_n^2 - k^2} V_j .$$

Finally by comparing with the second equation (13-59) there results

(13-61) $$Y_{lj} = ikY \sum_1^\infty {}_n \frac{\beta_{nj}\beta_{nl}}{k_n^2 - k^2}.$$

Thus the components of the tensor admittance have been explicitly evaluated.

§ 12. The form of the right-hand side of (13-61) is of great interest. We can replace k by ω/v and introduce ω_n such that $k_n = \omega_n/v$. Then (13-61) becomes

(13-62) $$Y_{lj} = i\omega v Y \sum_1^\infty {}_n \frac{\beta_{nj}\beta_{nl}}{\omega_n^2 - \omega^2}.$$

It is natural to interpret the ω_n as resonant frequencies. The admittance Y_{lj} tends to infinity for $\omega = \omega_n$ (in the present case it becomes really infinite because we have disregarded the losses). This means that, if a fixed voltage is maintained in the jth mode (which may belong to any one of the guides feeding the cavity), the response obtained in the lth mode (which in turn may belong to any guide) is a current presenting a resonance peak whenever ω approaches one of the values ω_n.

We may note that the resonance frequencies are the same for all the components of the tensor admittance $\boldsymbol{Y}$. We may define a set of tensors $\boldsymbol{B}_n$ as follows

$$\boldsymbol{B}_n = ivY\beta_{nj}\beta_{nl}\boldsymbol{i}_j\boldsymbol{i}_l.$$

With this position (13-62) may be written

(13-63) $$\boldsymbol{Y} = \sum_1^\infty {}_n \frac{\omega \boldsymbol{B}_n}{\omega_n^2 - \omega^2}.$$

When the frequency of the field is in the vicinity of a resonance frequency it is sufficient to apply very small voltages to the guides to obtain very intense currents. If ω coincides exactly with one of the ω_n the voltages may be zero and nevertheless the currents will not vanish. This means that the guide terminals may be short-circuited or closed by perfect plane conductors while the field inside the cavity will still be different from zero. Hence the ω_n represent the natural frequencies of the cavity.

§ 13. A similar approach will be followed in the evaluation of the tensor impedance.

To begin with the functions $\boldsymbol{c}_n$ on Σ_0 will be expanded in series of eigenfunctions $\boldsymbol{e}_T$ of the guides as follows

$$\boldsymbol{c}_n(\Sigma_0) = \gamma_{nj}\boldsymbol{e}_{Tj}.$$

This expansion is possible because the $\boldsymbol{c}_n$ are transverse at the terminals. Substituting this expression and (13-58) into (13-57) written for Σ_0 with $\boldsymbol{n} = -\boldsymbol{k}$ we get

$$V_j\boldsymbol{e}_{Tj} = \sum_1^\infty {}_n \left[\frac{ikZ\gamma_{nk}I_l}{k^2 - k_n^2} \iint_{\Sigma_0} \boldsymbol{k}\wedge\boldsymbol{h}_{Tl}\cdot\boldsymbol{e}_{Tk}\,\mathrm{d}\Sigma\right]\gamma_{nj}\boldsymbol{e}_{Tj}.$$

Making use of (11-60, 74) and equating the coefficients of $\boldsymbol{e}_{Tj}$ in both sides we have

$$V_j = \sum_1^\infty {}_n\, ikZ\,\frac{\gamma_{nl}\gamma_{nj}}{k_n^2 - k^2} I_l.$$

Hence comparing with the first equation (13-59) we finally obtain

$$Z_{jl} = ikZ\sum_1^\infty {}_n \frac{\gamma_{nl}\gamma_{nj}}{k_n^2 - k^2}, \tag{13-64}$$

which represent the components of the tensor impedance. Setting again $k_n = \omega_n/v$ we may also write

$$Z_{jl} = i\omega vZ\sum_1^\infty {}_n \frac{\gamma_{nl}\gamma_{nj}}{\omega_n^2 - \omega^2}. \tag{13-65}$$

We have thus found a series of anti-resonance frequencies ω_n for which Z_{jl} becomes infinite. It will be noted that these anti-resonance frequencies are different from the resonance frequencies of the previous chapter in spite of the fact that we have represented them by the same symbol.

Let us now introduce the tensors

$$\boldsymbol{C}_n = ivZ\gamma_{nl}\gamma_{nj}\boldsymbol{i}_l\boldsymbol{i}_j.$$

With this position, (13-65) may be written

$$Z = \sum_{1}^{\infty} {}_n \frac{\omega C_n}{\omega_n^2 - \omega^2}. \tag{13-66}$$

We thus see that the anti-resonance frequencies apply in the same way to every component of the tensor impedance.

Finally it is evident that, if the losses in the cavity had been taken into account, the resonant and anti-resonant terms of (13-63, 66) would have acquired the complete form similar to (6-35) where the Q appears.

INDEX